THE NOBEL PRIZE WINNERS

Chemistry

THE NOBEL PRIZE WINNERS

Chemistry

Volume 3
1969 – 1989

Edited by
FRANK N. MAGILL

SALEM PRESS
Pasadena, California   Englewood Cliffs, New Jersey

∞ The paper used in these volumes conforms to the
American National Standard for Permanence of Paper
for Printed Library Materials, Z39.48-1984.

Library of Congress Cataloging-in-Publication Data
The Nobel Prize winners: chemistry/edited by Frank N.
Magill. p. cm.
Includes bibliographical references.
Contents: v. 1. 1901-1937—v. 2. 1938-1968—v. 3. 1969-
1989.
1. Chemists—Biography. 2. Nobel prizes.
I. Magill, Frank Northen, 1907-
QD21.N64   1990   90-8092
540'.79—dc20   CIP
ISBN 0-89356-561-x (set)
ISBN 0-89356-564-4 (volume 3)

PRINTED IN THE UNITED STATES OF AMERICA

CONTENTS

ALPHABETICAL LIST OF PRIZE WINNERS

THE NOBEL PRIZE WINNERS

THE NOBEL PRIZE WINNERS

THE NOBEL PRIZE WINNERS

THE NOBEL PRIZE WINNERS

Chemistry

1969

Chemistry
Derek H. R. Barton, Great Britain
Odd Hassel, Norway

Physics
Murray Gell-Mann, United States

Physiology or Medicine
Max Delbrück, United States
Alfred D. Hershey, United States
Salvador E. Luria, United States

Economic Sciences
Ragnar Frisch, Norway
Jan Tinbergen, The Netherlands

Literature
Samuel Beckett, Ireland

Peace
International Labour Organisation

DEREK H. R. BARTON
1969

Born: Gravesend, Kent, England; September 8, 1918

Nationality: British
Areas of concentration: Conformational analysis and organic synthesis

*Barton demonstrated the fundamental importance of the three-dimensional con-
formations that molecules assume, a concept that revolutionized the understanding
of modern organic chemistry. His discoveries had far-reaching implications for
biologically important molecules such as steroids and led to significant advances in
synthesis*

The Award

Presentation

Derek Barton was awarded the Nobel Prize in Chemistry on December 10, 1969.
In his presentation address, Arne Fredga, member of the Nobel Committee for
Chemistry of the Royal Swedish Academy of Sciences, briefly explained that molecules are constantly bending, turning, or twisting in different ways, and that the
term "conformation" is applied to a shape that the molecule actually assumes.

Fredga noted that each conformation has a different stability. Only the most
stable conformations are favored, or present to a significant degree. Reactive sites in
the molecules are therefore influenced by the molecular conformation. A reactive
moiety, or group, may be shielded by the molecule in its most stable conformation
and therefore becomes much less reactive. When more than one such group is
present, a knowledge of the conformation allows the prediction of which group will
react, or of how the molecule will behave under a specific set of reaction conditions. This is fundamental to the manipulation of organic molecules during synthesis, isolation, or conversion into a different compound.

Fredga concluded with the statement that Barton's contribution lay in his extension of the work of Odd Hassel, joint recipient of the 1969 Nobel Prize. He noted
that it was Barton's research and publications on the steroid ring systems, which are
present in hormones, cholesterol, and other biological molecules, such as venoms,
that drew attention to the work by Hassel on cyclohexane rings.

Nobel lecture

Derek Barton delivered his Nobel lecture, "The Principles of Conformational
Analysis," on December 11, 1969. He treated the topic from a historical perspective,
citing Friedrich August Kekulé's theories on the constitution of organic molecules
and following up with a summary of the advances that led to his own contributions.
He pointed out that the constitution of a molecule only revealed which atoms were
bonded to which. Since different compounds possessing the same constitution were

known, the concept of stereochemistry, which deals with the three-dimensional structure of molecules, was recognized as an important aspect of structural theory, and rapid advances were made in that area.

In his lecture, Barton acknowledged the pioneering work of Odd Hassel, with whom he was sharing the prize, on the cyclohexane system. Hassel had demonstrated that of the three main structural possibilities for cyclohexane, a six-carbon cyclic compound, it was the chair form that the molecule actually assumed. "Conformation" was the term that came into use to describe those configurations of a molecule that differed from one another only by the rotation of atoms about bonds. It was therefore made clear that some conformations are much more stable than others and that a given system will tend to assume the conformation of greatest stability.

Hassel continued his work with decalin, which consists of two fused cyclohexane rings, while Barton focused his attention on the stereochemistry of steroids. At the time, steroid chemistry was a major area of organic chemistry, which had just received further recognition from the discovery of the therapeutic properties of cortisone. Most steroids contain three cyclohexane rings and a cyclopentane ring fused together and are commonly found throughout nature, in hormones, bile acids, digitalis glycosides, cholesterol, saponins, and the venoms of potato tops and toads.

Barton presented his research on the application and elucidation of stereochemical principles in summary form. His work led to the predictability of the reaction pathways of steroids and significantly increased knowledge of the detailed, step-by-step processes (mechanisms) followed in common organic reactions, such as elimination reactions, neighboring-group participation, and ring-opening of small rings. He cited Ernest Eliel for his contributions in defining the actual energies involved in conformational analysis.

In his closing remarks, Barton mentioned his discovery of the phenomenon that he called "conformational transmission," which described the influence of conformation on one side of a molecule on the outcome of a reaction occurring at a remote site. Finally, he pointed out that biological processes are intimately dependent on the three-dimensional interactions of molecules, such as those between enzymes and substrates, and that chemistry had now advanced so far in this direction that important discoveries in the biological areas of science would certainly be forthcoming.

Critical reception

In general, chemists throughout the world were most positive about the presentation of the Nobel Prize in Chemistry to Derek Barton (and Odd Hassel). Ernest Eliel, a recognized authority in the area of conformational analysis, reviewed the event in *Science*, where he described Barton's original paper in this field as "electrifying" and stated that it had revolutionized not only organic chemistry but chemistry as a whole. Eliel made note of Barton's expressions of indebtedness to Hassel's ideas. He praised Barton's research on the influence of three-dimensional molecular structure on reactivity and mentioned several resulting discoveries, including biochemical rearrangements such as the cyclization of squalene to lanosterol. He also credited Barton's development of conformational analysis with the revolution in the synthesis and structure elucidation of naturally occurring biomolecules.

According to Eliel, one of the factors that stimulated the rapid recognition of Barton's ideas was his interaction with chemists at Harvard University during his visiting lectureship in 1949-1950. Undoubtedly, the influence of his colleagues in the University of London system, where the ideas of mechanistic organic chemistry were being developed throughout the century by Christopher Ingold and others, was also of great significance. The article concluded with a comment on the continuing significance of Barton's work, as revealed by the expanding scope and importance of the concepts, not only in small-molecule research but also in the polymer and biopolymer areas, including proteins.

The announcement that the Nobel Prize in Chemistry was to be awarded to Derek Barton and Odd Hassel was also hailed in *Chemical and Engineering News*. Robin Johnson's article emphasized the close relationship between the ideas, concepts, and research of the two prizewinners. He pointed out that it was Derek Barton who combined all the knowledge that evolved from the foregoing two decades of research on the shapes of molecules, much of which was pioneered by Odd Hassel, and produced the flash of inspiration from which he developed his theories of molecular conformations. He also stated that Barton's ideas were enthusiastically accepted by the chemistry community, as evidenced by the rapid application of the concepts to chemistry in general and their immediate incorporation into university chemistry courses.

There is no doubt that the chemistry community strongly supported the choices for receipt of the 1969 prize. The explosive growth of steroid research, of organic synthesis, and of the mechanistic approach to the understanding and teaching of organic chemistry can all be traced back to the initial work of Derek Barton on the conformation of steroids.

Biography

Derek Harold Richard Barton was born to William Thomas and Maude Henrietta Barton in Gravesend, on the Thames River near London, on September 8, 1918. He received his early education at Tonbridge School and later went on to Gillingham Technical College. In 1938, he transferred to the Imperial College of Science and Technology, University of London, where he obtained his B.S. degree, with first-class honors, in 1940 and his doctorate in 1942. Two years later, Derek Barton was married to Jeanne Kate Wilkins, with whom he had one son. This marriage was later dissolved, and he married Christiane Cognet, a professor at the Lycée Français de Londres.

Barton was a visiting professor at Harvard University from 1949 to 1950. He considered it a special year in his life, not only because it was during this time that his ideas on conformational analysis took root but also because he developed strong relationships with the chemists at Harvard. He often referred to his "friends at Harvard University." He had already known Robert Burns Woodward for some time, and Woodward had once stated that Barton was his "secret collaborator."

One of the most notable indicators of Barton's character is the consideration and, indeed, self-confidence that he displayed by repeatedly voicing his indebtedness to Odd Hassel's pioneering research into the structural analysis of the cyclohexane ring system. Eliel commented upon Barton's outgoing nature in an article in *Science*. He described Barton as a scientist who was aware of the need to expose his ideas constantly, not only through publications and reviews but also by traveling and accepting lecture engagements, and who stimulated others to understand what had become one of the most significant areas of chemistry.

Scientific Career

Barton obtained his doctoral degree in 1942 under the auspices of Sir Ian Heilbron, at Imperial College, London. Heilbron was actively engaged in steroid research, and so, even while pursuing his doctoral degree, Barton was becoming familiar with the field that he would later revolutionize with his three-dimensional concepts of the structure of molecules.

He spent the remaining war years working on a government project. In 1944, he took a position at Albright and Wilson, Birmingham, and in 1945 he returned to the academic environment at Imperial College. At first, he was assistant lecturer in the department of inorganic and physical chemistry, and, from 1946 to 1949, he was an I.C.I. Research Fellow. In 1948, the Chemical Society awarded Barton the Harrison Memorial Prize. At that time, he was involved in research related to the transformations undergone by organic chlorides when subjected to relatively high temperatures.

It was during the period 1949-1950, as a visiting lecturer at Harvard University, that Barton became taken with the idea of how the three-dimensional arrangement of the atoms in steroids affected their properties and reactions. He was familiar with Odd Hassel's findings regarding the preferred arrangement of atoms (conformation) in the six-carbon cyclohexane ring system. While listening to a lecture at Harvard regarding some steroid reactions that were not then understood, Barton immediately saw that the missing parts of the puzzle were tied in with the three-dimensional conformations of the steroid molecules. Hassel's most important work was originally published in relatively obscure Norwegian journals, which were not readily available after the war. It was not only Barton's scientific curiosity that drove him to seek out the work of other scientists but also a conviction that there is value in the ideas and research of all scientists.

Barton published his revolutionary ideas in *Experientia*, in 1950, in his famous paper entitled "The Conformation of the Steroid Nucleus." In this paper, he discussed Odd Hassel's research and drew on his own knowledge of the chemical literature to establish his new concepts of the actual conformations of steroids. Steroids are molecules composed of three cyclohexane rings and one cyclopentane ring joined together. Using numerous examples, he showed how a vast number of previously unexplained observations in steroid chemistry, and in organic chemistry in general, could be understood and rationalized if the three-dimensional structures of molecules were taken into consideration. The paper was so lucid, and the previously unexplained phenomena were so well rationalized, that it received immediate recognition and worldwide acclaim in the scientific community. Many research groups initiated new projects in the area of conformational analysis, and the more basic aspects of Barton's ideas were quickly incorporated into undergraduate university courses in chemistry.

When he returned to London in 1950, Barton became a reader in organic chemistry at Birkbeck College, University of London, and was awarded the first Corday-Morgan Medal of the Chemical Society. In 1953, he was elected full professor and, in 1955, became Regius Professor of Chemistry at Glasgow University, Scotland.

During the period 1949-1960, Barton's research centered on the chemistry and structural analysis of organic compounds. Utilizing his own theories, he predicted the structures of various complex, naturally occurring compounds, such as alkaloids. Subsequent laboratory synthesis of the alkaloid under investigation supplied corroborative evidence of the predicted structure. The final step of his elegant procedure was to feed the plant, from which the alkaloid was first isolated, with suitable precursors in which radioactive atoms had been incorporated. By isolating all the radioactive compounds finally present in the plant after a suitable amount of time, he was able to determine the synthetic pathway to the alkaloid followed by the plant. Barton elucidated the biosynthetic pathway to various classes of compounds, including morphine, indole, erythrina, and Amaryllidaceae alkaloids.

In 1956, Barton was awarded the Fritzsche Medal by the American Chemical Society. In its review of the event, *Chemical and Engineering News* mentioned his successful proof of the structure of caryophyllene, a naturally occurring compound obtained from oil of cloves, and praised Barton by acknowledging that there was hardly any research in the area of organic chemistry that did not utilize Barton's concepts. He returned to Imperial College as professor of organic chemistry the following year.

The Royal Society awarded Barton the Davy Medal in 1961. A review of the award in *Nature* commented upon his pioneering work on conformational analysis and the far-reaching effect on scientists' understanding of the relationship between the conformation of a molecule and its reactivity. The article illustrated the vast amount of research and knowledge that Barton had already contributed to chemistry. Specific examples were noted within various fields, including sesquiterpenes, di- and triterpenes, steroids, biochemical pathways, and the use of light (photochemistry) to effect chemical transformations. The photochemical synthesis of aldosterone was developed at the Research Institute for Medicine and Chemistry, Boston, of which Barton was a director. The photochemical transformation has been named the "Barton reaction."

Barton believed the ability to see scientific discoveries from different angles to be a significant advantage. He fostered this philosophy by actively seeking constant interaction with other scientists, as a guest lecturer and as a visiting professor. He dedicated his Tilden lecture (1953), which was published in the *Journal of the Chemical Society*, to all of his colleagues, claiming that they had taught him more of chemistry than he had taught them. In 1958, he was Arthur D. Little Visiting Professor at the Massachusetts Institute of Technology; in 1959, Karl Folkers Visiting Professor at the Universities of Illinois and Wisconsin; and, in 1960, Peter C. Reilly Visiting Professor at the University of Notre Dame. Among his many guest lecturing engagements, he was the Max Tischler lecturer (Harvard University, 1956), Simonsen Memorial lecturer (Chemical Society, 1958), Falk-Plaut lecturer (Columbia University, 1961), Aub lecturer (Harvard Medical School, 1962), Renaud lecturer (Michigan State University, 1962), Inaugural 3-M lecturer (University of Western Ontario, 1962), 3-M lecturer (University of Minnesota, 1963), Sandin lecturer (University of Alberta, 1969), and Graham Young lecturer (University of Glasgow, Scotland, 1970).

A further indication of Barton's desire to communicate with fellow scientists on a worldwide basis is the list of honorary degrees and memberships that he has been granted during his travels by many organizations and universities. These include the American Academy of Arts and Sciences (Foreign Honorary Member, 1960), Montpellier University (D.Sc., 1962, France), Dublin University (D.Sc., 1964, Ireland), Deutsche Akademie der Naturforscher "Leopoldina" (Honorary Fellow, 1967, Germany), Sociedad Quimica de Mexico (Honorary Member, 1969), St. Andrews University (D.Sc., 1970, Scotland), the Belgian Chemical Society (Honorary Member, 1970), the Chilean Chemical Society (D.Sc., 1970), and Coimbra (D.Sc., 1971, Portugal). In addition to these honors, Barton won numerous awards for his continuing research contributions to chemistry. After receiving the Nobel Prize in Chemistry in 1969, Barton was awarded the Royal Medal (1972) and the Copley Medal (1980) of the Royal Society.

Although he was not active in conformational analysis after 1960, Barton has continued his work in the areas of natural products and biosynthesis. His research on tetracycline antibiotics formed the substance of the Royal Society's Bakerian lecture in 1970. He also worked extensively and has made significant advances in the chemistry of penicillins and transformation into the related antibiotic cephalosporins.

Barton's development of conformational analysis was of such fundamental importance to organic chemistry that the area is introduced to students in basic university-level organic courses throughout the world. Perhaps the most significant aspect of his revolutionary ideas was that molecules should be imagined in three dimensions. Considering the various conformations that molecules can adopt in their bending and twisting motions makes it possible to rationalize and predict the outcome of chemical reactions, even in the most complex naturally occurring systems.

Barton's ideas were immediately applied to all aspects of organic and biological synthetic pathways and form the basis for analyzing the structure of complex molecules and for understanding their chemistry. These ideas have been invaluable to chemists in all areas of the science.

Bibliography

Primary

CHEMISTRY: "The Conformation of the Steroid Nucleus," *Experientia*, 1950; "The Stereochemistry of Cyclohexane Derivatives," *Journal of the Chemical Society*, 1953; "Some Approaches to the Synthesis of Tetracycline," *Proceedings of the Royal Society of London, A*, 1970; "Chemical Relationships Between Cephalosporins and Penicillins," *Proceedings of the Royal Society of London, B*, 1971.

Secondary

Campbell, W. A., and N. N. Greenwood. *Contemporary British Chemists*. New York: Barnes & Nobel Books, 1971. The book consists of brief, two-page chapters on the most prominent British chemists at the time of publication. The chapter on Barton has a very brief biographical sketch, followed by an excellent overview of Barton's discoveries specifically written for readers with little or no background in organic chemistry. The chapter closes with mention of a few of the awards and honors granted to Barton.

"Davy Medal: Prof. D. H. R. Barton, F. R. S." *Nature* 192 (December 9, 1961): 906. Detailed information on the specific areas in which Barton applied his revolutionary theories to earn the Royal Society's Davy Medal. Invaluable to anyone wishing to investigate further any aspect of Barton's research up to 1961.

"Derek Barton." In *McGraw-Hill Modern Scientists and Engineers*. Vol. 1. New York: McGraw-Hill, 1980. Gives a concise summary of Barton's research. There is a brief description of the findings of Odd Hassel, followed by an account of Barton's research, which is quite technical. The summary of the various subjects on which Barton worked is interesting, and mentions areas not found in other sources.

Eliel, Ernest L. "Nobel Laureates in Economics, Chemistry, and Physics." *Science* 166 (November 7, 1969): 718-720. This long article is a review of the research carried out by Barton and Odd Hassel that led to their Nobel Prizes. The author, a recognized authority in the field of conformational analysis, used substantial technical language and provided a number of important literature references. The discussion of the impact of Barton's work on the science of chemistry is especially pleasing and well-suited to general reading. A major part of the biographical summaries is devoted to awards and honors.

Nobelstiftelsen. *Nobel Lectures: Chemistry, 1963-1970*. Vol. 4. New York: Elsevier, 1972. The chapter on Derek Barton gives the English translation of the Nobel Prize presentation speech by Professor Arne Fredga, member of the Nobel Prize Committee for Chemistry of the Royal Swedish Academy of Sciences. This is followed by Barton's Nobel lecture, the text of which is clarified by illustrations of six-carbon rings and steroid conformations. Some exposure to organic chemistry would be most helpful in understanding the material. There are many references to published research, many of them by Barton. The chapter closes with a biographical essay.

Wasson, Tyler, ed. *Nobel Prize Winners*. New York: H. W. Wilson, 1987. The article on Barton is aimed at the nontechnical reader and is written in biographical form. The description of Barton's contribution to chemistry is extremely brief but easy to understand. Many of the other areas in which Barton worked are mentioned. The article closes with a few references to selected works, which are not well defined.

Massimo D. Bezoari

1969

Chemistry
Derek H. R. Barton, Great Britain
Odd Hassel, Norway

Physics
Murray Gell-Mann, United States

Physiology or Medicine
Max Delbrück, United States
Alfred D. Hershey, United States
Salvador E. Luria, United States

Economic Sciences
Ragnar Frisch, Norway
Jan Tinbergen, The Netherlands

Literature
Samuel Beckett, Ireland

Peace
International Labour Organisation

ODD HASSEL
1969

Born: Kristiania (modern Oslo), Norway; May 17, 1897
Died: Oslo, Norway; May 11, 1981
Nationality: Norwegian
Areas of concentration: X-ray crystallography, conformational analysis, and charge-transfer complexes

Hassel performed experiments that demonstrated the concepts of conformational analysis, especially in six-membered organic ring structures. Conformational analysis allows the prediction of reactions of many types of chemicals, including many of the biochemical systems

The Award

Presentation

Arne Fredga of the Royal Swedish Academy of Sciences presented the Nobel Prize to Odd Hassel and Derek Barton on December 10, 1969. In his address, Fredga commented that one of the fundamental conditions for life on earth is that carbon atoms can bond together in an almost unlimited number of arrangements. These molecules can be classified by constitution, by the number of atoms of each element in the molecule, and by configuration, the three-dimensional arrangement of the atoms. Molecules are not rigid structures; they have a certain flexibility and may also be able to change from one shape, called conformation or conformer, to another.

One conformer is usually favored because it is more stable. Using cyclohexane, a molecule that has six carbon atoms bonded together to form a ring, Odd Hassel performed the fundamental experiments that demonstrated that one conformer, called the chair form, is the more favored. Fredga noted that Hassel also showed how the predominant conformer leads to certain reactions when other groups are bonded to the six-member ring. Hassel's work on the compound decalin extended the concept of conformational analysis to compounds of more than one ring. Conformational analysis is the study of how the three-dimensional shape controls the reaction of organic compounds, including complex ring structures, many of which are important in biochemistry. The favored conformation may protect a reactive group from other molecules or may make that group easily accessible. Fredga used as an example the ring system of the steroids, which are important in bile acids, sex hormones, cortisone, cholesterol, and venoms of toads.

Fredga told how Hassel had first laid the foundation by his experimental work and Derek Barton had then drawn attention to Hassel's work as he advanced the concept of conformational analysis in his classic work "The Conformation of the Steroid Nucleus" and extended the concept to biochemical molecules.

Nobel lecture

Odd Hassel delivered his Nobel lecture on June 9, 1970. It is an indication of the versatility of this scientist that his Nobel lecture was on a topic different from the topic for which he was awarded the Nobel Prize, conformational analysis. His lecture, "Structural Aspects of Interatomic Charge-Transfer Bonding," concerned the bonding in compounds formed by a transfer of a negative electrical charge, or electron, from a donor molecule to an acceptor molecule. Electron donors can be molecules with nonbonding pairs of electrons (lone pairs) or molecules with pi electrons (electrons not located on a particular atom and thus not as tightly bound). The electron acceptors can be several different types of molecules, even molecules that normally would be electron donors.

Beginning during the 1950's, X-ray crystallographic studies of compounds formed by charge transfer bonding were performed by Hassel's research group. One of the first studies found that in a solid made from a one-to-one mixture of bromine and 1,4-dioxan, almost endless chains of alternating molecules were formed with linear oxygen-bromine-bromine-oxygen arrangements. The oxygen had acted as a donor to the acceptor bromine and both bromines acted as acceptors to different oxygens.

In studies with other combinations of molecules, Hassel found that the same oxygen (having two lone pairs) could serve as the starting point for two bromine molecule bridges. From these data, it was expected that nitrogen in amine groups (nitrogen having one lone pair) would participate in only one bromine molecule bridge. Hassel noted that this conclusion had been consistent with the data from several molecule combinations. The action of a halide, an atom of chlorine, bromine, or iodine, acting as an acceptor exists also in solid compounds formed by halide atoms bonded to a nonhalide atom.

Hassel explained that charge-transfer bonding was analogous to hydrogen bonding. Hydrogen bonding is the attraction of a hydrogen on nitrogen, oxygen, or fluorine to a lone pair of electrons on nitrogen, oxygen, or fluorine. X-ray studies of solid compounds formed by hydrogen bonding or by charge-transfer bonding have led to the formulation of rules that are able to predict atomic arrangements and, to some extent, bond lengths in both types of solids.

Critical reception

Conformational analysis perhaps aided in the discovery of the shape of deoxyribonucleic acid (DNA), which may be the outstanding discovery of the decade. This was the claim made by *Science News* in discussing the Nobel Prize awarded to Hassel and Barton. The article stated that Hassel's chief contributions lay in proving that the chair form of cyclohexane is predominant and thus lower in energy, and in differentiating between the two types of carbon-to-hydrogen bonds.

Chemical and Engineering News noted that the enthusiasm of chemists for the basic idea of conformational analysis was shown by the rapidity of its application and by the fact that it is taught in many university chemistry courses. The article also mentioned the difficult conditions, such as being in a Nazi concentration camp and having to start from scratch after the war, suffered by the Norwegian scientist. A personal insight from Hassel about research was that it is a good thing "to attack problems with different methods, not always with one."

The New York Times published two articles on Hassel. One discussed the work of Hassel, Barton, and Murray Gell-Mann, the physics prizewinner; the other discussed the men themselves. The work of the men was described as plumbing nature, as using their intelligence "to make order out of chaos and then to translate that order into pristine principles of scientific understanding." The work of Hassel and Barton took the field of six-member carbon rings out of the two-dimensional realm into the real three-dimensional world. The other article quoted Hassel as saying, "I have been among the chemistry candidates before, but did not expect to get the prize now. It was indeed very pleasing." Although he did go to Sweden to accept the prize, his first reaction was negative: "I detest public appearances and have to think it over thoroughly." A student is credited as stating that Hassel preferred molecules.

"Conformational analysis has changed the face of chemistry," begins the article in *Science.* The importance of the concept is said to be shown by the large number of important molecules, such as steroids, terpenes, alkaloids, and some carbohydrates, whose reactions can be described by knowing the conformation. Hassel's work was popularized as "the way molecules shape up when they are isolated." The three-page article also discussed the connection between conformational ideas and structure elucidation and synthesis of natural product. These ideas led to new principles, such as conformational stereochemical control, used by Robert B. Woodward, the Nobel laureate of 1965, in the synthesis of reserpine.

A later response of the Norwegian people is indicated by the article by Otto Bastiansen in the obituary of Odd Hassel in *Chemistry in Britain.* He stated that Hassel's Nobel Prize was a great inspiration to Norwegian chemistry: "Other Norwegians had won this great honor but . . . he was the first scientist to receive the prize for research carried out almost entirely in Norway."

Perhaps the best evaluation of Hassel's Nobel Prize was offered by the cowinner, Sir Derek Barton. Barton graciously wrote the following words for this publication:

Odd Hassel spent his scientific life from 1925 to 1950 working essentially on the same problem. He studied the preferred conformations of substituted cyclohexanes. At a time when this subject was of little interest, he steadily gathered the evidence that showed that the preferred conformation of cyclohexane and its congeners was always the chair. He summarized his work clearly in an article published in Norwegian in 1943 in an obscure journal, not generally available outside of Norway. So the value of his work was not immediately appreciated. Furthermore, his use of dipole moments and of electron diffraction, two techniques that were not regarded at that time as reliable, also delayed the recognition of the importance of his contribution. However, his article in *Nature* in 1946 on the preferred conformations of *cis-* and *trans*-decalin did attract much attention and his further publications in the *Acta Chemica Scandinavica* completed his international recognition.

Hassel was almost always right in the conclusions that he drew from his careful experimentation. Finally, when an objective method (densitometry) of evaluating electron diffraction patterns became available, the scene was set for a full recognition of the value of his work.

Hassel richly deserved the honor he received.

Biography

Odd Hassel was born in Kristiania (modern Oslo), Norway, on May 17, 1897, to Ernst and Mathilde (née Klaveness) Hassel. Ernst Hassel was a gynecologist; he died when Odd and his twin brother were age eight. The family of four boys and a girl was then reared by an intellectual and cultured mother. Hassel did not like school and performed well only in mathematics and the sciences. His interest in chemistry developed in high school. In 1915, Hassel entered the University of Oslo to major in chemistry, although, for a family of position, chemistry was a peculiar choice. His other brothers chose civil engineering and law; even his twin, Lief, chose law.

Hassel was graduated in 1920. After a year of travel in Italy and France, he worked for K. Fajans in Munich. The next year he moved to Berlin, where he completed his Ph.D. in 1924. On Fritz Haber's recommendation, he was awarded a Rockefeller Fellowship to stay a year in Germany. In 1925, Hassel returned to Oslo, where he received a university fellowship for a year. He became associate professor (docent) in 1926, professor in physical chemistry and head of the new department of physical chemistry in 1934.

When the Germans occupied Norway in 1940, Hassel stopped publishing in German journals, instead choosing less well-known Norwegian journals. He also participated in anti-Nazi projects. In 1943, he was arrested and placed in a concentration camp at Grini with the rest of the faculty of the University of Oslo. Release from the camp occurred in November, 1944, and Hassel returned to the University of Oslo. In 1973, he continued his efforts, joining other Nobel laureates in a letter addressed to President Nikolai Podgorny of the Soviet Union, published in *The New York Times* on December 2. The letter expressed the "profound distress that we hear of the resumption of suppression of our colleagues and the campaign of harassment against them in the Soviet Union"; Andrei Sakharov and Aleksandr Solzhenitsyn were mentioned by name.

After retirement in 1964, Hassel lived in Oslo and was involved in research, publishing papers as late as 1971. His twin brother's death marked a loss of zest for life, and, roughly a year later, Odd Hassel died, on May 11, 1981.

Scientific Career

Odd Hassel made his mark on science not only in conformational analysis but also in several other areas of chemistry. His first international recognition was for introducing adsorption indicators, now used in standard analytical procedures. While working in Fajans' laboratory in Munich, Odd studied spectral sensitization of silver halides through the addition of organic dyes. From this work developed the use of a dye as an adsorption indicator in analysis for silver ions and halide ions. The dye adsorbs onto the particles of silver halide as they form, which allows the particles to be seen before they are large enough to be seen by the naked eye without the dye. By the use of adsorption indicators, the analysis of silver or halide ions can be accomplished with greater accuracy. Two papers were published on the work—one with Fajans introducing the method and one by Hassel alone about the mechanisms of the adsorption. Hassel's first publication was from his work as an undergraduate. A publication and his thesis covered a kinetics (the rate of reaction) study of the reduction of nitro compounds with stannous chloride.

Hassel went to the Kaiser Wilhelm Institute in Dahlem, Berlin, after leaving Fajans' group. In Berlin he learned X-ray crystallography, a technique that he continued to use extensively when he returned to Oslo. While still at Berlin, Hassel published the corrected structure for graphite from his X-ray work. In Oslo, he pioneered work on Werner complexes (compounds in which bonds are formed by sharing a pair of electrons from one atom), fluoroxy, and other fluoro compounds. One of his many notable studies was of water substituted for ammonia in Werner complexes. Water could substitute without rupture of the structure.

Many individual compounds were studied, both in powder and in single-crystal form. One compound studied was cadmium iodide; the results obtained by Hassel corrected the classification of its structural type. These seemingly individual studies continued to lay a solid experimental foundation for the understanding of crystals.

Isomorphous solids are not crystalline in nature; that is, the atoms and molecules are not arranged in the systematic ordered array of crystalline solids. This field is one avoided by many X-ray crystallographers. Hassel attacked the field in a systematic way. He studied compounds that were similar in formula to determine if they corresponded in structure and also to determine quantitatively the difference. This study led to the concept of the "radii of action," the size of the sphere of influence of multiatomic ions. He found that many compounds of similar formula do have similar atomic arrangements and that often the difference in distance between atoms is systematic.

The crowning achievement in the study of crystals was to bring him international fame. In 1934, he published a book, *Kristallchemie*, that provided an up-to-date review of both experimental work and theoretical considerations. By 1935, the book had been translated by R. C. Evans of Cambridge from German to English (*Crystal Chemistry*). The book was also translated into Russian and became a standard reference for chemists and crystallographers. Until its publication, no one place contained all the work on crystals. This collection of most of the work on crystals allowed others not only to gain access to the experimental work but also to see the current theories and to be able to work toward new theories. Hassel even suggested new directions in which the tool of X-ray methods might be used.

In approximately 1930, Hassel began to work more and more on organic molecules. X-ray methods of that time could not determine positions of light atoms, such as carbon, hydrogen, and oxygen, within a molecule. Substituting a heavy atom helped but not enough to determine the complete molecular shape. One technique that he viewed as a possible help was the measurement of dipole moments. Dipole moments are caused by a separation of positive and negative charges in a molecule. In molecules where the positive and negative charges coincide, one end is no more negative than the other. Many molecules, however, have one end more positive than the other, creating a dipole moment analogous to that of the magnetic field of a bar magnet. The greater the difference in charge and the farther apart the charges, the greater the dipole moment.

Hassel used dipole moments as a tool to understand the shape of a molecule, the interactions between molecules, and the distribution of electric charge. An example of the information determined by Hassel and his research group is that in p-nitro-benzonitrile one nitrogen is negative compared to carbon but not in phenylcar-bylamine. This type of data is used today in the synthesis of organic compounds. The extra charge will often direct a substitution to one place instead of another.

The number of organic compounds that are crystalline is limited and thus limited Hassel's work. Needing another tool to be able to study organic molecules, he looked for a method to study free molecules. The method chosen in 1938 was electron diffraction. Similar to X-ray diffraction, the electrons in the compounds deflect the incoming electrons in a systematic pattern, which can be detected by a photographic plate or film. The pattern on the film can be used to determine the structure of molecules even in the gas phase. It was used to study not only organic compounds but also inorganic compounds, such as molecules of bromine and iodine, carbon dioxide, disulfide, tetrachloride and tetrabromide, phosphorus tri-sulfide, and di-iron hexachloride. Information on molecular shape and bond distances (distance between atoms bonded together) was acquired as both the experimental and the computational areas of the method were improved. Studies of organic compounds, especially cyclohexane and substituted cyclohexanes, where another element or group of elements replace a hydrogen in cyclohexane, were a major part of the research program. Although there had been suggestions that the six carbons were not all in the same plane, some scientists had published that cyclohexane was planar, based on spectroscopic data. The electron diffraction work showed that the six carbons were not in the same plane. There were two distinct conformers of cyclohexane, called the "chair" and the "boat" after the appearance of their shapes. One way in which to visualize the shapes is to number the carbons in order around the ring. In the boat conformer, carbons two, three, five, and six are in the same plane (or, on each side of a canoe); carbons one and four are raised above the plane like the bows of a canoe. The chair conformer is different, as carbon four is below the plane of the four carbons. The shape is similar to a person's shape while sitting in a recliner and is the more prominent conformer.

In roughly 1943, more detailed analysis allowed the differentiation of the two hydrogens bonded to each carbon. One hydrogen is almost in the plane of the carbons, the other is almost perpendicular to the plane. A cyclohexane with one hydrogen substituted by another element or group of elements is more stable with the substituted group in the position close to the plane of the molecule. It was also found that the groups could change from one position to the other as the ring inverted. When more than one group were substituted on the ring, the positions of the groups were often determined by the groups being far enough apart so that they interfered with each other the least.

Much of the scientific work that Hassel accomplished during this period was not reaching scientists in most of the world. Although almost all of his early work was published in German journals, when Germany invaded Norway, Hassel switched to Norwegian journals, which were not as well known, as well distributed, or as widely translated. The outside world did not learn of his outstanding work until after the war.

In 1943, Hassel was arrested and placed in a concentration camp. He stayed busy even in the camp; he taught general chemistry lectures and even a full physical chemistry course, illegally. He recruited scientists such as Per Andersen, who worked with him after the war. As his publication record shows articles every year, he must have spent some time in the camp collecting ideas and planning experiments to be done upon release. The articles published in 1944 were probably submitted before his arrest.

In 1953, Hassel began studies in a new field, charge-transfer complexes. He found the theories prevalent in the 1950's unacceptable for stereochemical reasons. Using X-ray crystallography again, he studied several of these compounds. The results from his work explained charge-transfer bonding, made the analogy to hydrogen bonding, worked out systematic bond distance, and established concepts to use in describing the charge transfer complexes. His work in charge-transfer bonding allowed explanation of compounds that had puzzled science. Molecules such as molecular bromine were not expected to make complexes, but they did. His work has explained the structure of these compounds. Crystals of molecules containing both electron accepting and electron donating groups have also puzzled scientists; the bond lengths are too short for the known types of intermolecular interactions. The work of Hassel, however, indicates that the bonds are the right length for charge-transfer bonds.

Hassel has received many richly deserved awards, including honorary degrees from the universities of Copenhagen (1950) and Stockholm (1960). He was recipient of the Guinerus Medal from the Royal Norwegian Academy of Sciences (1964) and the Guldberg and Waage's Law of Mass Action Memorial from the Norwegian Chemical Society (1964). The American Chemical Society honored him as a foreign Centennial Fellow. The Norwegian government made him a knight of the Order of Saint Olav. Perhaps the highest compliment was paid by his colleagues in 1967, when the Hassel Lecture, a lecture to be given by an outstanding foreign scientist, was established. Hassel has also given of his time and effort to advance science. He did much work on the steering body of the Norwegian Research Council for Science and Humanities; he served as chairman of the Norwegian Chemical Society and as Norwegian editor from 1947 to 1957 of the scientific journal *Acta Chemica Scandinavica*. Many of the University of Oslo faculty members trace their scientific heritage back to the inspiration of Odd Hassel.

Bibliography

Primary
CHEMISTRY: *Kristallchemie*, 1934 (*Crystal Chemistry*, 1935, translated by R. C. Evans); "Results of Electric Moment Measurements of Cyclohexane Derivatives and Their Relationship to Conclusions Drawn from X-Ray Crystallographic Work," *Transactions of the Faraday Society*, vol. 30, 1934; "Cykloheksanproblemet," *Tidsskrift for Kjemi, Bergvaesen og Metallurgi*, vol. 3, 1943 ("The Cyclohexane Problem," *Topics in Stereochemistry*, vol. 6, 1968); "Structure of the So-Called *cis*-Decalin," *Nature*, vol. 157, 1946; "Electron Diffraction Investigations of Molecular Structures," *Acta Chemica Scandinavica*, vol. 1, 1947; "Stereochemistry of Cyclohexane," *Quarterly Reviews*, 1953; "Nomenclature of Cyclohexane Bonds," *Science*, vol. 119, 1954 (with D. H. R. Barton, K. S. Pitzer, and Vladimir Prelog); "Structural Aspects of Interatomic Charge-Transfer Bonding," *Science*, vol. 170, 1970; "The Gas Electron Diffraction Method," *Physical Methods in Heterocyclic Chemistry*, 1971 (with P. Anderson).

Secondary
Anderson, Per, Otto Bastiansen, and Sven Furbery, eds. *Selected Topics in Structure Chemistry*. Oslo: Universitetsforlaget, 1967. This book is a collection of papers dedicated to Odd Hassel on his seventieth birthday. It includes a delightful biography and a summary of his work written by those who knew him well. Articles are by his scientific heirs.
Bastiansen, Otto. "Obituaries." *Chemistry in Britain* 18 (1982): 442. A short but excellent article about Odd Hassel by someone who knew and loved him.
Blakeslee, Sandra. "Winners Plumbed the Nature of Matter." *The New York Times*, October 31, 1969: 20. This is a discussion of the work of the two prizewinners in chemistry and that of Murray Gell-Mann, the winner in physics.
Eliel, Ernest L. "Nobel Laureates in Economics, Chemistry, and Physics." *Science* 166 (November 7, 1969): 718-720. Eliel is a scientist from the field of conformational analysis. He discusses the importance of the work of Hassel and Barton and the men themselves.
Johnson, Robin. "Barton, Hassel Win Chemistry Nobels." *Chemical and Engineering News* 47 (November 10, 1969): 11. Another article to announce the Nobel Prize and its importance, with personal insights not seen in other articles.
"Nobel Prizes in Chemistry, Physics." *Science News* 96 (November 1, 1969): 421-442. This article is an announcement of the Nobel Prize to Derek Barton and Odd Hassel with comments about the importance of the award.
Nobelstiftelsen. *Nobel Lectures: Chemistry, 1963-1970*. New York: Elsevier, 1972.

This book reprinted the Nobel lecture and a short biography of each prizewinner in chemistry.

"Odd Hassel." *McGraw-Hill Modern Scientists and Engineers*. Vol. 2. New York: McGraw-Hill, 1980. This article, reviewed by Odd Hassel, provides a short review of his accomplishments.

Ramsay, O. Bertrand. *Stereochemistry (Nobel Prize Topics in Chemistry)*. New York: John Wiley & Sons, 1982. This monograph traces the history of stereochemistry, emphasizing the influence of the Nobel Prize winners—Hassel, Barton, Vladimir Prelog, and John Cornforth. Biographical notes and reprints of their most important paper in English are included.

"The Three New Nobel Scientists." *The New York Times*, October 31, 1969: 20. This article includes the reaction of Odd Hassel to winning the Nobel Prize. It also mentions that Ragnar Fritsch, the economics laureate, and Odd Hassel are close friends.

Wasson, Tyler, ed. *Nobel Prize Winners*. New York: H. W. Wilson, 1987. This is a short but informative article about Odd Hassel. It does tell of his quiet, reserved personality.

C. Alton Hassell

1970

Chemistry
Luis F. Leloir, Argentina

Physics
Hannes Alfvén, Sweden
Louis-Eugène-Félix Néel, France

Physiology or Medicine
Julius Axelrod, United States
Sir Bernard Katz, Great Britain
Ulf von Euler, Sweden

Economic Sciences
Paul A. Samuelson, United States

Literature
Aleksandr Solzhenitsyn, Soviet Union

Peace
Norman E. Borlaug, United States

LUIS F. LELOIR
1970

Born: Paris, France; September 6, 1906
Died: Buenos Aires, Argentina; December 2, 1987
Nationality: Argentine
Areas of concentration: Biochemistry and carbohydrate chemistry

Leloir delineated the mechanism for the biosynthesis of carbohydrates with his discovery of sugar-nucleotide compounds, showing that transfer reactions using cofactors were involved. He determined the process of glycogen synthesis taking place in the body, and of sugar and starch synthesis in green plants

The Award

Presentation

The Nobel Prize in Chemistry for 1970 was presented by Professor Karl Myrbäck of the Royal Swedish Academy of Sciences to Luis Leloir on December 10, 1970. In his speech, Myrbäck surveyed the nature of carbohydrates, from simple sugars to polysaccharides such as glycogen and cellulose, and their vital roles in all living organisms. In particular, he stressed the importance of plants in sugar manufacture and the subsequent metabolism of such compounds. The breakdown of these compounds had been known for a long time, but information on synthesis reactions was fragmentary even into the 1950's.

In 1949, Leloir discovered how sugars could be transformed from one form to another by the use of nucleotides acting, in conjunction with sugar molecules, as an activation intermediary. By forming sugar-nucleotide combinations, more complex sugars could be easily synthesized, an idea that was quickly picked up by numerous research scientists worldwide. In fact, Leloir's procedure showed how an immense number of metabolic reactions could be studied, thereby opening a tremendous range of biochemical research.

With the discovery of the sugar-nucleotides, Leloir showed that all reactions involved were transfer reactions in which the sugar moieties were transferred to other molecules, allowing even high-molecular-weight polysaccharides to be formed. By 1959, Leloir had applied the reaction buildup mechanism to glycogen, one of the most important molecules in the body, showing that nature performs independent processes for synthesis and breakdown of carbohydrate molecules.

Nobel lecture

On December 11, 1970, Leloir presented his Nobel lecture, entitled "Two Decades of Research on the Biosynthesis of Saccharides." Detailing the early history of his work, including studies on fatty acid oxidation, renal hypertension, and glycogen transformation, Leloir first concentrated on his work on lactose breakdown, discovering its mechanism of using cofactors. His group worked with 1,6-diphosphate, in the process discovering the second major cofactor to be uridine. They synthesized the first sugar-nucleotide, uridine diphosphate glucose (UDPG), the structure of the molecule being confirmed five years later. In subsequent experiments, UDPG was found to act as a glucose donor, assisting in building larger molecules. Similar transfer reactions were found in wheat-germ extract, including two enzymes, allowing Leloir to explain the mechanism of sucrose synthesis in plants. At the same time, he managed to isolate a new sugar moiety, N-acetylglucosamine, essential in the biosynthesis of bacterial cell walls and mucoproteins. Numerous other sugar-nucleotides were isolated in further studies, and their complicated transformation processes were delineated.

Leloir mentioned many of the transfer reactions detected by other workers, work leading to his own detection of the formation of glycogen from UDPG with liver and muscle enzymes. His work showed that the process was not a simple reversal of the phosphorylase reaction. After finding the correct pathway, he extended his study to investigating the formation of starch in plants, discovering the enzymes catalyzing the transfer of glucose to starch molecules.

Leloir became interested in lipids as intermediates in the formation of polysaccharides and illustrated the first lipid intermediary detected in bacteria, undecaprenol pyrophosphate. He showed the equations advanced for the role of the carrier lipid in the formation of *Salmonella lipopolysaccharides*, a key ingredient in the formation of bacterial cell walls (murein). He also detailed the mechanisms by which the cell walls were assembled.

As a new issue, Leloir became interested in polyprenols. The type compound, isolated from animal tissues, was called dolichol. Twenty isoprene units form the molecule. Leloir worked with this compound found in the liver, and he detailed the reaction mechanisms discovered, suggesting additional problems for further research.

Leloir closed with special acknowledgments of Professor Bernardo A. Houssay and of coworkers and various organizations involved in his research.

Critical reception

The official announcement of the 1970 Nobel Prize in Chemistry seemed to provoke no great response either in major national magazines or in relevant scientific publications, with a single exception. In *Chemistry* (January, 1971), for example, the award, along with those for physics, medicine, and the Nobel Peace Prize, was simply noted, with a brief, simplified explanation of the work done by Leloir on sugar-nucleotides and their role in carbohydrate metabolism. In *Newsweek* (November 9, 1970) and *Time* (November 6, 1970), the award was noted with even greater brevity; *Time*, for example, spent much more space on a program suggested to increase the production of physicians in the 1980's.

The major recognition of the prizewinner came in an article written by Enrico Cabib, one of Leloir's numerous coworkers, and published in *Science* (November 6, 1970). Filled with enjoyable anecdotal material, Cabib's article delineated Leloir's early work in Argentina, including the trials of working in a makeshift laboratory with a dearth of good equipment. Indeed, it is almost amazing the results he achieved by employing money-saving inventions, homemade apparatus, and ingenious gadgetry. Cabib remarked on Leloir's powerful influence in maintaining a calm and soothing atmosphere in the laboratory. His remarks on this Nobel winner's character are quite illuminating: He depicts Leloir donating all of his prize money and his professor's salary to the institute because of its needs and not missing a single day in the laboratory despite the pressure of administrative and other duties. Perhaps it could be no higher honor than to quote a coworker's opinion of the laureate: "The world is made richer by the presence of persons like Leloir. With his example he taught many of us a style of life and with his work, he has enlarged the horizons of human adventure."

Biography

Luis Leloir was born in Paris, of Argentine parents, on September 6, 1906. When he was two, his family moved to Buenos Aires, where he lived for the rest of his life with only minor exceptions. Upon taking the necessary tests, he was graduated with a medical degree from the University of Buenos Aires in 1932, and he went to work at the University Hospital for the next two years. Interested in advancing medical knowledge, he went to work with Dr. Bernardo A. Houssay at the Institute of Physiology, doing research on the role of the adrenal gland in carbohydrate metabolism. Becoming more involved in research, in 1936 he went to the University of Cambridge Biochemistry Laboratory, where he worked with Malcolm Dixon on succinic acid dehydrogenase, with Norman Edson on ketogenesis in the liver, and with David Green on other research. After the year, he returned to the Institute of Physiology to begin research with J. M. Muñoz on fatty acid oxidation, and, subsequently, with several other researchers on the formation of angiotensin.

In 1943, he resigned, because of the dismissal of Houssay from the university. Also in 1943, he married Amelia Zuberbuhler; they had a daughter, Amelia. In 1944, he became a research assistant at Carl Cori's Laboratory in St. Louis, Missouri, working on the formation of citric acid and, with David Green of Columbia University, on the problems of aminotransferases.

In 1945, he returned to Argentina to head the Instituto de Investigaciones Bioquímicas, beginning work on carbohydrate metabolism, particularly that of galactose, and the study of cofactors. That work, along with research on lipids and polyprenols, continued until 1987. He spent the rest of his life in Buenos Aires, with the exception of trips to meetings abroad, until his death on December 2, 1987.

Scientific Career

After spending a year working at the University of Cambridge, Leloir returned to the Institute of Physiology in Buenos Aires. With J. M. Muñoz, he did interesting work on ethanol metabolism and fatty acid oxidation. In fact, they were the first to obtain an enzymatic system capable of oxidizing fatty acids in vitro that was reproducible. Leloir also teamed with other coworkers, under Eduardo Menendez, to investigate the mechanism of renal hypertension. The work, resulting in the discovery of a new substance they named hypertensin, saw Leloir in the primary role of establishing the mechanism by which angiotensinogen was transformed into angiotensin (as it is known chemically today) by the enzyme renin.

In 1947, after a time spent in the United States, Leloir set up his own privately financed Biochemical Research Institute in Buenos Aires, putting together an excellent research team. Undertaking the study of the biosynthesis of lactose, or milk sugar, the decision was made to approach the research by seeing how lactose was degraded by a yeast, *Saccharomyces fragilis*. He began with a hydrolysis of lactose to glucose and galactose, following with a phosphorylation, or addition of phosphorus, of the galactose, to give galactose 1-phosphate, with the phosphorus being in the quite unusual position on the first carbon atom. The next step, which changed the molecule to glucose 6-phosphate, was determined to require heat-labile enzymes and two heat-stable cofactors. The first cofactor identified was glucose 1,6-diphosphate, found to be a coenzyme for the intermediate phosphoglucomutase reaction, the enzyme that catalyzes the conversion of glucose 1-phosphate to glucose 6-phosphate. The second cofactor was, after a great tour de force, identified as uridine diphosphate glucose (UDPG): the first identified sugar-nucleotide.

The mechanism by which uridine diphosphate glucose acted as a cofactor was determined to be acting as a transfer point for sugar molecules, in that the uridine diphosphate glucose acted as a glucose donor. With the basic mechanism known, other mechanisms of the sugar-nucleotide groups were investigated immediately, including ones of guanosine, adenosine, cytidine, and thymidine with sugar molecules, and ones with more complex sugars, such as UDP-N-acetylglycosamine, extremely important in the biosynthesis of bacterial cell walls. All this work was initially done on yeast extracts. A similar procedure was performed on wheat-germ enzymes, which allowed for the explanation of sucrose biosynthesis, providing an explanation for the mechanism of sucrose synthesis in plants. The discovery of this new group of substances, known as sugar-nucleotides, and their function in the biosynthesis of complex carbohydrates in living forms is the basis for the awarding of the Nobel Prize in Chemistry to Leloir.

The mechanism by which uridine diphosphate glucose acts in the conversion of galactose 1-phosphate to glucose 1-phosphate was established by Leloir himself. The uridylyl group was found to transfer from uridine diphosphate glucose to galactose 1-phosphate enzymatically, resulting in UDP-galactose. An epimerase, another enzyme, converted that nucleotide back into UDP-glucose, allowing the cycle to restart. This essentially established the role of sugar-nucleotides as substrates for monosaccharide interconversion into higher molecular weight forms.

Leloir also pushed to find the role of UDP-acetylglucosamine. The roles established for that molecule included formation from UDP-acetylgalactosamine in the liver, and in the sugar moiety used in building up chitin. Enough was known by the mid-1950's to identify the sugar-nucleotides' two main functions: serving as substrates for enzymes that interconverted monosaccharides and acting as donors in glycosyl transfer reactions. This identification of function led Leloir to a new investigation, that of glycogen formation.

In 1957, Leloir's group announced an alternative mechanism for the synthesis of glycogen. He had found that he could catalyze the formation of glycogen from UDP-glucose by using liver extracts and muscle enzymes. Prior to his work, it had been believed that the synthesis occurred as a reversal of the basic phosphorylase reaction of glucose reacting with inorganic phosphate, with the same enzyme being involved in both synthesis and degradation. He found that glucose 6-phosphate acted as an activator of glycogen synthetase. Leloir's group discovered a new co-enzyme, uridine triphosphate (UTP), analogous to ATP (adenosine triphosphate), which combined with glucose 1-phosphate to form the new sugar-nucleotide, uridine diphosphate glucose. In the presence of a specific enzyme of glycogen synthetase, a molecule of uridine diphosphate glucose, and a primer, the reaction would result in uridine diphosphate and would transfer glucose to a growing glycogen chain. In the presence of adenosine triphosphate, the uridine diphosphate is converted back into uridine triphosphate, and the reaction can continue again. The continuous nature of the reaction is regulated by the concentrations of meta-bolites and by reversible conversions of active to inactive forms of compounds brought about by several enzymes acting on one another.

Leloir then extended the work to investigate the formation of starch in plants. Enzymes were found that catalyzed the transfer of glucose from UDP-glucose to starch. Quite incidentally, it was also found that adenosine diphosphate glucose (ADP-glucose) worked ten times faster, a result that Leloir was able to show actually occurred, for example, in corn. Enzymes for synthesizing ADP-glucose were also discovered.

After Peron's dictatorship was overthrown in Argentina, the new government, much more inclined toward the development of science, improved the Institute of Physiology by granting it much larger buildings and newer equipment and adding it to the University of Buenos Aires. Leloir was appointed Professor Extraordinarius and was later made chairman of the Department of Biochemistry.

In the mid-1960's, Leloir became interested in the idea of lipid intermediaries in polysaccharide biosynthesis, discovery of which had been made in 1965 during studies of the biosynthesis of lipopolysaccharides by Salmonella organisms. These intermediates were identified as polyprenyl phosphate-sugars. Using mass spec-troscopy to assist in the structure determination of the intermediate compound, Le-loir's group discovered undecaprenol pyrophosphate. The role of that molecule in Salmonella involved the transfer of galactose 1-phosphate so that the lipid pyrophos-phate and uridine monophosphate are formed. Leloir derived the series of steps—six repeatable steps—to show how the polyrenol phosphate could be synthesized in living organisms.

In the 1970's, Leloir became very interested in the exact role played by poly-prenols in the synthesis of complex polysaccharides. In 1970, his work showed the presence, in animal tissues, of a microsomal acceptor lipid which accepted glucose residues from uridine diphosphate glucose, the compound being called dolichol. With N. Behrens, he studied a liver process that involved dolichol, a process that involved glucosyl residues from uridine diphosphate glucose being accepted to form UDP and dolichol-phosphoglucose. They were able to determine that the controlling product formed was dolichol monophosphate, the glucose given off in the reaction combining with a protein to become a glucosylated protein. Only a few such are known, one of which is collagen. The study of those polyprenol intermediates fascinated him, because of the large variety of polyprenols and the fact that they could vary in chain length, number of *cis* or *trans* double bonds, degree of saturation, and the number of phosphates and sugars attached to the molecule.

Leloir spent much of his productive years on the Faculty of Sciences at the University of Buenos Aires. He was a member of many scientific organizations, including the National Academy of Sciences, American Academy of Arts and Sciences, Academia Nacional de Medicina, American Philosophical Society, Pontifical Academy of Sciences, and the Biochemical Society of England (as an honorary member). He received honorary degrees from various universities, including Granada (Spain), Paris, and Tucumán and La Plata, in Argentina. He had, over his research years, received numerous awards besides the Nobel Prize, including awards from the Argentine Scientific Society, Helen Hay Whitney Foundation, Severo Vaccaro Foundation (Argentina), Bunge and Born Foundation (Argentina), Gairdner Foundation (Canada), Louisa Gross Horowitz (United States), and Benito Juarez (Mexico). He also acted as president of the Pan American Association of Biochemical Societies.

Because of his numerous contributions to biochemistry, particularly in the clarifying of the basic mechanisms of carbohydrate metabolism in both plants and animals, Luis Leloir deserves a prominent place among the important scientists developing biochemistry in the twentieth century. His solving of the glycogen problem alone ensures his importance—his other scientific researches and discoveries only increase his contributions to the biochemical understanding of the world.

Bibliography

Primary
CHEMISTRY: "Synthesis of Glucose-1,6-Diphosphate," *Methods in Enzymology*, vol. 1, 1955 (with R. E. Trucco); "Biosynthesis of Glycogen from Uridine Diphosphate Glucose," *Journal of the American Chemical Society*, vol. 79, 1957 (with C. E. Cardini); "Characterization of Phosphorus Compounds by Acid Lability," *Methods in Enzymology*, vol. 3, 1957 (with C. E. Cardini); "Synthesis of Glycogen from Uridine Diphosphate Glucose in Liver," *Journal of Biological Chemistry*, vol. 235, 1960 (with S. H. Goldembe); "Starch and Oligosaccharide Synthesis from Uridine Diphosphate Glucose," *Journal of Biological Chemistry*, vol. 236, 1961 (with M. A. Rongined and C. E. Cardini); "Nucleoside Diphosphate Sugars and Saccharide Synthesis," *Biochemical Journal*, vol. 91, 1964; "Two Decades of

Research on Biosynthesis of Saccharides," *Science*, vol. 172, 1971; "Biosynthesis of a N,N'-Diacetylchitobiose Containing Lipid by Liver-Microsomes—Probable Dolichol Pyrophosphate Derivative," *Biochemical and Biophysical Research Communications*, vol. 52, 1973 (with R. J. Stanelon); "Role of Dolichol in Protein Glycosylation," *Advances in Experimental Medicine*, vol. 83, 1977.

Secondary

Banks, Peter. *The Biochemistry of the Tissues*. New York: John Wiley & Sons, 1976. Presents a detailed overview of what is known of tissue chemistry, with topics as diverse as the origin of life, bioenergetics, and obesity in humans. Carbohydrate metabolism in the liver and other organs is covered in detail. Control of metabolic processes in cells is nicely explained. Numerous illustrations and references.

Borek, Ernest. *The Atoms Within Us*. New York: Columbia University Press, 1961. A beginner book on the nature of the chemicals that make up complex molecules within living organisms. Covers all the basics, including enzymes, sugars, genes, and specialty topics such as blood, viruses, and use of isotopes. It is well written and is a good starting place for anyone without a strong background in chemistry that wants to understand how biochemistry works.

De Bley, H. J. *Introduction to the Chain of Life*. Reading, Mass.: Addison-Wesley, 1975. A general introduction to the biochemistry of life, starting with the development of the science. Explains well the extensive characteristics of carbohydrates and lipids, the various metabolisms, including glycogen and glucose. Special section of interest on abnormalities of metabolism, the importance of nutrition, and chemistry of the environment. Contains a glossary.

Guthrie, R. D. *An Introduction to the Chemistry of Carbohydrates*. Oxford, England: Clarendon Press, 1968. This reference presents a well-written overview of carbohydrates, from mono- to polysaccharides. Included are the known reactions and pathways involving carbohydrates both in and outside the body. Also has a good chapter on physical methods of analysis for molecules up to sugar-nucleotides. This is detailed reading, providing additional references.

Harrison, Kenneth. *Guide-Book to Biochemistry*. 2d ed. Cambridge, England: Cambridge University Press, 1965. This reference gives a brief introduction to biochemistry on a level understandable by anyone with basic chemistry. Covers oxidation and the role of enzymes, with chapters on carbohydrate metabolism and its controls, Leloir's reactions involving glycogen synthesis using cofactors, and glucose synthesis. The work provides an appendix of complex formulas.

Larner, Joseph. *Intermediary Metabolism and Its Regulation*. Englewood Cliffs, N.J.: Prentice-Hall, 1971. This reference shows the approaches used to investigate the pathways chemicals follow in the body, making use of analytical tools such as tracers and radioactivity. It covers energy metabolism, sugars, glycogenesis, and numerous other cycles. Agents of control are stressed. There is an excellent, though detailed, chapter on integration and control of carbohydrate and lipid metabolism. Also provided are glossary, additional references.

Percival, Edmund George Vincent. *Structural Carbohydrate Chemistry.* Englewood Cliffs, N.J.: Prentice-Hall, 1950. This is an older book, but well written, detailing the analysis of various types of carbohydrates, from monosaccharides to polysaccharides. Studies include synthesis and breakdown, the actions of natural glycosides, and glycogen metabolism. There are numerous line drawings and extensive details on sugars in the body.

Westley, John. *Enzymic Catalysis.* New York: Harper & Row, 1969. This work presents the fundamentals of enzymology as applied to biochemistry. It details the mechanisms by which enzymes act and the constraints, particularly temperature, pressure, and chemicals present. Good chapter on regulatory enzymes that control metabolism as a basal level. Complicated mathematics in some places, but it provides a problem-solving appendix. Numerous references provided.

Arthur L. Alt

1971

Chemistry
Gerhard Herzberg, Canada

Physics
Dennis Gabor, Great Britain

Physiology or Medicine
Earl W. Sutherland, Jr., United States

Economic Sciences
Simon Kuznets, United States

Literature
Pablo Neruda, Chile

Peace
Willy Brandt, West Germany

GERHARD HERZBERG
1971

Born: Hamburg, Germany; December 25, 1904

Nationality: Canadian
Areas of concentration: Molecular spectroscopy and structure determination

Herzberg was a leader in molecular spectroscopy, a method of study that can identify molecules and provide precise information on their electronic structure and motions. He performed pioneering work with free radicals, the highly reactive molecular fragments which occur as intermediates in chemical reactions

The Award

Presentation

The 1971 Nobel Prize in Chemistry was presented to Gerhard Herzberg on December 10, 1971; Professor Stig Clæsson of the Royal Swedish Academy of Sciences made the presentation address. Clæsson began his address by noting that Herzberg not only is regarded as "the world's foremost molecular spectroscopist," but also he has made his Ottawa Institute (The National Research Council of Canada) into the world center for spectroscopic research. Herzberg and his laboratory play a leadership role in the field with as great an impact as Niels Bohr's Copenhagen Institute and the Cavendish Laboratory at Cambridge once had.

Molecular spectroscopy studies the interaction between molecules and electromagnetic radiation (which consists, for example, of visible light, ultraviolet radiation, and infrared radiation). Analysis of the radiation energies that are emitted or absorbed by a molecule can provide extremely precise information about its size, shape, movement, energy, and electronic structure. Although Herzberg was originally a physicist, he was eventually able to use spectroscopy to study molecular systems complicated enough to be of interest to chemists. In particular, in the 1950's, Herzberg was the first to investigate free radicals, the molecular fragments which are created by the violent collisions of molecules as they undergo a chemical reaction. Radicals exist for only an infinitesimal length of time before recombining into new molecules, but they hold the key to the mechanisms of chemical reactivity and reactions. By the time he was awarded the Nobel Prize, Herzberg had extensively studied more than thirty radicals. One of Herzberg's intriguing discoveries is that many radicals change their shape dramatically when they absorb energy.

Throughout his presentation, Clæsson emphasized both Herzberg's experimental skill and his theoretical insight. He credited Herzberg with advancing both the field of quantum mechanics (the branch of physics that describes the behavior of microscopic systems) and the development of molecular spectroscopy.

Nobel lecture

Herzberg's Nobel lecture, delivered on December 11, 1971, and entitled "Spectroscopic Studies of Molecular Structure," was a detailed summary of some of the most important results obtained during his many years of work in spectroscopy. Herzberg reviewed the spectroscopic data and the calculated results for about twenty molecules, some of which exist as electrically charged ions or radicals. His studies had differing aims. Some provided precise data against which to check theoretical predictions, while others identified chemical species present in the interstellar medium, in flames, and in electrical discharges. Much of Herzberg's work, however, was done in the spirit of basic research, with no specific goal other than the cataloging of molecular properties for their own sake.

One way to obtain the spectrum of a molecule is to irradiate it with electromagnetic radiation and compare the wavelengths of the emerging radiation to those of the incident radiation. The "missing" wavelengths have been absorbed by the molecules, giving them energy to vibrate, rotate, rearrange and/or lose their electrons, or break apart. From knowledge of the missing wavelengths, one can calculate basic molecular properties such as bond lengths and strengths, molecular shape, vibrational and rotational frequencies, the nature and energy of the electron distribution, and dissociation and ionization energies (the energies needed to break bonds and to remove electrons, respectively). During his Nobel address, Herzberg showed how these properties manifest themselves in the spectra, and he displayed many of their values.

The simplest molecule that Herzberg described is hydrogen. A neutral hydrogen molecule consists of two hydrogen atoms, that is, two electrons and two protons, and while a four-particle system is still very complicated, it is possible to calculate many of its expected properties on the basis of theory alone. In order to evaluate the soundness of the theory, Herzberg analyzed the spectra of hydrogen and related gases, obtaining experimental values for the separation distance between the two atoms and for the dissociation and ionization energies. The importance of Herzberg's hydrogen work lies in its precision; for example, his experimental hydrogen ionization energy was measured to better than one part in a million. The theoretically derived ionization energy agrees with his experimental value in six digits, giving strong support to the model of the hydrogen atom on which the theory is based.

Many of the other species that Herzberg discussed are radicals. Because radicals are often very short-lived, occurring only as intermediates in chemical reactions, they are impossible to isolate for detailed study. Instead, when spectra are obtained from a reactive system, the identities of the radicals present must be deduced from the spectral features. The presence of a radical is confirmed only if it can be independently made and found to have a spectrum identical to the one in question. To illustrate this chain of detective work, Herzberg described how he identified the C_3 radical (a molecular fragment containing three carbon atoms) in comets by its distinctive spectral features and through laboratory experiments, even though C_3 had never before even been postulated as an intermediate in any chemical reaction. Herzberg concluded his survey by acknowledging Ronald Norrish and George

Porter, the developers of the principal experimental method Herzberg used to create his radicals and ions, and by stressing the work that still needed to be done in the field.

Critical reception

The 1971 Nobel Prize winners were announced while Herzberg was participating in a two-week Canadian-Soviet scientific exchange program. Herzberg had heard rumors that the prize was his after finishing a lecture at the Leningrad State University, but it was not until he was at the Leningrad station, leaving for Moscow, that the news was confirmed by the Foreign Secretary of the Soviet Academy of Sciences.

At the Moscow station, Herzberg told correspondents that he was "very surprised and very honored and very happy," although he was also confused as to whether he had won the Nobel Prize in chemistry or in physics. He said, "The award is for me as a physicist. I was brought up as a physicist. But my recent work, for example, in free radicals and molecules, has in a way been more appreciated by chemists. . . . I've had many awards in chemistry, but this is the first major award in physics." When told that the award was actually in chemistry, Herzberg blurted, "Ah ha, I was somewhat surprised," but showed no disappointment at the correction.

Reaction to Herzberg's selection in the professional journals, newspapers, and magazines was approving but matter-of-fact. For example, Alex E. Douglas of the National Research Council of Canada wrote in *Science*, November 12, 1971, that "Scientists . . . who have been involved in any way with problems of atomic and molecular structure will be pleased, but not surprised, by this announcement." Many of the popular publications strove to link Herzberg's basic research to applications that they apparently thought the public would better appreciate. *The Globe and Mail* of November 3, 1971, published in Toronto, stressed the importance of Herzberg's work to the understanding of air pollution, while *The New York Times* of November 4, 1971, wrote that "conceivably [Herzberg's studies] could ultimately contribute to solving such riddles as the origin of cancer."

The 1971 Nobel Prize winner in physics was Dennis Gabor, the discoverer of holography. The fact that both Herzberg and Gabor had been forced to flee Nazi Germany in the 1930's was a coincidence that was remarked upon in several of the reports about them. *The New York Times* of November 4, 1971, for example, ran an editorial entitled "Hitler's Gift to a Free World" that paid homage both to the prizewinners and to the "several thousand men and women involved in this vast scientific exodus [who] have long since richly repaid the nations which gave them sanctuary."

Herzberg was the first Canadian to win the Nobel Prize in either chemistry or physics. Even before winning the award, Herzberg had been a critic of Canadian science policy, being particularly outspoken about the need for scientists themselves, rather than "politicians, accountants, and committees," to determine the direction of their work. Besides attacking the bureaucracy of the Canadian system,

Herzberg has also deplored the tilt from basic toward applied research, saying, "Government people and laymen think of science only as a means to improve the economy. But the maser and laser, for example, were discovered not to provide implements but to gain understanding. You can't plan discoveries, nor can you direct science into undiscovered areas, because it's impossible to know what they are or might mean." He has stated firmly that "the exclusive or predominant support of mission-oriented work can only lead to mediocrity." Herzberg's views were so well known that a typical reaction from his peers at the time of the award was that his selection as the Nobel Prize recipient would be seen as an important affirmation of the value of pure research.

Biography

Gerhard Herzberg was born on December 25, 1904, in Hamburg, Germany, to Ella Biber and Albin Herzberg. His father died when Herzberg was ten. After attempting several business ventures, his mother left her two sons with family friends and emigrated to the United States, where she worked as a domestic to help with their support. Herzberg received his early education from the Technische Universität (technical university) at Darmstadt, now in West Germany. He obtained his master's degree in engineering in 1927, and his Ph.D. in physics in 1928 under Hans Rau, who had been a pupil of Wilhelm Wien. His Ph.D. thesis was concerned with the spectra of various forms of gaseous nitrogen.

After his studies at Darmstadt, Herzberg spent one postdoctoral year at the University of Göttingen under Max Born and James Franck, and another at the University of Bristol under A. M. Tyndall. By 1929, Herzberg had already published twenty scientific papers. In 1929, Herzberg married Luise Öttinger, a fellow physics student he had met at Göttingen. They eventually had one son and one daughter. Luise earned her Ph.D. from Frankfurt University in 1933 and was a scientific collaborator of Herzberg until her death in 1971.

From 1930 until 1935, Herzberg worked as *Privatdozent* (unsalaried specialized lecturer) and senior assistant in the physics department at Darmstadt. As Nazism became more entrenched in Germany, the Herzbergs were pressured to leave because Luise was Jewish. In 1935, the Carnegie Foundation made funds available for a temporary guest professorship at the University of Saskatchewan in Saskatoon, Canada, and a few months after his arrival there, Herzberg was given a permanent position as Applied Research Professor of Physics.

Herzberg became a Canadian citizen in 1945. From 1945 to 1948, he held the position of professor of spectroscopy at the Yerkes Observatory of the University of Chicago, Williams Bay, Wisconsin, where he investigated the molecular spectra of stars, comets, and planets. On his return to Canada, he joined the National Research Council in Ottawa as Principal Research Officer. Soon afterward, he was appointed Director of the Physics Division, a post he held from 1949 to 1955. In 1955, the division was divided into pure and applied physics, and Herzberg served as the Director of the Pure Physics Division until 1969 when a new title, Distinguished

Research Scientist, was created for him.

Sadly, Herzberg's wife died only a few months before he won the Nobel Prize in 1971. He married Monika Tenthoff, an acquaintance from Germany, in 1972. In 1975, the Herzberg Institute of Astrophysics, an interdisciplinary facility associated with the National Research Council, was founded. Herzberg continued to work well past the usual retirement age at the institute, along with about two hundred others, on problems in astronomy, space science, and molecular spectroscopy.

Scientific Career

Throughout his career, Herzberg has used the tools of spectroscopy to tackle questions of atomic and molecular structure. He has published more than two hundred original papers and five texts, three of which are considered to be classics in their field. His work is characteristically precise, clear, and extremely detailed, and his data have been repeatedly republished separately in handbooks for use by other researchers.

One of the earliest problems that Herzberg addressed is the structure of the atomic nucleus. In the 1920's, the only particles known to exist were protons and electrons, and therefore it was postulated that atomic nuclei were compound particles consisting only of these two kinds of particles. The protons would provide the bulk of the nuclear mass, and the electrons, together with the protons, would give the nucleus its characteristic electrical charge. The nitrogen nucleus, for example, would have fourteen protons and seven electrons. Together with Werner Heitler, Herzberg showed that this accepted picture of the nitrogen nucleus was not compatible with certain features of the nitrogen spectrum. Their analysis was published in 1929, influencing the search for a new nuclear model. Nuclei are now known to contain protons and neutrons; the neutron was discovered by James Chadwick in 1932.

During his years at Darmstadt, Herzberg devoted much of his time to improving and refining both the experimental techniques and the theoretical methods of analysis used in the then fledgling field of spectroscopy. In 1933, he published an important paper with Edward Teller describing how a molecule's symmetry affects its spectrum, and he showed how to derive extremely accurate values for the dissociation energy of many diatomic molecules.

One of Herzberg's early experimental discoveries was that the spectrum of molecular oxygen contains certain features never before observed, representing a "forbidden transition" made by the molecules as they absorb light energy. An understanding of this transition is important in the analysis of the chemistry and physics of the upper atmosphere, and therefore these "Herzberg bands" have been extensively studied by Herzberg and by other scientists. Later, in 1952, Herzberg was able to do a definitive analysis of the "Herzberg bands" and other forbidden transitions in oxygen using a sample cell that allowed for multiple transversals of the exciting light through the oxygen gas inside. With such a long path length for the radiation, the cell was as sensitive as a single transversal cell 5,000 meters long.

During the Nazi regime, many German academics were forced to flee the country, and it became increasingly difficult to find positions elsewhere. After a long search, Herzberg accepted a professorship at the University of Saskatchewan in Canada, even though it had no suitable research laboratory for him, few funds, and no advanced graduate students to work with him. Despite these drawbacks, Herzberg achieved much in his ten years there. For the first few years, he worked with experimental data that he and others had acquired in Germany, and, in 1937, Herzberg was able to show that within a molecule, the length of a carbon-carbon single bond depends upon the other bonds to which it is adjacent. This discovery was an important first step in understanding molecular shape, since carbon-carbon bonds are found in a wide variety of molecules. With small grants, Herzberg ultimately was able to set up a spectroscopy laboratory at Saskatchewan, where he and his graduate students studied gas molecules as well as the spectra from some stars and comets.

Perhaps the most important of Herzberg's accomplishments during his Saskatchewan years was the result of his somewhat forced slow research pace. As he improved the facilities there, he wrote the first two books of his major three-volume study of spectroscopy, *Molecular Spectra and Molecular Structure*. Volume 1 was entitled *Spectra of Diatomic Molecules* (1939); volume 2, *Infrared and Raman Spectra of Polyatomic Molecules* (1945). The third volume, *Electronic Spectra and Electronic Structure of Polyatomic Molecules*, was published in 1966. All three of these monumental works have been widely used as texts in advanced courses and are considered to be invaluable research aids.

In 1945, Herzberg accepted a research position at the Yerkes Observatory at the University of Chicago, where he could work in impressive laboratory facilities with advanced graduate students and colleagues within his field. While at Yerkes, Herzberg perfected new experimental techniques which enabled data to be collected under insensitive and difficult conditions. One of his important studies there showed that hydrogen is present in the atmospheres of several of the planets in this solar system. Herzberg also studied Earth's atmosphere, focusing on the changes that occur in the presence and absence of sunlight. Other astronomical contributions of his include the identification, along with Alex Douglas, of several carbon and hydrogen species in comets and in the interstellar medium and the confirmation of the presence of water in comets.

Despite the excellent facilities at Yerkes, the Herzbergs were glad to return to Canada when Herzberg obtained a position at his final professional destination, the National Research Council of Canada in Ottawa. Herzberg's Ottawa research has been mainly concerned with the spectroscopy of simple molecules, which he has investigated using a wide range of techniques including different light frequencies and excitation methods, very high and very low temperatures and pressures, and innovative sample cell configurations. Many of his studies have been directly motivated by questions in astronomy.

Herzberg is not the inventor of spectroscopy, and the application of quantum mechanics to atoms and atomic spectroscopy was becoming understood by scientists even by the end of the 1920's. The molecules are much more complicated than atoms, however, and Herzberg is credited with having worked out and systematized many of these complications. The simplest molecules are diatomic, containing only two atoms. Herzberg measured and compared the characteristics of many of the diatomics to each other, trying to understand what makes different molecules different; he also compared his experimental data to theoretical predictions to test various theories. A list of the diatomic molecules that he studied reads like the index of an elementary chemistry textbook: hydrogen, deuterium, oxygen, nitrogen, fluorine, chlorine, iodine, carbon monoxide, and various hydrides and oxides.

Of particular interest has been Herzberg's detailed descriptions of the geometries of many common polyatomic molecules. For example, he found that hydrogen cyanide (a three-atom molecule consisting of hydrogen, carbon, and nitrogen atoms bonded together) and acetylene (a four-atom molecule consisting of a pair of bonded carbon atoms, each of which is bonded to an end hydrogen atom) are linear in their least energetic states. Both molecules, however, are bent in their next most energetic states. Hydrogen cyanide forms an angle of 125 degrees between the carbon-hydrogen and carbon-nitrogen bonds, and acetylene forms an angle of 120 degrees between each carbon-hydrogen bond and the carbon-carbon backbone. In addition, in both molecules, the bonds stretch in the excited state by about 10 percent. This kind of detailed geometrical description is crucial to the understanding of the relationship between molecular shape and electronic energies and distributions.

Herzberg is perhaps most famous for his work on radicals. When he first began investigating radicals, they had never before been observed, and little was known about their nature, although their existence had long been suspected. Because of their fleeting lifetimes and usually very low concentrations, radicals present a difficult challenge to the experimentalist, and Herzberg needed to use special techniques in order to create them in detectable amounts. Along with other methods, he made excellent use of flash photolysis, whereby an intense flash of light is used to excite molecules to such a high energy that they break apart. The method of flash photolysis was developed by Ronald Norrish and George Porter, who won the Nobel Prize in 1967 for their work. Two other techniques specifically developed by Herzberg's group to study electrically charged molecules and fragments are flash discharge, which is closely related to flash photolysis, and flash radiolysis, in which a beam of electrons creates charged molecules and ions as it passes through the sample cell.

As a result of systematic investigations performed on a wide range of radicals, Herzberg was able to build up the theory needed to explain the many spectral features they produce. Most of the radicals that he has studied are so simple, and yet so rarely seen under normal conditions, that they have no common names and are referred to only by their chemical formulas. Typical of the radicals he has characterized are C_2, CO, NH, CS, C_2^-, CO^+, NO^+, HCO, HNO, HCF, C_3, CNC,

NCN, and HNCH: charged and uncharged molecular fragments consisting of only two to four common atoms.

Two radicals for which Herzberg is particularly well known are methylene (consisting of a carbon atom bonded to two hydrogen atoms) and methyl (a carbon atom bonded to three hydrogen atoms). Methyl and methylene groups are ubiquitous throughout organic chemistry and occur within a majority of the molecules found in living systems, and thus the behavior and characteristics of their radicals have implications for biology as well as chemistry. Herzberg found that the isolated methyl radical is nearly flat, a fact which is of great theoretical interest, since when attached to a molecule the methyl group resembles a pyramid. In contrast, a host of studies indicates that the methylene radical is bent. In its least energetic state, the hydrogen-carbon-hydrogen bond angle is 134 degrees; in its next two higher energy states, the bond angle first decreases to 102 degrees, and then increases back to about 140 degrees, reflecting the different electron distributions in the three states.

The Nobel Prize is awarded for outstanding contributions to scientific knowledge. Sometimes the contribution is a single, electrifying discovery that will immediately be of benefit in an applied or theoretical way. In other cases, the prize is awarded for a body of work that as a whole has transformed the thinking in a field or has even brought a new field into being. Herzberg's prize belongs to this latter category. His lifetime of work has had ramifications throughout all of chemistry: in providing an understanding of the mechanisms and rates of chemical reactions, in giving a "picture" of the structure and motions of molecules, and in showing how to unravel the information buried in complicated spectra. Herzberg can be credited with having pioneered and developed the application of spectroscopy to the study of radicals, and with having been a leader in the field of spectroscopy in general.

Bibliography

Primary
CHEMISTRY: *Atomic Spectra and Atomic Structure*, 1937; *Molecular Spectra and Molecular Structure*, vol. 1, *Spectra of Diatomic Molecules*, 1939; *Molecular Spectra and Molecular Structure*, vol. 2, *Infrared and Raman Spectra of Polyatomic Molecules*, 1945; *Molecular Spectra and Molecular Structure*, vol. 3, *Electronic Spectra and Electronic Structure of Polyatomic Molecules*, 1966; *The Spectra and Structure of Simple Free Radicals: An Introduction to Molecular Spectroscopy*, 1971.

Secondary
Davis, Jeff C., Jr. "Introduction to Spectroscopy: Part I. The Nature of Spectra." *Chemistry* 47 (October, 1974): 6-10; "Part II. The Spectrometer." *Chemistry* 48 (January, 1975): 11-14; "Part III. Light and the Electromagnetic Spectrum." *Chemistry* 48 (May, 1975): 19-22; "Part IV. Interaction of Light and Matter." *Chemistry* 48 (July/August, 1975): 15-18. This series of articles covers the fundamental concepts and techniques of spectroscopy at a leisurely and very accessible level.

Chemistry was created specifically for high school students, who generally do not study spectroscopy. Therefore, Davis is careful to define his terms carefully and to explain the rationale behind the various experimental and theoretical methods.

Herzberg, Gerhard. "Molecular Spectroscopy: A Personal History." *Annual Review of Physical Chemistry* 36 (1985): 1-30. This autobiography details Herzberg's academic training and professional career and includes descriptions of many of the other contributors to his field. Although he is technical in his discussions of his work, much of the account is historical and is easily understood by the nonscientist. The reader especially gets the sense of Herzberg's intense devotion to his work.

——————. *The Physical World.* Washington, D.C.: American Association for the Advancement of Science, 1974. This is a lecture that Herzberg presented to the XIV General Assembly of the International Union of Pure and Applied Physics under the title "Spectroscopy and Molecular Structure." A college-level background in spectroscopy is needed to benefit fully from this lecture. Reproductions of some of the illustrations from the lecture are included, but enough are missing so that it is sometimes difficult to follow Herzberg's remarks.

Stokes, Lawrence D. "Canada and an Academic Refugee from Nazi Germany: The Case of Gerhard Herzberg." *Canadian Historical Review* 57 (June, 1976): 150-170. This article is a detailed and fascinating account of how and why Herzberg and his wife left Germany for Canada during the Nazi years. It concludes that the Herzbergs were extremely fortunate, since "only a handful" of the nearly seventeen hundred displaced German scholars were ultimately accepted into Canada.

Stoner, John Oliver, Jr. "Principles of Spectroscopy." In *The New Encyclopædia Britannica.* 15th ed. Chicago: Encyclopaedia Britannica, 1982. Located under "Spectroscopy, Principles of," this is a comprehensive and detailed description of the history, principles, and methods of spectroscopy. The writing is dense, but the article may be useful as the starting point for a reader who needs to get a feeling for the vocabulary of the field.

Leslie J. Schwartz

1972

Chemistry
Christian B. Anfinsen, United States
Stanford Moore, United States
William H. Stein, United States

Physics
John Bardeen, United States
Leon N Cooper, United States
John Robert Schrieffer, United States

Physiology or Medicine
Gerald M. Edelman, United States
Rodney Porter, Great Britain

Economic Sciences
Sir John Hicks, Great Britain
Kenneth J. Arrow, United States

Literature
Heinrich Böll, West Germany

Peace
no award

CHRISTIAN B. ANFINSEN
1972

Born: Monessen, Pennsylvania; March 26, 1916

Nationality: American
Areas of concentration: Biochemistry and molecular biology

Anfinsen demonstrated that a protein's three-dimensional active structure is determined within its primary amino acid sequence. He proved this by studying the unfolding (inactivation) and refolding (reactivation) of enzymes, primarily ribonuclease. He advanced the understanding of the relationship between protein structure and cellular function

The Award

Presentation

Professor Bo G. Malmström of the Royal Swedish Academy of Sciences presented the Nobel Prize in Chemistry to Christian B. Anfinsen, Stanford Moore, and William H. Stein on Sunday, December 10, 1972. He honored all three recipients for their studies involving the molecular structure and function of the enzyme ribonuclease. He began his presentation address with a philosophical discussion of enzymes, catalytic molecules which are responsible for all life processes in all living organisms. Malmström cited Jöns Jakob Berzelius, the Swedish chemist who first proposed that life processes are catalytic in nature.

In the cells of living organisms, the macromolecule deoxyribonucleic acid (DNA) serves as the carrier of inheritable traits by encoding information necessary for the construction of thousands of different proteins. Each protein has a unique role in specific tissues of the organism. In essence, proteins are the expressed traits that constitute the organism. The proteins called enzymes are catalytic, thereby producing cellular changes via the regulation of chemical reactions. Each protein is unique in that it is a variable-length chain of twenty types of amino acids arranged in a unique sequence determined by DNA.

Anfinsen's experiment showed that a protein's complex functional structure is determined by its primary amino-acid sequence, and ultimately by the genetic code DNA. Moore and Stein showed that of all the amino acids in a protein's primary sequence, a few (three or four) highly reactive amino acids come together to form the active catalytic center of the enzyme.

Nobel lecture

On Monday, December 11, 1972, Anfinsen delivered his Nobel lecture, entitled "Studies on the Principles that Govern the Folding of Protein Chains." He began his lecture with a presentation of the enzyme ribonuclease, a protein consisting of 124 amino acids isolated from the bovine pancreas. Eight of the 124 amino acids interact to produce four disulfide bonds, in which chemical bonding occurs between sulfur-containing amino acids. Ribonuclease can potentially form 105 different patterns of four disulfide bonds; however, only one specific pattern of four bonds yields a fully functional three-dimensional structure.

The problem at hand was how the enzyme folded to form this specific pattern. Anfinsen and coworkers believed that the three-dimensional structure of a functional protein was determined by the lowest energy state of the physiological system, an idea termed the "thermodynamic hypothesis." In other words, a protein's functional structure was determined by its primary amino-acid sequence.

A major experiment confirming the thermodynamic hypothesis was the unfolding and refolding of ribonuclease. The enzyme was unfolded to its inactive state by adding urea, which broke the enzyme's disulfide bonds. Removal of the urea initiated refolding, or renaturation, back to the enzyme's active, or native, state.

In the laboratory, protein renaturation required hours to complete, whereas in living cells, the process required approximately two minutes. Other proteins required only seconds. It was apparent that ribonuclease was randomly searching through the 105 possible disulfide bond configurations en route to the native thermodynamically stable functional structure. The focus switched to how the cellular protein performed this random process so rapidly, yet so precisely.

Inactivation, or catalytic removal of certain amino-acid sequences from ribonuclease, had little effect upon enzyme activity, whereas removal of other sequences did affect activity. Therefore, each protein had specific amino acids, in addition to those associated with the active center, that were essential for proper folding. These critical structural amino acids included the sulfhydryl amino acids cysteine and methionine.

Even under optimum conditions (for example, ideal temperature and pH), an unfolded protein searches through thousands of possible configurations before arriving at the correct functional structure. Yet the process requires only seconds— minutes at the most. Anfinsen proposed that the protein-folding process was not completely random, not requiring every possible structure to be tested. Instead, proteins folded systematically, folding progressively from one stable state to an even more stable state, until the most stable functional state was achieved.

The primary amino-acid sequence of the protein dictates this folding process. Ultimately, the genetic code within the DNA molecule is the deciding factor. Mutations within DNA affect the amino-acid sequences of proteins, thereby altering protein structure and function, resulting in positive effects (evolution), neutral effects, or negative effects (molecular disease, cancer).

Critical reception

Christian Anfinsen received the Nobel Prize at a time when all scientific disciplines, especially biochemistry and molecular biology, were rapidly accelerating. Structural analysis of molecules had produced many breakthroughs, including the DNA structure by James Watson and Francis Crick, the genetic code by Robert

Holley, H. Gobind Khorana, and Marshall Nirenberg, and protein structure discoveries by Linus Pauling and Frederick Sanger, among others. These accomplishments had set the stage for the elucidation of more fundamental questions, such as the relationship of molecular structure to molecular function within the cell.

Anfinsen's analyses of protein denaturation/renaturation and Moore and Stein's work on enzyme catalytic sites, both performed on bovine pancreatic ribonuclease, constituted major steps toward the resolution of this question. Frederick M. Richards, a Yale University biophysicist writing for *Science* magazine, elaborated on the role of these three scientists in the "ribonuclease saga." While contrasting the differing styles of the three scientists, he illustrated their insights and diligent works leading to their respective discoveries. Anfinsen was characterized as a uniquely talented scientist who could draw brilliant conclusions from limited data and then pursue his ideas with comprehensive experimental tests. Richards also mentioned the influences of Armour ribonuclease and the Carlsberg Laboratory in Copenhagen upon Anfinsen's work.

Science News cited Moore, Stein, and Anfinsen for establishing a pathway for future investigations in protein chemistry. Approximately two dozen enzymes had been elucidated as of 1972, but their works opened the door for major breakthroughs involving hundreds, possibly thousands, of enzymes. The applications of Anfinsen's work to future molecular medicine was also noted.

Scientific American cited Anfinsen for his demonstration of spontaneous folding of protein structures in ribonuclease and related proteins, thus demonstrating that protein folding was ultimately determined by the protein's amino-acid sequence and genetic code. Both *Time* and *Newsweek* also cited Anfinsen's ribonuclease studies, although more attention focused on American physicist John Bardeen, the first individual to win two Nobel Prizes in the same field.

Anfinsen was awarded half the prize, with Moore and Stein splitting the remainder. The prize was a fitting tribute to all three scientists, whose classic experiments set the standard for protein biochemistry research. Their work was almost immediately cited in many undergraduate and graduate biochemistry texts, including Lubert Stryer's *Biochemistry*. Stryer discussed their development of ideas and experimental methodology in addition to stressing the importance of their discoveries.

The Nobel Prize elevated Anfinsen, who already enjoyed considerable respect in the scientific community, to the stature of a giant in protein biochemistry. He continued his studies on protein formation with the enzyme staphylococcal nuclease and the popular antiviral protein interferon. He also used his position to support important popular causes, speaking out on the dangers of nuclear power and the threat of nuclear war. He staunchly defended dissident Soviet scientists, bringing worldwide attention to their plight.

Biography

Christian Boehmer Anfinsen was born on March 26, 1916, in Monessen, Pennsylvania, the son of Christian Boehmer and Sophie (née Rasmussen) Anfinsen. He received his B.A. degree from Swarthmore College in 1937. He then studied organic chemistry at the University of Pennsylvania, receiving the M.S. degree in 1939. He subsequently visited the Carlsberg Laboratory in Copenhagen, Denmark, through the American-Scandinavian Foundation.

Anfinsen returned to the United States in 1940 to work on doctoral research in biochemistry at Harvard Medical School. He received the Ph.D. degree in 1943. He married Florence Bernice Kenenger on November 29, 1941. They had three children, Carol Bernice, Margot Sophie, and Christian Boehmer Anfinsen. He continued at Harvard as assistant professor of biological chemistry until 1950. In 1947, he was a senior cancer research fellow, working with Dr. Hugo Theorell at the Medical Nobel Institute in Stockholm, Sweden. He was a Markle Scholar at Harvard from 1948 to 1950.

Anfinsen was director of the Laboratory of Cellular Physiology and Metabolism at the National Heart Institute in Bethesda, Maryland, from 1950 to 1962. He received a Rockefeller Foundation Public Service Award in 1954 and a Guggenheim Fellowship for research at the Weizmann Institute of Science in Israel in 1958.

Anfinsen briefly returned to Harvard Medical School in 1962 as professor of biochemistry. He became director of the Laboratory of Chemical Biology at the National Institute of Arthritis and Metabolic Diseases in Bethesda in 1963. He received several honorary degrees, including doctorates from Swarthmore College in 1965, Georgetown University in 1967, and New York Medical College in 1969. He served as president (1971-1972) of the American Society of Biological Chemists and served on the Board of Governors of the Weizmann Institute of Science. He has been an editor for *Advances in Protein Chemistry* and a member of the United States' National Academy of Sciences and the Royal Danish Academy.

Scientific Career

Christian B. Anfinsen's scientific career has emphasized the intricate relationship between molecular structure and function. His thermodynamic hypothesis, by which molecules arrange themselves according to their lowest energy state, presents a view of a complex but orderly cellular machinery, consisting of a hierarchy of information molecules, beginning with the inheritable deoxyribonucleic acid (DNA). The information encoded in DNA is transcribed into ribonucleic acid (RNA), which is subsequently translated into a long chain of amino acids called a protein. Proteins provide cellular structure and help control the rates of chemical reactions (enzyme proteins): In essence, proteins are life, the expression of the information encoded in DNA. The information transfer scheme DNA→RNA→protein is the major theme of molecular biology, and Anfinsen's brilliant work has played a major role in establishing this theme and in advancing the field of molecular biology.

In the 1950's, Anfinsen selected the enzyme ribonuclease, which catabolizes (that is, breaks down) RNA, as his research focus. This particular protein was of interest to many protein scientists worldwide because it had been highly purified from bovine pancreases by Armour, Inc., during World War II. His early investigations with this enzyme concentrated on determination of enzyme size and shape by paper chromatography, plus determination of the enzyme's amino-acid sequence by Frederick Sanger's end-group analysis technique. Sanger was awarded the Nobel Prize in Chemistry in 1958 for the first protein amino-acid sequence determination, performed on insulin in 1953. Sanger showed that each protein has a unique specific amino-acid sequence. Anfinsen was to take Sanger's important work a major step further.

During a sabbatical at the Carlsberg Laboratory in Copenhagen, Denmark, Anfinsen studied new techniques for the analysis of ribonuclease, including the behavior of proteins under denaturing (that is, in unfolded, inactive) conditions. This work, under the direction of K. U. Linderstrøm, was a major turning point in Anfinsen's young career. Upon returning to the United States, he worked with Michael Sela and Frederick H. White, Jr., to study the breakage of disulfide bonds in ribonuclease. Disulfide bonds form between nonadjacent amino acids bearing sulfhydryl groups, methionine and cysteine in particular. They unfolded the enzyme in beta-mercaptoethanol, observing a steady decline in activity (the ability to break down DNA) as the reaction proceeded. Refolding of the denatured (inactive) enzyme then yielded an increase in activity as various intermediate stages of folding were reached.

Anfinsen and A. P. Ryle obtained evidence that the three-dimensional disulfide bonding pattern of ribonuclease was closely associated with formation of the enzyme's catalytic active center. Furthermore, hydrogen bonding appeared to play a major role in ribonuclease formation, especially in the case of one lysine amino acid.

In 1961, Anfinsen, Sela, White, and Edgar Haber continued with the ribonuclease denaturation/renaturation experiments. The thermodynamic hypothesis had emerged as a major explanation for a protein folding into its active state. The information for the three-dimensional protein structure was believed to lie within the protein's primary amino acid sequence. Their results indicated that protein folding was not caused by structural alterations between various active protein states, but instead involved the random sequential shifting of disulfide bonding patterns until the active native structure was achieved.

In 1962, Haber and Anfinsen performed a more thorough analysis of ribonuclease, in which they denatured the protein and then allowed it to refold in the presence of disulfide bond inhibitors. The inhibitors 8M urea and 4M guanidine blocked correct disulfide bond formation, thus producing a variety of ribonuclease folding intermediates. These intermediates had varying degrees of native enzymatic activity. Furthermore, they found that the amino acids tyrosine and histidine were important drivers of the refolding process. These experiments provided strong evidence that the correct disulfide-paired native enzyme was thermodynamically the most stable and the most active state of the enzyme.

As further support for the thermodynamic hypothesis, Anfinsen, David Givol, and Robert F. Goldberger discovered an enzyme from bovine pancreas that accelerated the renaturation of bovine pancreatic ribonuclease. The enzyme functions in sulfhydryl-disulfide bond formation and is enhanced by the presence of thiol compounds. Its molecular weight was determined to be approximately 42,000 daltons by analytical ultracentrifugation. The enzyme's activity is dependent upon the number of disulfide bonds per substrate.

The thermodynamic hypothesis was gaining considerable support as a description of protein folding. Specific amino acid residues within the protein's primary amino acid sequence provided the information for a step-by-step folding pattern that culminated in the fully functional protein. The folding process relied not only upon disulfide bonding but also upon other factors, such as hydrogen bonding and the activation of zymogens, inactive precursor proteins. While Anfinsen had championed disulfide bonding, he was keenly aware of the importance of other mechanisms for protein folding as well.

Beyond ribonuclease, Anfinsen shifted attention to similar enzymes, including staphylococcal nuclease, a 149-amino-acid protein that does not form disulfide bonds and that catabolizes DNA and RNA. Anfinsen, in collaboration with Ladislav Moravek and Hiroshi Taniuchi, showed that staphylococcal nuclease is resistant to digestion by proteolytic enzymes (such as trypsin and chymotrypsin, which break down proteins into amino-acid subunits) when protected with ligands such as calcium. Furthermore, trypsin digestion of unprotected staphylococcal nuclease produces an enzyme fragment that retains normal activity, again illustrating that only specific amino-acid sequences are critical for protein function.

In the presence of calcium, staphylococcal nuclease excludes solvent water from its native structure. This observation supported another potential folding mechanism, in which a solvent such as water would direct the sequential folding of the protein. Such a hydrodynamic mechanism would rely upon interactions between the solvent and specific amino acid residues, but the primary amino-acid sequence still would thermodynamically dictate the course of interactions. The native protein would consist of compartments into which solvent could penetrate, thus contributing to the stability of the structure in addition to the disulfide and hydrogen bonding patterns.

David H. Sachs, Alan N. Schecter, Ann Eastlake, and Anfinsen then used antibodies to prove the enzyme's active center. They found that antibodies generated against specific regions of the native enzyme inactivated the enzyme. Even though one target sequence, amino acids 99-149, did not include the active center, inactivation of this sequence still eliminated enzyme activity. It was apparent that proper folding of this sequence, and other regions, was critical for formation of the active center, thus adding another proof for the thermodynamic hypothesis.

Anfinsen's studies of protein denaturation/renaturation and antibody binding of the enzymes ribonuclease and staphylococcal nuclease culminated in the 1972 Nobel Prize in Chemistry. The award elevated Anfinsen's stature both in the United States and worldwide. He became a leader in protein biochemistry, inspiring an entire generation of protein chemists to continue the elucidation of molecular structure. The award also firmly established the thermodynamic hypothesis for protein folding, as well as the biological information flow concept of DNA to RNA to protein.

During the late 1970's, Anfinsen continued his studies of protein conformation with staphylococcal nuclease. He concentrated on the kinetics of enzyme formation as well as the characterization of the antibodies used in his earlier experiments. He advanced the use of antibodies in molecular analysis, a technique eventually utilized widely in protein and nucleic acid research. His studies continued to support the thermodynamic hypothesis.

While all proteins are of critical importance to cellular activities, one protein in particular, interferon, attracted widespread attention during the late 1970's and early 1980's. Interferon is a glycoprotein (that is, a protein with carbohydrate residues) that possesses antiviral activity. It is produced by human immune and connective tissue cells such as leukocytes and fibroblasts. It has been used in the treatment of some cancers.

Anfinsen directed his research toward the structural and functional analysis of interferon, an enzyme composed of protein and sugar. He discovered that removing sugar from the enzyme did not affect its antiviral activity. Anfinsen's laboratory also determined the amino-acid sequence and molecular weight (18,500 daltons) of the major component of human lymphoblastoid interferon. The sequence is different from interferons of other species.

In addition to his continued scientific studies, Anfinsen has used his position as Nobel laureate to defend popular causes, including the use of alternative energy sources over nuclear power, the dangers of nuclear war, and especially support for dissident scientists within the Soviet Union. Anfinsen is among the thirty-three Nobel laureates and seventy-nine hundred other international scientists representing forty-four countries who belong to Scientists for Sakharov, Orlov, and Shcharansky (SOS). He has been outspoken in his support for prisoners of conscience in the Soviet Union and was a leader in SOS's drive to limit American-Soviet scientific exchanges during the late 1970's and early 1980's as a protest against Soviet oppression. The efforts of Anfinsen and other SOS scientists appear to have been highly successful in the wake of Mikhail Gorbachev's program of reform in the Soviet Union, which included the release of many political prisoners and more freedom of movement for Soviet scientists.

Bibliography

Primary

CHEMISTRY: "Reductive Cleavage of Disulfide Bridges in Ribonuclease," *Science*, vol. 125, 1957 (with Michael Sela and Frederick H. White, Jr.); "The Kinetics of Formation of Native Ribonuclease During Oxidation of the Reduced Polypeptide Chain," *Proceedings of the National Academy of Sciences, USA*, vol. 47, 1961 (with E. Haber, Michael Sela, and Frederick H. White, Jr.); "The Reversible Reduction of Disulfide Bonds in Polyalanyl Ribonuclease," *Journal of Biological*

Chemistry, vol. 237, 1962 (with Michael Sela and Juanita Cooke); "The Identification of Unreactive Amino Groups in Ribonuclease and Their Significance to Enzymatic Activity," *Journal of Biological Chemistry*, vol. 238, 1963 (with Juanita Cooke and Michael Sela); "Disulfide Interchange and the Three-Dimensional Structure of Proteins," *Proceedings of the National Academy of Sciences, USA*, vol. 53, 1965 (with David Givol, Francesco De Lorenzo, and Robert F. Goldberger); "Purification and Properties of an Enzyme from Beef Liver Which Catalyzes Sulfhydryl-Disulfide Interchange in Proteins," *Journal of Biological Chemistry*, vol. 241, 1966 (with Francesco De Lorenzo, Robert F. Goldberger, David Givol, and Edward Steers, Jr.); "Ligand-Induced Resistance of Staphylococcal Nuclease and Nuclease-T to Proteolysis by Subtilisin, Chymotrypsin, and Thermolysin," *Journal of Biological Chemistry*, vol. 244, 1969 (with Hiroshi Taniuchi and Ladislav Moravek); "A Solid Phase Synthetic Study of the Active Site Region of Staphylococcal Nuclease-T," *Journal of Biological Chemistry*, vol. 246, 1971 (with Irwin M. Chaiken); "An Immunologic Approach to the Conformational Equilibria of Polypeptides," *Proceedings of the National Academy of Sciences, U.S.A.*, vol. 69, 1972 (with David H. Sachs, Alan N. Schechter, and Ann Eastlake); "Studies on the Principles that Govern the Folding of Protein Chains," *Science*, vol. 181, 1973; "Apparent Dispensability of the Carbohydrate Moiety of Human Interferon for Antiviral Activity," *Journal of Biological Chemistry*, vol. 251, 1976 (with Sikta Bose, Dalia Gurari-Rotman, Urs Th. Ruegg, and Lila Corley); "Amino Terminal Sequence of the Major Component of Human Lymphoblastoid Interferon," *Science*, vol. 207, 1980 (with Kathryn C. Zoon, Mark E. Smith, Pamela J. Bridgen, Michael W. Hunkapiller, and Leroy E. Hood).

Secondary

Debus, Allen G., ed. *World Who's Who in Science*. Chicago: Marquis-Who's Who, 1968. This reference work provides concise, one-paragraph summaries of the lives of major twentieth century world scientists, including information on marriages, children, and honors.

Epstein, Charles J., Robert F. Goldberger, and Christian B. Anfinsen. "Genetic Control of Tertiary Protein Structure: Studies with Model Systems." *Cold Spring Harbor Symposia on Quantitative Biology* 28 (1963): 439-449. One of Anfinsen's many research contributions, this review article is a clear, comprehensive presentation of protein folding mechanisms. It includes many example systems, including ribonuclease, lysozyme, and trypsin. The authors advocate the thermodynamic hypothesis for protein formation.

Kim, Peter S., and Robert L. Baldwin. "Specific Intermediates in the Folding Reactions of Small Proteins and the Mechanism of Protein Folding." *Annual Review of Biochemistry* 51 (1982): 459-489. This review article is a very comprehensive, detailed summary of all major research in protein biochemistry, especially in terms of protein folding. More than two hundred references are cited, and major protein systems are described, including ribonuclease, lysozyme, and cytochrome c.

Phillips, David, C. "The Three-Dimensional Structure of an Enzyme Molecule." *Scientific American* 215 (November, 1966): 78-90. In this article, which is very readable for the layperson, Phillips presents the structure and folding pattern for the enzyme lysozyme. His three-dimensional diagrams are impressive, as is his clear presentation of protein folding research.

Richards, Frederic J. "Areas, Volumes, Packing, and Protein Structure." *Annual Review of Biophysics and Bioengineering* 6 (1977): 151-176. This is another major review article concerning the nature of protein folding, with special emphasis upon solvent interactions with protein side groups. The article is both detailed and comprehensive, with more than one hundred references cited.

Stryer, Lubert. *Biochemistry*. 3d ed. San Francisco: W. H. Freeman, 1988. Stryer's textbook is a classic biochemistry text for undergraduates. It is very clearly written, with excellent diagrams and illustrations. The chapter on protein structure includes an interesting discussion of the contributions of several Nobel chemistry laureates.

Zubay, Geoffrey L. *Biochemistry*. Reading, Mass.: Addison-Wesley, 1983. Zubay's biochemistry textbook is a detailed work for advanced undergraduate and graduate students. It provides extensive biochemical information and has outstanding diagrams, including three-dimensional molecular structures.

David Wason Hollar, Jr.

1972

Chemistry
Christian B. Anfinsen, United States
Stanford Moore, United States
William H. Stein, United States

Physics
John Bardeen, United States
Leon N Cooper, United States
John Robert Schrieffer, United States

Physiology or Medicine
Gerald M. Edelman, United States
Rodney Porter, Great Britain

Economic Sciences
Sir John Hicks, Great Britain
Kenneth J. Arrow, United States

Literature
Heinrich Böll, West Germany

Peace
no award

STANFORD MOORE

WILLIAM H. STEIN

STANFORD MOORE and WILLIAM H. STEIN
1972

Stanford Moore

Born: Chicago, Illinois; September 4, 1913
Died: New York, New York; August 23, 1982
Nationality: American
Areas of concentration: Protein chemistry and analytical biochemistry

William H. Stein

Born: New York, New York; June 25, 1911
Died: New York, New York; February 2, 1980
Nationality: American
Area of concentration: Protein chemistry

Moore and Stein developed new methods to elucidate the structural properties of protein molecules, and they applied that methodology to determine the sequence of amino acids within the enzyme ribonuclease. This was the first enzyme for which the amino acid sequence was resolved

The Award

Presentation

The 1972 Nobel Prize was presented to Stanford Moore, William H. Stein, and Christian B. Anfinsen on December 10, 1972. Bo G. Malmström, a professor of biochemistry and a member of the Royal Swedish Academy of Sciences, made the presentation address. An authority on the study of enzymes, Malmström began by noting the early work of Jöns Jakob Berzelius, who introduced the concept of chemical catalysis. Catalysts are agents that can accelerate chemical reactions, and Berzelius had correctly proposed that catalysts might exist in biological tissues. Enzymes are a class of proteins that serve as biological catalysts. Each different enzyme catalyzes a unique biochemical reaction, and each is composed of twenty different types of amino acid building blocks arranged in a specific, unique linear sequence. Malmström acknowledged the important work of the Nobel Prize recipients in determining the linear sequence of the amino acids in a single enzyme that degrades ribonucleic acid: ribonuclease.

Malmström discussed the understanding of the complexity of protein structure that had been attained as a result of the elegant experimental work by Stein, Moore, and Anfinsen. A protein molecule does not exist simply as a linear chain of amino acid units with random three-dimensional structure; the chain folds and bends in a unique and specific way, often into a globular form.

Anfinsen's research had shown that information inherent in the amino acid sequence of a protein directs folding of the molecule into a specific three-dimensional shape and that precise folding is essential for catalytic activity of enzymes. Moore and Stein's complementary studies showed that the folding of the enzyme molecule brings certain amino acids into close proximity to form an active site, the region where the catalytic event takes place.

Nobel lectures

Stanford Moore and William Stein presented their Nobel Prize lectures on December 11, 1972. In the spirit of the inseparable collaboration between the two scientists, the published texts of their lectures were combined and entitled "The Chemical Structures of Pancreatic Ribonuclease and Deoxyribonuclease." In opening remarks, Moore and Stein stressed the incredible complexity that exists within the chemical structures of proteins. Each protein molecule contains many different types of chemical groups, which can interact with one another in almost limitless numbers of ways, and which can be involved in various types of chemical reactions. As a result, myriad possible variations in the structures of proteins could theoretically exist, and thus, the chain of amino acid units can assume specific three-dimensional arrangements favorable for promoting chemical catalysis.

Moore and Stein summarized some historical aspects regarding the identification and purification of ribonuclease, a heat-stable enzyme found in the pancreas that, during digestion, catalyzes the degradation of nucleic acids present in food. Although partial purification of the enzyme had been accomplished previously, Moore and Stein's structural studies would require a pure molecular species. To accomplish further purification, they utilized ion-exchange chromatography, a procedure that separates molecules on the basis of their electrical charge. Ribonuclease and another protein, cytochrome c, were the first molecules of such large size to be purified by this technique. Later, gel filtration chromatography, which separates molecules by size, was also used.

A significant portion of the address focused on the development of analytical methods to separate and quantitate the specific types of amino acid that make up ribonuclease. The procedures developed over a number of years resulted in a rapid, automated system that took advantage of the differential interactions of the various amino acids with columns containing chromatographic media.

Having elucidated the composition of the amino acid units in ribonuclease, the next task was to determine the sequence of the units within the linear chain of the protein. Moore and Stein described the techniques they utilized to break the long, linear chains into smaller, more manageable pieces. The amino acids that composed the protein fragments were then sequentially removed chemically and identified, until the entire sequence of amino acids within the enzyme was deduced.

In the next part of their lecture, Moore and Stein explained how amino acids on different parts of the linear chain could interact with one another through the folding of the chain and discussed their experiments to investigate which of the amino acids might be involved in the catalytic process. These studies required their development of methods to modify certain amino acids chemically and then to determine how such a modification affected the catalytic properties of the enzyme. These experiments provided insight both into the types of amino acids making up the active site of the enzyme and into how the protein was folded in three-dimensional space.

The authors concluded their discussion of ribonuclease by considering important studies on the enzyme by other scientists. They noted the work of their Nobel Prize corecipient Christian Anfinsen in understanding the importance of the disulfide cross-linkages that exist between certain amino acids, cysteines, within the ribonuclease molecule. In addition, they stressed the importance of research by Bernd Gutte and Robert Bruce Merrifield on the chemical synthesis of ribonuclease, which made possible the substitution of amino acids for those that are found in the naturally occurring enzyme in order to examine the effect of the substitutions on the catalytic properties of the enzyme.

After a brief discussion of their work on a related enzyme, deoxyribonuclease, the authors concluded by suggesting that the elucidation of the detailed structures of several enzymes would be necessary to begin understanding the underlying principles of enzymatic catalysis and stating that such knowledge may lead to important and practical benefits in medicine.

Critical reception

In the articles that appeared following the announcement of the recipients of the 1972 Nobel Prize in Chemistry, there was a consensus that the awarding of the prize to Stein, Moore, and Anfinsen was a just and deserved reward for the great contribution that these scientists had made to the discipline of protein chemistry. An article by Bernard Weinraub in *The New York Times* referred to the work of the recipients as "pioneering studies in enzymes, considered in many respects the key substances of life." An article in the journal *Nature* stated that "nobody has done more in these past twenty years to determine the shape of the field [of protein chemistry] as we know it today." Frederic Richards of Yale University noted in an article in *Science*, "The work has spanned and in a major way contributed to the most exciting era in biochemistry so far."

The key contributions of Moore and Stein were consistently recognized in the articles that appeared after the announcement of the prize, particularly their contribution to the understanding of the chemical structure of the enzyme ribonuclease, the first enzyme for which the amino acid sequence had been determined. An article in *Nature* called this structure determination "a great technical *tour de force*" for its time and discussed the potential medical importance of the work.

Since the Nobel Prize was awarded to Moore and Stein several years after their initial studies, the scientific impact of the research could be assessed. By 1972, several other enzymes had been sequenced, and protein chemistry laboratories routinely analyzed structure/function relationships utilizing the principles they had described. Referring to the sequencing and structural determination of ribonuclease, an article from *Science News* stated that the work had "opened the door for the synthesis of ribonuclease." The article further noted that with the capability to conduct protein synthesis, scientists might begin to understand various genetic diseases resulting from enzyme disorders, research which "may set the stage for eventual repair of defective enzymes in patients."

The close working relationship between Moore and Stein, which resulted in joint authorship of nearly all of their scientific works, was discussed in several articles. In *Nature*, Stein and Moore were referred to as "inseparably linked" by their work, and a *Science* article noted that "they have worked at Rockefeller and published together to the point where their names have become inseparable in the minds of most biochemists." Several articles also made note of the abundance of Nobel laureates from Rockefeller University, with Moore and Stein being the eleventh and twelfth.

Biographies

Stanford Moore was born in Chicago on September 4, 1913, and spent most of his childhood in Nashville, Tennessee. His father, John Howard M. Moore, was a professor of law at Vanderbilt University, and his mother, Ruth (née Fowler) Moore, was a graduate of Stanford University; the scholarly achievements of both parents were influential in stimulating Moore's education. Moore developed an interest in chemistry while in high school, and in 1931 he entered Vanderbilt University, where he especially enjoyed the challenges of organic chemistry. Although initially un-decided between majors in chemistry and aeronautical engineering, Moore was graduated summa cum laude in 1935 with a bachelor's degree in chemistry.

Moore received a Wisconsin Alumni Research Foundation Fellowship in 1935, which supported his graduate studies in organic chemistry under the direction of Karl Paul Link at the University of Wisconsin. Upon completing his Ph.D. in 1938, Moore accepted a research position in the laboratory of Max Bergmann, a re-nowned protein chemist and friend of Link, at the Rockefeller Institute for Medical Science in New York. Moore spent most of his career at the institute, which later became the Rockefeller University.

Moore was said to have had little time for nonscientific activities, especially later in life. He never married, and he lived modestly in an apartment in New York City. In the mid-1970's, Moore became incapacitated by the degenerative effects of amyo-trophic lateral sclerosis (Lou Gehrig's disease), but he continued to be involved with research at the Rockefeller University until he died on August 23, 1982.

William Howard Stein was born in New York City on June 25, 1911. His father, Fred M. S. Stein, retired from a business career at an early age to devote his time to community health concerns in New York City. His mother, Beatrice (née Borg) S. Stein, was also involved in community affairs and was concerned with improving the environment for underprivileged city children. Stein's parents were of consider-able influence in his choice to study science or medicine. As a teenager, Stein obtained a progressive education at the Lincoln School of the Teacher's College of

Columbia University in New York and then transferred to Phillips Exeter Academy in New Hampshire at the age of sixteen.

In 1929, Stein began college at Harvard and, in 1933, was graduated with a bachelor's degree in chemistry. He remained at Harvard as a graduate student, studying organic chemistry for a year, before deciding that his primary interests were in the area of biochemistry. Stein transferred to the department of biochemistry in the College of Physicians and Surgeons at Columbia University. In 1936, while a graduate student at Columbia, Stein married Phoebe Hockstadter; they had three sons in the following eight years.

Stein joined Max Bergmann's laboratory at the Rockefeller Institute in 1937 and was appointed to a permanent position there in 1944, following World War II. Stein spent 1960 as a visiting professor at the University of Chicago and 1963 as a visiting lecturer at Harvard University. After many years of affiliation with the *Journal of Biological Chemistry* as an associate editor, he became editor-in-chief in 1968, a position which he retained only until 1969, when he was stricken with Guillain-Barre syndrome. This condition resulted in paralysis and his being confined to a wheelchair until his death on February 2, 1980. During this time of physical incapacitation, he continued to contribute whenever possible to discussions with Moore and others in the laboratory at Rockefeller University.

Although Moore and Stein could have gained tremendous financial rewards from their development of the fraction collector and the automated amino acid analyzer, they never patented these inventions, and they freely circulated their ideas to those who were interested. Moore willed his estate to the Rockefeller University to fund an endowment to provide salary and research expenses for an investigator in the field of biochemistry.

Scientific Careers

Stanford Moore's studies of the molecular structure of proteins were a logical outgrowth of his interest in organic chemistry, which evolved during his undergraduate years. His interest was further developed through his graduate research at the University of Wisconsin, for which he synthesized chemically modified carbohydrates and subsequently characterized the products. This experience would prove beneficial later both for amino acid analysis and sequencing and for studies in which amino acids within the structure of ribonuclease were specifically modified.

After graduate school, Moore spent three years in Max Bergmann's laboratory at the Rockefeller Institute developing methods to quantitate the relative amounts of amino acids resulting from the digestion of proteins. Protein molecules are composed of long chains of amino acids linked by chemical bonds. Treatment of the protein with acid breaks (hydrolyzes) these bonds to produce a hydrolysate, a mixture of all the amino acids which had composed the original intact protein.

William H. Stein was introduced to the study of protein chemistry while a graduate student at Columbia University, working under the research direction of Edgar G. Miller, Jr. For his thesis, he analyzed the amino acid content of the protein elastin, a major component of the walls of veins and arteries, thought at that time to be an important factor in the regulation of coronary artery disease. Stein used techniques that had been developed by Max Bergmann of the Rockefeller Institute for Medical Research. Bergmann's research group was involved with the structural determination of protein molecules and the specificity of proteolytic enzymes (enzymes that degrade proteins).

Upon receiving his Ph.D. from Columbia in 1937, Stein joined the outstanding research staff working in Bergmann's laboratory at the time. Stein's efforts there focused on improving some of the methods for the analysis of certain amino acids. The work involved developing procedures to modify amino acids chemically and then to quantify them gravimetrically (by weight). A year after Stein began in the Bergmann laboratory, Stanford Moore joined the group. At Bergmann's suggestion, Stein and Moore collaborated on research that led to the development of gravimetric methods for the analysis of two amino acids, glycine and leucine. This marked the beginning of the lifelong collaboration between Stein and Moore.

During World War II, the members of the laboratory were committed to wartime projects for the Office of Scientific Research and Development. These projects included studies of the physiological effects of vesicant gases utilized for chemical warfare. Stein's efforts concentrated on the chemical reactions between mustard gas and amino acid and protein molecules; Moore had left the laboratory to coordinate chemical warfare research efforts for the U.S. government, working in Washington, D.C.

Bergmann's death in 1944 left a vacancy in the area of protein chemistry on the staff at the Rockefeller Institute. Following the completion of the war, the director of the Rockefeller Institute, Herbert Gasser, offered both Moore and Stein positions to develop a research program. They accepted the offer and occupied the laboratory space that had been vacated by Bergmann's group. Although the position was initially offered on a trial basis, their research into amino acid analysis progressed rapidly and they were granted permanent positions. Both Moore and Stein were promoted to associate member in 1949 and to member in 1952, a title that changed to professor of biochemistry when the Rockefeller Institute became the Rockefeller University in 1955. Moore was the John D. Rockefeller Professor from 1981 until his death in 1982.

The collaborative effort between Stein and Moore was a close one, and their accomplishments cannot be singularly ascribed to one or the other. Their research led to the development of landmark methodology for the measurement and quantification of the amino acid building blocks of protein molecules; it led as well to their elucidation of the primary structure of the enzyme ribonuclease. Proteins consist of long, linear chains comprising twenty different types of amino acid units which are bound to one another by covalent chemical bonds. The challenge undertaken by Moore and Stein was to determine the types, and the specific sequence, of the amino acids within a single protein—the enzyme ribonuclease. This enzyme is found in high levels in the pancreas and is responsible for catalyzing the breakdown of ribonucleic acid during digestion.

The first step in their elucidation of the amino acid sequence of the ribonuclease molecule was to obtain a homogeneous form of the purified enzyme. Although the enzyme had been purified and crystallized as early as 1940 and was commercially available, Werner Hirs, Moore and Stein's first postdoctoral research associate, pioneered the use of ion-exchange chromatographic techniques for purposes of protein isolation. This type of chromatographic separation, which is based on differences in the net electrical charge of molecules, revealed that two distinct forms of the enzyme could be fractionated chromatographically and that the two forms were different protein molecules with distinct properties. Subsequent investigations of the structural details of the enzyme involved one of the two forms, ribonuclease A.

The determination of the relative numbers of the different types of amino acids in the purified ribonuclease was a logical next step in the elucidation of the enzyme's structure. To accomplish this analysis, Moore and Stein utilized methodology which they had developed for the quantitative analysis of the products after degradation of the protein into its amino acid substituents by treatment with aqueous acid. The principles of partition chromatography established by Archer Martin and Richard Synge, Nobel laureates in chemistry in 1952, were utilized to develop methods to separate each of the twenty different types of amino acids from one another. The amino acids in the resulting separated samples were detected, and the levels quantified, by reaction of the eluted fractions with ninhydrin. Moore and Stein improved upon previously described methods for the detection and quantification of amino acids with ninhydrin, a reagent that forms a colored product upon reaction with the amino group of an amino acid. For the purpose of collecting the fractions that eluted from the chromatographic columns, Moore and Stein invented the automatic drop-counting fraction collector, which has become a standard apparatus in nearly every biochemistry laboratory throughout the world.

The amino acid separation technology evolved through various phases of improvement. Initially, the separation of amino acids was carried out with chromatographic columns containing starch, and the amino acids were sequentially washed off the column by elution with ethyl alcohol, a procedure that required about two weeks for a complete quantitative analysis for all twenty types of amino acids. Eventually, a system was developed by which the amino acids were separated by a multistep elution of the amino acids from ion-exchange resins containing negatively charged sulfonate ions, a process that was fully automated and required only about six hours for a complete analysis. The automated amino acid analysis system that was developed as a result of this research became commercially available, and it became a standard, indispensable instrument in laboratories involved in various aspects of protein chemistry. The utilization of these novel, rapid analytical techniques allowed Moore and Stein both to determine that ribonuclease was a protein containing 124 amino acid residues and to determine the numbers of each type of amino acid present within the molecule.

The next step in the elucidation of the structure of ribonuclease was to determine the specific sequence of the different amino acids within the linear polypeptide chain. Utilizing methods similar to those developed by Nobel laureate Frederick Sanger for the amino acid sequencing of a smaller protein molecule, insulin, Werner Hirs began the process of preparing smaller fragments of the ribonuclease molecule by partial digestion with specific proteolytic enzymes. After determining the amino acid sequence of each fragment using variations of the methodology developed by Pehr Edman, the order in which these sequenced fragments fit together to form the intact protein could be deduced. The sensitive, quantitative methods developed by Moore and Stein for amino acid analysis greatly facilitated this process and made feasible the determination of the complete amino acid sequence of this relatively large protein. Ribonuclease was the first enzyme for which the amino acid sequence was determined.

Following the amino acid sequence determination of ribonuclease, Moore and Stein began experiments to obtain information on the three-dimensional arrangement that results when the parts of the ribonuclease protein chain fold in space. Such folding of an enzyme molecule allows the interactions between certain amino acids necessary for their participation in the mechanism of enzymatic catalysis. By specific chemical modification of amino acid residues, Stein, Moore, and their coworkers identified some of the important amino acid residues that make up the active site of ribonuclease where the catalytic event occurs. For example, by characterizing the reaction of the chemical iodoacetamide with two different residues of the amino acid histidine within ribonuclease, it was demonstrated that a histidine residue twelve amino acids from one end of the molecule was only five angstroms from a histidine residue that was the 119th amino acid from the end of the molecule. This indicated that the molecule was folded in such a way that these two parts of the chain were placed in close proximity. Eventually, other researchers verified some details of the three-dimensional arrangement proposed by Stein, Moore, and coworkers by using the X-ray crystallographic methods for structure determination that became a feasible technique for the structural analysis of protein molecules as a result of the Nobel Prize-winning work of Max Perutz and John Kendrew.

The importance of Moore and Stein's research was not only in their elucidation of detailed structural information of a specific enzyme, ribonuclease, but also in their development of the methodology that revolutionized protein chemistry. This marked the beginning of an era in biochemical research that led to the determination of the structures of many proteins and enzymes, which in turn provided considerable information concerning the chemical mechanisms of enzymatic catalysis.

Bibliography

Primary

Joint publications

CHEMISTRY: "Chromatographic Determination of the Amino Acid Composition of Proteins," *Cold Spring Harbor Symposia on Quantitative Biology*, vol. 14, 1949; "A Chromatographic Investigation of Pancreatic Ribonuclease," *Journal of Bio-*

logical Chemistry, vol. 200, 1953; "The Amino Acid Composition of Ribonuclease," *Journal of Biological Chemistry*, vol. 211, 1954 (with C. H. W. Hirs); "The Structure of Proteins," *Scientific American*, vol. 204, 1961; "Alkylation and Identification of the Histidine Residues at the Active Site of Ribonuclease," *Journal of Biological Chemistry*, vol. 238, 1963 (with A. M. Crestfield); "Properties and Conformation of the Histidine Residues at the Active Site of Ribonuclease," *Journal of Biological Chemistry*, vol. 238, 1963 (with A. M. Crestfield); "The Chemical Structures of Pancreatic Ribonuclease and Deoxyribonuclease," *Les Prix Nobel en 1972*, 1973; "Bovine Pancreatic Deoxyribonuclease A. Isolation of Cyanogen Bromide Peptides: Complete Covalent Structure of the Polypeptide Chain," *Journal of Biological Chemistry*, vol. 248, 1973 (with T. H. Liao and J. Salnikow).

Secondary

Anfinsen, Christian B. "Studies on the Principles That Govern the Folding of Protein Chains." *Science* 181 (1973). This is the Nobel address of Anfinsen, the corecipient of the Nobel Prize in Chemistry in 1972 with Moore and Stein. He performed studies on structural aspects of ribonuclease that were complementary to their work.

Bailey, J. Leggett. *Techniques in Protein Chemistry*. New York: Elsevier, 1967. This book includes a comprehensive description of amino acid analysis methodology, including chromatographic separation techniques, quantitation by the ninhydrin reaction, and use of the automatic amino acid analyzer.

Blackburn, Stanley. "Ribonuclease." In *Enzyme Structure and Function*. New York: Marcel Dekker, 1976. In this chapter, the author provides a thorough scientific coverage of the enzyme with respect to structure, details of the active site, and the mechanism of catalytic activity. The book also includes a general overview of the techniques used in enzyme structure/function studies.

Desmond, Peter. "Stanford Moore." In *The Annual Obituary, 1982*, edited by Janet Podell. New York: St. Martin's Press, 1983. This short biographical memoir emphasizes Moore's scientific career and is written for a reader with little scientific knowledge.

Effink, Maurice R., and Rodney L. Biltonen. "Pancreatic Ribonuclease A: The Most Studied Endonuclease." In *Hydrolytic Enzymes*, edited by A. Neuberger and K. Brocklehurst. New York: Elsevier, 1987. This chapter, specifically devoted to the enzyme that Moore studied, discusses the enzyme's biological function, structure, active site, and details of the chemical reaction.

Hirs, C. H. Werner. "The Structure of Ribonuclease." *Annals of the New York Academy of Sciences* 85 (1960). This article discusses many aspects of the details of the structural elucidation of the ribonuclease molecule, written by one who was a key contributor to the research carried out in Stein and Moore's laboratory.

King, Jonathan. "Deciphering the Rules of Protein Folding." *Chemical and Engineering News* 67 (1989): 32-54. This article discusses the state of knowledge about protein structure in 1989, work which has developed and evolved from the early studies carried out by Stein and Moore in the 1950's and 1960's. The article discusses the importance and relevance of the understanding of the details of protein structure to accelerate new areas of biotechnology.

Moore, Stanford. "William H. Stein." *National Academy of Sciences Biographical Memoirs* 56 (1987): 415-442. This article is an insightful and personal biography written by Stein's lifelong colleague and collaborator Moore, after Stein's death in 1980.

Smith, Emil L., and C. H. Werner Hirs. "Stanford Moore." *National Academy of Sciences Biographical Memoirs* 56 (1987): 355-386. This biography, written after Moore's death, outlines his personal and scientific life and includes several autobiographical notes to give some insight into his personality.

H. David Husic
Diane W. Husic

1973

Chemistry
Ernst Otto Fischer, West Germany
Sir Geoffrey Wilkinson, Great Britain

Physics
Leo Esaki, Japan
Ivar Giaever, Norway and United States
Brian D. Josephson, Great Britain

Physiology or Medicine
Karl von Frisch, Austria
Konrad Lorenz, Austria
Nikolaas Tinbergen, The Netherlands

Economic Sciences
Wassily Leontief, United States

Literature
Patrick White, Australia

Peace
Henry Kissinger, United States
Le Duc Tho, North Vietnam

ERNST OTTO FISCHER
1973

Born: Solln (near Munich), Germany; November 10, 1918

Nationality: German
Area of concentration: Organometallic chemistry

Fischer recognized that the stability of certain organic compounds containing metals was best explained by considering the metal atom to be enclosed between two flat organic molecules—hence, the name "sandwich compounds." The bonding theory proposed to account for these structures led to the synthesis of many interesting compounds and contributed to advances in catalysis

The Award

Presentation

Professor Ingvar Lindqvist, a member of the Royal Swedish Academy of Sciences, presented Ernst Otto Fischer to the King of Sweden, who awarded him the 1973 Nobel Prize in Chemistry. Lindqvist pointed out that chemists are often viewed by the general public as scientists who concentrate on developing new technology. This stereotype is a source of irritation to chemists, because it conceals the fact that applied chemistry has developed from the quest for new theoretical concepts. Few people appreciate the imaginative insights that have enriched the history of chemistry. Lindqvist pointed out that this is especially applicable to the research of Fischer, which exemplifies the thesis of Arthur Koestler, that scientific research is related to the process of artistic creation.

Lindqvist noted that, although the facts pertaining to sandwich compounds were known to all chemists, it took a flash of genius to visualize their structure. This gave rise to intensive research efforts that in turn produced a variety of new compounds. The first sandwich compound, which contained an iron atom enclosed between two flat organic groups, known as cyclopentadienyl groups, had properties similar to those of benzene. For that reason, it was labeled ferrocene. Fischer later prepared a compound in which a chromium atom was sandwiched between two benzene molecules. This was followed by the synthesis of "open sandwich" molecules, which had a flat molecule on one side of the metal atom and smaller molecules—such as carbonyl groups, containing one carbon and one oxygen atom—on the other side.

In closing, Lindqvist noted that the opening of this research territory, which has also led to advances in the theory and practice of catalysis, resulted from the concept of the bonding that was postulated for these sandwich compounds.

Nobel lecture

On December 11, 1973, Ernst Otto Fischer delivered his Nobel lecture, entitled

"On the Path to the Carbene and Carbyne Complexes." He chose this topic because he had already presented his findings on sandwich compounds in 1960 in a lecture at the same Royal Technical University of Stockholm.

In his introductory remarks, he pointed out that certain types of organometallic compounds were discovered more than one hundred years earlier by chemists Robert Bunsen and Sir Edward Frankland. In these compounds, the hydrogen atom in a hydrocarbon was replaced by a metal atom. This single bond between metal and carbon atom, which consists of an electron pair, is labeled a sigma bond. Later, Victor Grignard synthesized such compounds with magnesium atoms, for which he received the Nobel Prize in 1912. Karl Ziegler synthesized organic compounds containing aluminum, which formed the basis for the low-pressure polymerization of ethylene. For this he was awarded the Nobel Prize, jointly with Giulio Natta, in 1963.

There are carbon compounds that contain double bonds—that is, two electron pairs between the carbon atoms. The one pair constitutes a sigma bond. The other pair is a pi bond, which can be visualized as a pair of electrons above the two carbon atoms. This pi bond can also form a bond with metals. This type of bonding occurs in sandwich compounds between the metal atom and the flat organic molecules encasing it. Here, however, the bond does not involve two pi electrons in the organic molecule. Rather, the pi electrons in the cyclic flat molecule are considered to be diffused over the entire ring. These diffused electrons, called delocalized electrons, form the pi bonds with electrons on the metallic atom. An example of this is dibenzene chromium, in which the chromium atom is located between two benzene rings.

There is a third type of organometallic compound that can be formed with organic compounds containing double bonds between the carbon atoms. This is realized when both the sigma pair of electrons and the pi pair of the carbon atom are shared directly with the metallic atom. The research on these compounds, called carbenes, constituted the first part of Fischer's lecture.

There are also organic compounds containing triple bonds—that is, having three pairs of electrons between the carbon atoms. One pair is a sigma bond. The other two are pi bonds. In these compounds, as in their double-bonded analogues, the carbon atoms can form three types of bonds with metal atoms. The metal atom can form a sigma bond. The two pi bonds between can also form pi complexes with two metal atoms. Finally, the carbon atom can also share its three electron pairs entirely with a metal atom, forming a compound called a carbyne. The carbyne complexes constituted the second half of Fischer's lecture.

The synthesis of the first carbene, which contained a double bond between carbon and tungsten, was reported by Fischer and Alfred Maasböl in 1964. The first carbynes contained a triple bond between carbon and the metals chromium, molybdenum, and tungsten. These were reported by Fischer and Gerhard Kreis in 1973.

Double bonds are shorter than single bonds, and triple bonds are even shorter. These distances, measured by X rays, confirmed the postulation of the double and triple bonds. Fischer concluded his lecture with the hope that he had demonstrated that there are still many research possibilities open in the field of organometallic chemistry.

Critical reception

The Nobel Prize in Chemistry in 1973 was awarded jointly to Ernst Otto Fischer of Munich and Sir Geoffrey Wilkinson of London because, after both had deduced the structure of ferrocene to be that of a "sandwich compound" independently of each other, they set out on research programs that were very fruitful in expanding the domain of organometallic chemistry.

In its report on the award, *The New York Times* (October 24) cited a spokesman of the Royal Swedish Academy of Sciences, who stated that the prize was "in chemistry for chemists" and explained that "a very essential part of scientific discipline is its structure and its concepts. Fischer and Wilkinson widened the basic concepts of chemistry by their work and therefore also changed the structure of chemistry."

Professor Gunnar Brusewitz of the Swedish Academy pointed out that the new direction given to research in organometallic chemistry initiated by Fischer and Wilkinson might well have practical results. For example, since this research had led to a better grasp of the interaction between metal atoms and organic molecules, it might mean that the lead added to gasoline to improve its antiknock properties could be replaced with less dangerous metallic ingredients, which could reduce the pollution caused by engine exhaust. Brusewitz emphasized, however, that the prize had not been awarded for any potential practical developments that might ensue. He stressed, "For the first time in many years, we have awarded a prize for pure basic chemistry research, not for methods or discoveries that border both on the biological and the physical fields."

Time magazine (November 6), referring to the sandwich compounds, reported: "Unknown in nature, such man-made compounds are becoming increasingly important. They have already been used to manufacture a group of catalysts—substances that stimulate or retard chemical reactions in which they themselves remain unaltered—used in the production of new supertough plastics, the drug L-dopa (for treating Parkinson's disease), low lead fuels, and other materials of industrial importance." The American periodical *Science*, reporting in its November 16 issue, stated that the research of Fischer and Wilkinson had "revolutionized the field of organometallic chemistry and has had a very significant impact on the broader fields of inorganic, organic, and theoretical chemistry." The *Science* article also pointed out that the Inorganic Chemistry Laboratory of the Technical University of Munich had become one of the leading centers in the world for research in organometallic chemistry under the direction of Professor Fischer.

Professor P. L. Pauson, the discoverer of "ferrocene," commented in the British periodical *Nature* (November 2) that Fischer's discovery of the carbene complexes was "the result of a most skilful and purposeful search for suitable synthetic methods." All the articles that were written by scientists who knew Fischer also observed that he was a unique personality who was completely dedicated to his research and his students.

Biography

Ernst Otto Fischer was born on November 10, 1918, in Solln, a suburb of Munich. He was the third child of Dr. Karl T. Fischer, a professor of physics at the Technical University of Munich, and his wife, Valentine (née Danzer). Fischer attended the Theresien Gymnasium in Munich, from which he was graduated in 1937.

He had planned to major in art history at the university, but before he could matriculate he had to complete two years of military service. With the onset of World War II, this service brought him to Poland, France, and Russia. In the winter of 1941-1942, however, he was given a brief study leave, which enabled him to initiate his studies at the Technical University of Munich. Instead of art history, he elected to study chemistry. Returning to the service, he was wounded and finally captured by the Americans. He was released in the fall of 1945 and resumed his studies at the Technical University, which reopened in 1946. In 1949, he passed his diploma examination (comparable to the American baccalaureate) with distinction and initiated his doctoral research under Professor Walter Hieber in the Inorganic Chemistry Institute of the Technical University. He was awarded the doctorate in 1952. After two years of additional research, Fischer was appointed instructor at the Technical University in 1954. In 1957 he was invited to the University of Munich as associate professor and was promoted to full professor in 1959. In 1964, he accepted the chair of inorganic chemistry at the Technical University of Munich when his mentor, Professor Hieber, retired. He held this position until 1984, when he became professor emeritus.

Scientific Career

Ernst Otto Fischer had the good fortune to hear the chemistry lectures of Professor Walter Hieber when, as a soldier on leave from the front in 1941, he was permitted to attend the university. Hieber had pioneered in developing the chemistry of the metal carbonyl compounds. These are compounds that contain carbon monoxide molecules bound to metal atoms. Hieber was also an excellent lecturer, and he made a lasting impression on Fischer. Although he was unable to resume his studies until 1946, being obliged to continue service on the front, Fischer had set his sights on majoring in inorganic chemistry under Professor Hieber.

Fischer's doctoral dissertation dealt with the synthesis of nickel tetracarbonyl, a compound in which four carbon monoxide molecules are bound to a nickel atom. This compound had originally been formed by the direct interaction of nickel atoms and gaseous carbon monoxide. Fischer showed that the compound could also be formed from nickel compounds in aqueous solution, and he studied the mechanism by which the compound was formed.

Although Fischer had been offered an attractive industrial position, Professor

Hieber was able to persuade him to choose an academic career. To be eligible for a professorship at a German university, candidates must complete an extensive research project. Fischer selected a topic in the field of organometallic chemistry that was not related to the carbonyls. After the completion of this research, he was appointed instructor at the Technical University of Munich.

He was intrigued by the stability of ferrocene, a compound formed from iron and two molecules of an organic ring compound. He postulated that it was a sandwich compound—that is, that the iron atom was enclosed between the two cyclic organic rings. This he confirmed in conjunction with W. Pfab by X-ray measurements. At about the same time, Geoffrey Wilkinson and Robert Burns Woodward of Harvard University postulated the identical sandwich structure. This led to a vigorous competition between Fischer and Wilkinson, who had relocated to the Imperial College of Science and Technology of the University of London.

If iron could form such a sandwich compound, Fischer reasoned, then chromium should also form such a compound if benzene molecules were used as the enclosing ring compounds. The basis for this argument is that a compound in which a chromium atom is sandwiched between two benzene molecules would have the same number of electrons as ferrocene, in which an iron atom is sandwiched between two cyclopentadienyl rings. Fischer validated this hypothesis in 1955, with Walter Hafner, by synthesizing dibenzene chromium, a compound that could be heated to 300 degrees without decomposition.

The synthesis of the diversity of organometallic compounds that was set in motion by the elucidation of the structure of the sandwich compounds in the early 1950's had its counterpart in industrial research, where organometallic compounds were also being synthesized, since they were found to be effective catalysts in the preparation of polymers. Thus, Karl Ziegler at the Max Planck Institute for Coal Research in Mülheim an der Ruhr used organometallic compounds containing aluminum and titanium to prepare polyethylene. At the beginning of the 1960's, chemists at the Wacker Company, including Hafner and R. Jira, both students of Fischer, discovered that solutions of palladium salts were effective catalysts in converting ethylene to acetaldehyde.

Industrial laboratories vied with one another and the university laboratories of Fischer and Wilkinson to synthesize these sandwich compounds. The industrial chemists were anxious to discover compounds that could be useful; the academic chemists were interested in finding new synthetic pathways and discovering novel types of bonding. On more than one occasion, the identical new compound was synthesized in the Fischer and the Wilkinson laboratory and in three industrial laboratories independently of one another. Despite the many industrial applications found for organometallic compounds, the research group directed by Fischer continued a systematic research program, ever looking for new classes of compounds.

After more than two hundred scientific papers were published describing the synthesis and characterization of organometallic compounds in Fischer's laboratory, an entirely new type of compound was reported by Fischer and Alfred Maasböl in

1964. This compound, called a carbene, contained a double bond between a carbon atom and a metal atom. Further research soon produced many compounds that contained such double bonds between metal and carbon atoms. Although this research was conducted to satisfy intellectual curiosity and to learn how atoms can be induced to form novel compounds, it has had many valuable practical applications for the chemical industry. The stability of these compounds has provided insight into the mechanism of many industrial processes. This, in turn, provides information on what factors can be varied to enhance yields or produce more stable products.

Since there are compounds that contain triple bonds between two carbon atoms, it is not surprising that the Fischer laboratories would try to synthesize a compound containing a triple bond between a metal atom and a carbon atom. Success crowned their efforts when Fischer and Gerhard Kreis reported the first compound containing such a triple bond between carbon and a metal atom in 1973. These compounds, called carbynes, can be prepared from carbenes by the interaction of boron trichloride, an inorganic compound containing boron and chlorine. It is interesting to note that the carbenes were formed from carbonyls by reactions that Fischer had learned while working on his own doctoral dissertation.

As creative as Fischer has shown himself to be, he also had the facility of stimulating creativity in his students and coworkers. He shared their victories and consoled them in their defeats, encouraging them to seek other pathways that would lead them to their goals. He recognized his students not for being a pair of hands but for making substantive contributions to research. In the 1950's, he had obtained financial rewards for some of his contributions to industrial chemistry, especially the patents involving the benzene sandwich compounds. He decided to purchase a chalet in the Austrian Tyrol that was ideally situated for skiing enthusiasts. He made this chalet available to his students, who, Fischer reasoned, had helped him obtain the results that made the patent possible and should share in the rewards. He also commented, when informed that he had been awarded the Nobel Prize, that his coworkers had made it possible. On more than one occasion, Fischer had been offered chairs at other universities. He declined all offers that would take him from Munich and the Bavarian Alps, which had been an inspiration to him his entire life.

Fischer's contributions are not confined to the research results published in chemical periodicals. He was a patient and understanding teacher who was able to set high standards that his students were anxious to meet. They soon learned that to synthesize a new compound was not enough. They had to find the optimal path for that synthesis. Once a new compound was isolated, its structure had to be determined by as many methods as were available. One of his maxims was "One method is no method." That his approach to developing chemical problem solvers was effective is seen in the publication record of the more than two hundred students who have conducted research under his guidance. They have made substantive contributions to organometallic chemistry, an interdisciplinary field that developed in large measure from the pioneering research of their mentor. By the year 1988, ten of Fischer's students had been called to head departments in West German universities.

Because of his dedication to research and to guiding his students to become effective problem solvers, there might be a tendency to picture Fischer as a professor in an "ivory tower." This is far from the truth. He was well aware that it required diligence to keep the university free from external influences in its traditional role of teaching and research. Students, too, were exposed to political polarization during the turbulent 1960's. Fischer exhorted the students to pursue pure science, free of any political extremism. He also recognized that journals must be available to publish the research results that continually pour forth from the chemical laboratories, serving on the publishing board of the *Journal of Organometallic Chemistry*, the most frequently cited journal in that field. Even after achieving emeritus status, Fischer continued to offer his services in the interests of science education. He not only participated in the annual meetings of Nobel laureates at Lindau on Lake Constance but also helped organize these meetings. There aspiring students have the opportunity to meet and learn from scientists who have been pioneers in their field.

He was often called upon to discuss the problems that have arisen with the development of technology. By virtue of his strong liberal arts background, he not only was conversant with the technical aspects of pollution and energy problems but also was aware of how ancient civilizations coped with comparable problems. Further, he was aware that philosophical considerations are needed to humanize decisions that affect all of us.

Bibliography

Primary

CHEMISTRY: "Über den Mechanismus der Kohlenoxyd-reaktion von Nickel (II)- und Kobalt (II)- Salzen bei Gegenwart von Dithionit," *Zeitschrift für anorganische und allgemeine Chemie*, vol. 269, 1952 (with Walter Hieber); "Neue Laboratoriumsmethoden zur Darstellung der Carbonyle von Nickel und Kobalt," *Zeitschrift für anorganische und allgemeine Chemie*, vol. 269, 1952 (with Walter Hieber and E. Böckley); "Cyclopentadien-Metallkomplexe: Ein neuer Typ metallorganischer Verbindungen," *Zeitschrift für Naturforschung*, vol. 7b, 1952 (with W. Pfab); "Di-benzol-chron," *Zeitschrift für Naturforschung*, vol. 10b, 1955 (with W. Hafner); "Compounds of Aromatic Ring Systems and Metals," *Advances in Inorganic and Radiochemistry*, vol. 1, 1959 (with H. P. Fritz); *Inorganic Syntheses: Bisbenzenechromium (O) and Bisbenzenechromium (I) Iodide*, vol. 6, 1960; "On the Existence of a Tungsten Carbonyl Carbene Complex," *Angewandte Chemie*, International Edition in English, vol. 3, 1964 (with A. Maasböl); *Metal Complexes*, 1966 (with H. Werner); "Hindered Rotation About the C-O Bond in Methoxy (Methyl) Carbene Ligands," *Angewandte Chemie*, International Edition in English, vol. 8, 1969 (with Cornelius G. Kreiter); "Ethoxydiethylaminocarbenepentacarbonyl-chromium (O)," *Angewandte Chemie*, International Edition in English, vol. 9, 1970 (with H. J. Kollmeier); "Structure, Bonding, and Reactivity of (Stable) Transition Metal Carbonyl Carbene Complexes," *Pure and Applied Chemistry*, vol. 24, 1970; "Ethoxydimethylaminocarbene-pentacarbonyl-chromium (O)," *Angewandte Chemie*, International Edition in English, vol. 10, 1971 (with Eberhard Winkler, Cornelius G. Kreiter, Gottfried Huttner, and Bernhard Krieg); "Recent Aspects of Transition Metal Carbonyl Carbene Complexes," *Pure and Applied Chemistry*, vol. 30, 1972; "Trans-Halogeno[alkyl (aryl) carbyne]-tetracarbonyl Complexes of Chromium, Molybdenum, and Tungsten," *Angewandte Chemie*, International Edition in English, vol. 12, 1973 (with Gerhard Kreis, Cornelius G. Kreiter, Jörn Müller, Gottfried Huttner, and Hans Lorenz); "Kinetik und Mechanismus der Isomerisierung von Cis- und Trans-Tetracarbonyl-Methoxymethyl-Carbene-Phosphine-Chrom (O)-Komplexen," *Journal of Organometallic Chemistry*, vol. 73, 1974; "On the Way to Carbene and Carbyne Complexes," *Advances in Organometallic Chemistry*, vol. 14, 1976.

Secondary

Cotton, F. Albert, and Geoffrey Wilkinson. *Advanced Inorganic Chemistry*. New York: John Wiley & Sons, 1988. The bonding between metal atoms and planar organic ring compounds—that is, the "sandwich" compounds—is presented, as well as the formation and reactions of carbenes and carbynes. It is pointed out that the nomenclature recommended by the International Union for Pure and Applied Chemistry should be employed for these compounds—"alkylidene" instead of "carbene" and "alkylidyne" instead of "carbyne."

Haiduc, Ionel, and Jerry J. Zuckerman. *Basic Organometallic Chemistry*. New York: De Gruyter, 1985. This advanced text presents the syntheses and the reactions of the "sandwich compounds" (pi complexes) and metal-carbene compounds, as well as metal-carbyne compounds.

Sharpe, Alan G. *Inorganic Chemistry*. 2d ed. New York: Longman, 1986. This text provides a brief introduction to the "sandwich" compounds as well as the carbene and carbyne complexes with metals.

Thayer, John S. *Organometallic Chemistry: An Overview*. New York: VCH Publishers, 1988. The introduction to this volume contains a history of the development of organometallic chemistry. The author points out the impetus given to this subdivision of chemistry by the discovery of ferrocene.

George J. Beichl

1973

Chemistry
Ernst Otto Fischer, West Germany
Sir Geoffrey Wilkinson, Great Britain

Physics
Leo Esaki, Japan
Ivar Giaever, Norway and United States
Brian D. Josephson, Great Britain

Physiology or Medicine
Karl von Frisch, Austria
Konrad Lorenz, Austria
Nikolaas Tinbergen, The Netherlands

Economic Sciences
Wassily Leontief, United States

Literature
Patrick White, Australia

Peace
Henry Kissinger, United States
Le Duc Tho, North Vietnam

SIR GEOFFREY WILKINSON
1973

Born: Todmorden, Yorkshire, England; July 14, 1921

Nationality: British
Areas of concentration: Structural and organometallic chemistry

Wilkinson proposed a radical structure for ferrocene and subsequently proved this structure through analytical experiments and the synthesis of similar sandwich compounds. This development opened a new field of chemistry to exploration

The Award

Presentation

Professor Ingvar Lindqvist, of the Royal Swedish Academy of Sciences, presented the 1973 Nobel Prize in Chemistry to corecipients Geoffrey Wilkinson and Ernst Otto Fischer. Lindqvist commented on existing stereotypes of chemists, which are misleading to the public and annoying to scientists. For example, people view chemists strictly as developers of technology rather than discoverers of "new concepts." Chemists are also perceived as using logic to the exclusion of imagination, although historically many examples of how both facets of thought led to important developments can be found.

Creative thought was important in the accomplishments of Wilkinson and Fischer, as they were the first to explain a particular set of facts by proposing a novel explanation. This was the idea of sandwich compounds, of which ferrocene is the best-known example. In these compounds, a metal atom is "sandwiched between two flat molecules." Furthermore, both recipients went beyond this insight and supported their claims by vigorous experimentation. This experimentation involved synthesis of many compounds structurally similar to ferrocene but with different metals and organic molecules. Lindqvist continued to draw culinary analogies, referring to development of open sandwiches, in which the metal is bonded to one flat molecule with other small groups occupying the other side. Among the many findings, he cited Wilkinson's synthesis of a metal-hydrogen bond, the first known example, as a discovery of great interest.

Lindqvist ended his remarks by reiterating that proving the sandwich molecule structure by theory and experimentation was the major accomplishment of both men. The existence of these compounds opened the door to new structural theories and research in applied catalysis. Wilkinson and Fischer will always be known as the founders of a major new field with untold future potential. Finally, Lindqvist congratulated them as discoverers of a milestone in chemistry.

Nobel lecture

Geoffrey Wilkinson presented his Nobel lecture, "The Long Search for Stable

Transition Metal Alkyls," on December 11, 1973. He listed several processes utilizing organometallic compounds containing a single chemical bond from a transition metal atom to a carbon atom, such as Ziegler-Natta catalysts for the production of polyethylene. Metal-carbon bonds in catalysts are usually unstable and highly reactive. Wilkinson was interested in synthesis of stable compounds in which a metal atom is bonded to a saturated carbon atom. Only single bonds are formed by unsaturated carbon atoms. Unstable diethylzinc was the first compound with this type of bond to be synthesized. In the early 1800's, Zeise's salt was first reported. This compound incorporates ethylene, with unsaturated carbon atoms, bound to platinum. The nature of the attachment of ethylene to platinum, however, would not be known for many years. Continued efforts to produce stable compounds with metal-carbon single bonds, commonly called metal alkyls, were not fruitful.

This difficulty in synthesis arises because transition metal compounds facilitate reactions in which organic groups couple to one another rather than attaching to the metal atom. An attempt to produce dihydrofulvalene, which is composed of two coupled cyclopentadiene groups, using this type of process resulted in formation of biscyclopentadienyl iron. Originally it was proposed that one carbon atom in each five-membered cyclopentadienyl ring formed a single bond to the iron atom. Wilkinson based his structural interpretation on the known instability of metal-carbon single bonds and his idea of the bonding in complexes such as Zeise's salt. Ethylene represents a class of organic compounds containing a carbon-carbon double bond in which two pairs of electrons are shared between the two atoms. Wilkinson postulated that one of these electron pairs, the pi electrons, could interact with the metal so that "the ethylene was bound sideways," with the metal atom equidistant from the two carbon atoms in ethylene. The cyclopentadienyl group contains double bonds that could interact with a metal atom in the same manner as ethylene. Finally, Wilkinson drew on the work of Linus Pauling. The pi electron pairs in the double bonds are delocalized in the cyclopentadienyl ring so that the five carbon-carbon bonds in the ring are identical and all five atoms are equidistant from the central metal. Ferrocene, then, is an iron atom sandwiched between two planar cyclopentadienyl groups.

Subsequently, several compounds were synthesized containing metal-carbon single bonds which were stable to varying degrees. All were related in that each contained a pi-electron-donating substituent. One of these, a manganese compound, was the first example of a fluctional molecule, one in which bonds rapidly shift position, so that averaged behavior is measured. Wilkinson postulated that metal-carbon bonds should be energetically stable so that the high reactivity of these compounds must be attributable to a pathway which facilitated rapid reaction. If that pathway could be blocked, then stable metal alkyls could be isolated. He delineated several pathways by which metal alkyls can decompose. One of these involves transfer of a hydrogen atom from the alkyl to the metal. For this to happen, one of the bonding sites in the metal must be vacant. By using substituents which occupy all of these sites, metal alkyl decomposition is inhibited. Another way to prevent decomposition was to make the hydrogen transfer impossible. Several organic groups can be used in this type of process. The simplest such group is the methyl group. Wilkinson believed that if a metal-methyl compound with no vacant reactive sites on the metal could be synthesized, then it would be stable. Chemically, tungsten was the best metal candidate. By treating methyllithium with tungsten hexachloride, hexamethyltungsten was obtained and, true to expectations, was stable. It displays interesting reactivity, as there is one vacant site left on the metal atom. Finally, Wilkinson noted that this type of synthesis is more art than science, and one is left with the realization that transition metal-carbon bonds are much stronger than was previously believed.

Critical reception

Announcement of the 1973 Nobel Prize winners in chemistry was made at a time when the interest of the public was already focused on science, although the particular science was astronomy, not chemistry. Comet Kohoutek, espoused by *Newsweek* magazine as the probable "celestial extravaganza of the century," was rapidly approaching its period of maximum visibility. This event had captured the attention of the popular press so that often articles on the comet and the Nobel Prizes in chemistry and physics for 1973 could be found on the same page of a periodical. Comet Kohoutek was not as spectacular as expected and is little remembered. This was the fate that Wilkinson predicted for public interest in his award, stating in *New Scientist* that "in six months' time it will all be over." This observation seems more applicable to the comet.

For the most part, reporters at the time of the announcement held views directly opposing Wilkinson's statement. Wilkinson and Fischer were credited with fostering remarkable advances within the field of organometallic chemistry, and even changing the very structure of chemistry in general. There was general agreement that the corecipients had taken an area of chemistry that was little explored or understood and turned it into a major area having impact on the fields of inorganic, organic, and theoretical chemistry.

It was widely held that organo-transition metal compounds of the type studied by Wilkinson and Fischer held much promise for industrial applications, although it was realized that no widespread industrial application had yet been devised. There was general recognition that their Nobel Prize was for basic research that was of interest in a theoretical rather than a practical vein. Victor McElheney stated in *The New York Times* that the work was "close to the heart of chemistry as a science." The 1973 award in chemistry was the first given in several years for fundamental chemical research, getting away from a trend noted in several publications of awarding workers for results that, as stated in *Science News*, "bordered both the biological and physical fields." Gunnar Brusewitsz of the Royal Swedish Academy of Sciences summed it up well when he said the prize was in "chemistry for chemists." In *Nature*, Dietmar Seyferth and Alan Davison stressed the importance of the award for basic research, as such recognition stimulates investigation in new, often nontraditional, areas and thus ultimately leads to some useful application. It was widely noted that the physics and chemistry Nobel Prizes for 1973 were for fundamentally different types of research. The physics prize was deemed the practical prize, as the phenomenon of electron tunneling, for which the recipients were awarded the prize, was expected to have immediate impact on the design of semiconductors and high-temperature superconductors.

With the awarding of the chemistry prize to Wilkinson and Fischer, *Chemical and Engineering News* noted that a tradition of preeminence of Germany and the United Kingdom in chemistry continued. Of the prizes awarded since 1901, 72 percent had been taken by the United States, the United Kingdom, and Germany.

Both *Nature* and *Science* stressed several important contributions to science made by Wilkinson during his investigation of sandwich complexes, quite apart from his elucidation of the structure of ferrocene. In particular, his use of nuclear magnetic resonance (NMR), then in its early stages of development, to elucidate structural features of compounds had wide-ranging impact on the use of this tool.

Public awareness of adverse environmental effects stemming from the use of tetraethyllead as an antiknock additive in gasoline was high at the time of the award. Not surprisingly, reports about the prize that year generally included statements about the likelihood that organo-transition metal compounds would replace lead additives in gasoline. Other potential applications for metallocenes and organometallic compounds included their use as catalysts for such processes as polystyrene production, as antianemic agents, and in drugs for the treatment of Parkinson's disease. There was in general much optimism expressed for the future of the field.

The fact that the award to Wilkinson was for research performed while he was on the faculty of Harvard University, where he was not granted tenure, did not escape notice in the popular press, although the scientific publications at the time made no note of it. According to *Time* magazine, "his senior colleagues were apparently unimpressed" by his results.

There was, in general, respect for the decision to award basic research the Nobel Prize. This was attributable in part to the willingness of Wilkinson and Fischer to propose theories of structure and bonding for the metallocenes which differed dramatically from the accepted rules. Their revolutionary ideas generated a flood of interest in a long-impoverished area of science, leading to developments of benefit to all—developments that will be remembered far longer than Comet Kohoutek.

Biography

Geoffrey Wilkinson was born near Todmorden, Yorkshire, England, to Henry and Ruth Crowther Wilkinson. An early interest in chemistry was fostered by his uncle, who owned a small chemical company. He was admitted to the Todmorden Secondary School, was graduated in 1939, and entered the Imperial College of Science and Technology, University of London, on a Royal scholarship. In 1941, he completed his bachelor of science degree, and in 1946 his doctorate. He joined the National

Research Council of Canada in 1942 as part of the joint United States-United Kingdom-Canada atomic energy project and remained in Canada until 1946. Wilkinson then became a research associate with Glenn Seaborg at the University of California, Berkeley, where he studied nuclear fission products. By his own admission, Wilkinson was "becoming a pseudophysicist rather than developing as a chemist." This, coupled with the scarcity of academic positions in England for nuclear chemists, prompted Wilkinson to move to the Massachusetts Institute of Technology (MIT) in 1950. The following year he joined the faculty of Harvard University as an assistant professor and shortly thereafter made his discovery of ferrocene's structure.

In 1951, Wilkinson married Lise Sølver Schau, the daughter of a rector of the Pharmaceutical High School in Denmark. While at Harvard, Wilkinson accomplished much; he also served in an administrative position as secretary to the chemistry department. For a period of nine months, Wilkinson worked in the laboratory of Jannik Bjerrum as a Guggenheim fellow. In 1955, he left Harvard and returned to the Imperial College of Science and Technology, which at the time had the only chair in inorganic chemistry in the United Kingdom.

Subsequently Wilkinson has received many academic honors for his significant contributions. He has two daughters and is generally acknowledged as a witty, congenial person. In recognition of his contributions, he was knighted in 1967.

Scientific Career

Without a doubt, Geoffrey Wilkinson is a giant in the field of inorganic chemistry. His research and writing have influenced most modern practitioners in the field. This is somewhat surprising when one surveys his career, as he originally established a reputation as a nuclear chemist.

During World War II, considerable effort and capital were expended in the race to develop the atom bomb. The Manhattan Project utilized nuclear fission, in which a heavy nucleus is split into smaller nuclei. Energy released in this process is utilized as the destructive force of the bomb. Fission processes may be induced by bombardment of a target nucleus with a small subatomic particle such as a neutron. Certain naturally occurring nuclei are intrinsically unstable and tend to undergo spontaneous fission.

While with the Research Council's program in Canada, Wilkinson classified the products of several nuclear fission reactions. This is a very involved process. Typically, the products of fission reactions are themselves radioactive and thus hazardous. Also, several products often result from a single fission step so that a mixture of particles results. Each substance decays by a certain type of radioactive emission, and each process has a characteristic half-life. A half-life is defined as the time required for one half of the original sample to decay. Thus it is possible to characterize radioactive substances by measurement of their radioactive decay rate and determination of the type of particle being emitted. In order to do this, the sample must be pure. Wilkinson therefore had the task of first separating the fission products from one another so that the individual substances could be studied and their characteristics determined. In order to effect this separation, Wilkinson made use of the fact that radioactive elements are still chemical elements and thus display differences in their chemical properties which enable them to be separated. With coworker Harry G. Hicks, Wilkinson developed and published several methods for the separation of fission products. The most useful of these was the technique of ion exchange chromatography.

Chromatographic processes involve passage of a mobile phase, containing the substances to be separated, over a stationary phase. Different substances interact with this stationary phase to varying degrees, with the net effect being that the materials in the mobile phase travel through the stationary phase at varying rates and are thus separated. In ion exchange chromatography, charged particles, or ions, displace a like charged material from the stationary phase. The net effect then is separation of the charged substances. Once the radioactive materials were separated in this fashion, they could be isolated by incorporating them into easily handled compounds. Radioactive decay processes of the resulting compounds could then be studied to determine the nature of the fission products. Through application of these techniques, Wilkinson was able to isolate and identify dozens of new radioactive isotopes of various elements. (Isotopes are substances that have the same number of positively charged protons in their nuclei but differing numbers of electrically neutral neutrons.) Wilkinson discovered new isotopes of such diverse elements as iridium, tantalum, and gold, with half-lives ranging from days to years.

Glenn Seaborg's laboratory was one of the best places to be in the race to discover new elements, and many of the transuranium elements were first produced there. Transuranium elements are those with more protons in their nuclei than exist in the nuclei of uranium atoms. They do not occur in nature except for trace amounts of plutonium. While at Berkeley, Wilkinson continued his studies of nuclear chemistry, focusing on the determination of the products of spallation reactions. In spallation processes, nuclei split as the result of bombardment with subatomic particles. During this time, he also characterized several examples of neutron-deficient elements. The atomic number of an element is the number of protons in the nucleus. In general, elements with large atomic numbers require a large number of neutrons to stabilize the high concentration of positive charge present in the nucleus of the atom. The number of neutrons is typically larger than the number of protons in these elements. Neutron-deficient elements do not have enough neutrons to make the nucleus stable so that these substances undergo some sort of radioactive decay to produce a more stable nucleus. Neutron-deficient elements decay by modes not found for naturally occurring radioisotopes. Wilkinson characterized the decay products of several of these isotopes.

Wilkinson found himself losing interest in what he termed an isotope synthesis "game." Furthermore, academic positions in the United Kingdom for nuclear chemists were rare. Therefore, when Wilkinson went to MIT as a research associate, he decided to shift his research into a new direction. He began to focus on the chemistry of the transition elements. These elements, in the center of the periodic table, are characterized by having more than one stable charge as well as interesting magnetic properties. While at MIT, Wilkinson made two major discoveries. Tenney Davis had hypothesized that certain phosphorus compounds could behave similarly to carbon monoxide and bond to nickel atoms. Wilkinson provided experimental evidence for this claim by synthesizing a compound in which a phosphorus trichloride molecule was attached to a nickel atom. This similarity in the reactivities of phosporus trihalide groups and carbon monoxide, or carbonyl, groups prompted one of the more exotic syntheses accomplished by Wilkinson. It is well known that carbon monoxide is a poisonous gas; it interacts with hemoglobin in the body. The active site in hemoglobin is an iron atom, and iron is a transition metal. Carbon monoxide occupies the site in hemoglobin normally occupied by oxygen, effectively blocking oxygen transport in the bloodstream. Wilkinson's work with nickel compounds had shown that phosphorus and carbonyl groups were similar. It thus seemed feasible that phosphorus groups may behave similarly toward hemoglobin. This postulate was confirmed by the successful isolation of hemoglobin containing a phosphorus trifluoride group bound to the iron atom. This finding explained the toxicity of phosphorus trifluoride.

Regardless of these accomplishments, it was Wilkinson's expertise in nuclear chemistry that resulted in his appointment, along with Dick Diamond, to the faculty of Harvard University in 1951. While hired primarily as a nuclear scientist, he found himself in the immediate position of teaching a course in inorganic chemistry, a novel experience for him. One significant event resulting from this course was that F. Albert Cotton decided to pursue his doctorate with Wilkinson. This began a very fruitful professional relationship.

When Wilkinson arrived at Harvard, he already was interested in the bonding in so-called pi complexes, in which the pi electrons in a bond are donated to a metal atom. Wilkinson was of the opinion that these groups "must be bound sideways." Early in 1952, Wilkinson read of the newly synthesized biscyclopentadienyl iron. In preparing for his course, Wilkinson had read about cyclopentadiene and the negatively charged cyclopentadienide ion, which was a highly symmetrical ring molecule with six pi electrons. Upon reading of the proposed structure of biscyclopentadienyl iron, Wilkinson was convinced that the reported structure was incorrect. Instead, he formulated the idea that the pi electrons in the carbon rings formed bonds to the iron atom, so that the molecule adopted a "sandwich" structure.

The final key was the application of Linus Pauling's theory of resonance. It is often possible to draw more than one structure for molecules with several pi electrons, which differ only by the placement of these electrons in the molecule. These are called resonance structures, and a molecule may be viewed as having a structure that is the average of these resonance structures. In the case of the iron cyclopentadiene complex, resonance in the two cyclopentadiene rings would make all the carbon atoms, and thus all the carbon-hydrogen bonds, in the cyclopentadienyl rings equivalent so that all of the iron-carbon internuclear distances were identical.

Remarkably, Wilkinson reached this proposed structure within a matter of hours. Robert Woodward had seen the same paper, and he and Wilkinson were both engaged in experimentation to prove the sandwich structure within days. Woodward coined the name "ferrocene" for the compound, in recognition of its similarity to the organic compound benzene. Wilkinson immediately launched efforts to synthesize compounds containing different transition metals. A wide variety of these compounds, dubbed metallocenes, were produced with such metals as ruthenium and cobalt.

Wilkinson pioneered the use of modern analytical techniques such as infrared spectroscopy, which determines the vibrational frequency of chemical bonds, and nuclear magnetic resonance (NMR) spectroscopy, which yields information about the chemical environment of hydrogen nuclei in compounds. With the aid of these techniques, different bonding modes were elucidated. In manganese cyclopentadienide, two types of cyclopentadienyl rings are present. One of these is bonded through the pi electrons as in ferrocene, but the other is attached by a single, or sigma-type, bond from the metal atom to one of the carbon atoms in the cyclopentadienyl ring. A related compound contained an iron atom and two carbon monoxide groups. One of Wilkinson's students, Stan Piper, studied the NMR spectrum and the infrared spectrum of this iron compound. Wilkinson and Piper expected that the NMR spectrum would be complicated, as there were several distinct proton environments in the proposed structure. The infrared spectrum was in agreement with this structure, but the NMR spectrum was simpler than expected. These anomalies were explained by the introduction of the concept of fluctionality, in which rapid interconversion of bonds occurs so that averaged behavior is seen. NMR is a slow experimental technique, so that averaged behavior is seen, whereas infrared measurements are faster than the time scale of interconversion. This fluctionality tends to make metal-carbon bonds fairly reactive. The class of compound studied by Piper was given the interesting name "ring whizzer."

Sandwich compounds, or metallocenes, were a new class of compounds. While synthesizing new compounds of this type, Wilkinson produced a rhenium metallocene which also contained a rhenium-hydrogen bond. This was the first time such a bond had been formed, and proof of its existence was offered by the presence of a peak at a very unusual position in the NMR spectrum. An additional class of compounds, the half sandwiches, in which there is only one cyclopentadienyl ring per molecule, was synthesized as well.

While at Harvard, Wilkinson made many significant contributions to the body of science. Harvard did not, however, offer him a tenured position. In 1973, he simply stated that he was fired and that Harvard "thought they could do without me." The significance of his work was noticed in the United Kingdom, and in 1955 he was offered the vacated chair of inorganic chemistry at London's Imperial College of Science and Technology. This was truly a return home for Wilkinson, who was graduated from the same institution as a Royal Scholar and Frank Hatton Prizeman. It was hoped that he would bring with him to the position an enthusiastic development of inorganic chemistry studies.

Wilkinson remained fascinated with the transition metal-hydrogen bond. He continued this line of investigation at the Imperial College. His emphasis gradually shifted from synthesizing these bonds to studying their role in catalytic processes. A catalyst is a substance that speeds up a desired reaction through participation in the mechanism of the reaction. A catalyst is converted back to its original form in one of the final steps of the process, so that it can be recovered and used again. Wilkinson found that transition metal-hydrogen bonding was important in certain types of catalytic processes. He focused on two types, olefin hydrogenation and hydroformylation reactions. Hydroformylation is the process of adding the elements in formaldehyde to an olefin, resulting in formation of a long-chain aldehyde from which alcohols can be produced. Olefin hydrogenation, as the name implies, is the addition of hydrogen atoms to the carbon atoms in the double bond of an olefin. Wilkinson found that a rhodium complex with a chlorine atom and three trichlorophosphorus groups bound to the metal atom was useful in olefin hydrogenation. This compound is now widely known as Wilkinson's catalyst. The compound has what is known as a square planar geometry, with all the elements bound to the metal in the same plane. In the hydrogenation process, Wilkinson elucidated that the hydrogen added to this complex, increasing the number of atoms bound to the central metal atom. Next, the olefin double bond attaches to the rhodium, as in Zeise's salt. Rearrangement gives the hydrogenated olefin and the original rhodium catalyst.

Wilkinson and Fischer both pioneered the field of pi bonded complexes. These materials tend to have metal atoms with a rather large electron density about the metal atom. It logically follows, then, that the metal must have a low charge, or oxidation state. There are many substances known, however, in which the transition metal has a very large positive charge. It thus seemed reasonable to suppose that organo-transition metal complexes with highly charged metal atoms could be synthesized. Many attempts were made, all unsuccessful, until 1975. Wilkinson and his associates found that when methyllithium and tungsten hexachloride are reacted, hexamethyltungsten is formed. This compound contains six metal-carbon sigma bonds, and the tungsten atom has an oxidation state of six. Tetramethylzirconium was produced as well. The isolation of these compounds provided concrete proof of the stability of high-oxidation-state metal alkyls.

Throughout his career as an inorganic chemist, Wilkinson has worked almost exclusively with transition metal complexes and helped make them an important subject in their own right. His research results have been reported in more than four hundred scientific publications. At least as important as his experimental program has been his contribution in the realm of texts and reference works. With F. Albert Cotton, he coauthored *Advanced Inorganic Chemistry*. Several editions of this milestone text have been published, and it is one of the standard works in the field. The significance of his contributions perhaps is best understood by the widespread recognition given to Wilkinson in the form of awards. In addition to the Nobel

Prize, he has received such honors as the Lavoisier Medal of the French Chemical Society in 1968, the Transition Metal Chemistry Award of the Royal Society in 1972, and the Galileo Medal from the University of Pisa, Italy, in 1973.

Wilkinson's career has spanned the development of organo-transition metal chemistry from its infancy to maturity. Organo-transition metal compounds are widely used in industry as catalysts for various processes. His pioneering work on instrumental methods for the determination of structure has borne fruit in the widespread use of infrared and NMR spectroscopy in chemistry and medicine (where NMR is more commonly referred to as magnetic resonance imaging). Theories of bonding and structure elucidated by Wilkinson paved the way for widespread research in the field. The body of fundamental scientific knowledge is much richer as a result, and perhaps that in itself is the greatest achievement of Wilkinson as a chemist.

Bibliography

Primary

CHEMISTRY: "Fission Products of Uranium-235," *Nature*, 1946 (with W. E. Grummit); "Neutron Deficient Radioactive Isotopes," *Journal of the Chemical Society*, 1949; "Chemical Separation of Fission Products by Oxidation-Reduction," *Nucleonics*, vol. 9, 1951 (with Grummit); "The Preparation and Properties of Tetrakistribromophosphinenickel and Tetrakistrifluorophosphinenickel," *Journal of the American Chemical Society*, vol. 73, 1951; "Phosphorus Trifluorohemoglobin," *Nature*, vol. 168, 1951; "The Structure of Biscyclopentadienyl Iron," *Journal of the American Chemical Society*, vol. 74, 1952 (with R. B. Woodward, M. C. Whiting, and M. Rosenblum); "Cyclopentadienyl Compounds of Chromium, Molybdenum, and Tungsten," *Journal of the American Chemical Society*, vol. 76, 1954; "Biscyclopentadienyl Rhenium Hydride," *Journal of the American Chemical Society*, vol. 77, 1955 (with J. M. Birmingham); *Advanced Inorganic Chemistry*, 1962 (with F. Albert Cotton); *Basic Inorganic Chemistry*, 1976 (with Cotton).

EDITED TEXTS: *Comprehensive Organometallic Chemistry: The Synthesis and Structures of Organometallic Compounds*, 1982 (with F. G. A. Stone); *Comprehensive Coordination Chemistry: The Synthesis, Reactions, Properties, and Applications of Coordination Compounds*, 1987.

Secondary

Basolo, Fred. "High Oxidation State Metals in Organometallic Chemistry." In *Encyclopædia Britannica Yearbook of Science and the Future*. Chicago: Encyclopædia Britannica, 1989. A brief summary of organometallic chemistry mentioning Wilkinson's work throughout. The nonrigorous treatment presented here is easier to follow and understand than treatments found in most textbooks and reference works.

Coates, G. E., M. L. H. Green, and K. Wade. *Organometallic Compounds*. London: Methuen, 1967. A systematic presentation of the types of organometallic compounds synthesized through 1966. As in Powell's work, excellent referencing is particularly useful to the advanced reader. The two-volume set is arranged according to the periodic table and the type of metal-carbon bonds.

Powell, P. *Principles of Organometallic Chemistry.* 2d ed. London: Chapman & Hall, 1988. This advanced text is one of the best in the field, providing in-depth information about organometallic chemistry. Wilkinson's work is seen as a significant proportion of that body. Well referenced, the book is an excellent source of detailed information about this subject.

Wilkinson, Geoffrey. "The Iron Sandwich: A Recollection of the First Four Months." *Journal of Organometallic Chemistry* 100 (1975): 273-278. Wilkinson's own narrative gives a clear picture of the frantic work which won for him the Nobel Prize. In this general article, the reader gains an understanding of the environment in which the academic chemist works and of the interaction between Wilkinson and other researchers at Harvard. A bibliography lists some of the early papers on metallocenes.

Wilkinson, G., E. Rochow, and R. Diamond. "Nuclear Chemistry at Harvard." *Journal of Chemical Education* 31 (1954): 474-475. This brief narrative is essentially a recruiting device. It does, however, provide a glimpse of the facilities and techniques of nuclear research. Historically, the perspective presented in this article differs from subsequent approaches to generating interest in nuclear science.

Craig B. Lagrone

1974

Chemistry
Paul J. Flory, United States

Physics
Sir Martin Ryle, Great Britain
Antony Hewish, Great Britain

Physiology or Medicine
Albert Claude, United States
Christian R. de Duve, Belgium
George E. Palade, United States

Economic Sciences
Gunnar Myrdal, Sweden
Friedrich von Hayek, Great Britain

Literature
Eyvind Johnson, Sweden
Harry Martinson, Sweden

Peace
Eisaku Satō, Japan
Sean MacBride, Ireland

PAUL J. FLORY
1974

Born: Sterling, Illinois; June 19, 1910
Died: Big Sur, California; September 9, 1985
Nationality: American
Area of concentration: Physical chemistry of macromolecules

Flory demonstrated that the physical and chemical properties of macromolecular systems could be understood in the light of the basic disciplines of chemical kinetics, thermodynamics, and statistical mechanics

The Award

Presentation

Professor Stig Clæsson of the Nobel Committee for Chemistry presented Paul J. Flory for the Nobel Prize in Chemistry on December 10, 1974. He began by comparing macromolecules to the chains of pearls worn by some members of the audience, but he emphasized that if a pearl were to represent a single atom in the molecule's backbone it would take all the necklaces in the audience strung end to end to produce a representative model. The length and flexibility of long-chain polymers require a statistical description of their size and shape.

Paul Flory made significant contributions to the theory of the configurations of long-chain molecules in solution. He introduced the concept of the theta point, an ideal state in which the configuration of the polymer in solution is determined only by its local chemical architecture and not by the solvent in which it is immersed. In relating the configurations of polymer molecules to their properties in solution he introduced a constant of broad significance, now called the Flory universal constant.

Professor Clæsson also noted a number of Paul Flory's other contributions. He stated that the outstanding characteristic of Flory's scientific work is that, in retrospect, it looks remarkably simple. This means, however, that the work was really a profound insight into a new area. Clæsson concluded by pointing out that the scientific work of Flory had helped to transform macromolecular chemistry from "primitive semi-empirical observations into a highly developed science."

Nobel lecture

Paul Flory's Nobel lecture, entitled "Spatial Configuration of Macromolecular Chains" and delivered on December 11, 1974, was both a historical review of some of his accomplishments and an exposition of current research. He began by pointing out that the science of macromolecules had been developed through the efforts of many investigators all over the world during the relatively short period of forty years. He then stated that he was appearing, "in a very real sense, as their representative."

The distinguishing characteristic of macromolecules is that the atoms or groups making up the molecule are connected in very long chains. The chemical bonds connecting these backbone atoms allow relatively free rotation of the attached groups. This means that the molecular chain is very flexible and, consequently, can adopt a large number of configurations in solution. This flexibility was recognized by early workers in the field, who applied the theory of random flights to the calculation of the size and shape of polymers in solution. This theory gives a qualitatively correct description of the chain configuration, provided that the effects of excluded volume can be neglected.

Excluded volume is a result of the unavoidable fact that the molecule cannot adopt a configuration in which two of its parts or segments occupy the same space at the same time. This produces an expansion of the chain (compared to an ideal chain as described by the theory of random flights in which this effect is neglected). The more compact configurations are prohibited, because they cannot occur unless a large number of chain segments are forced to be in the same place at the same time. This expansion, however, can be countered by the effects of the solvent, which, under certain circumstances, will oppose the swelling. Flory gave an outline of his famous theory, published in 1949, in which he correctly calculated the effects of volume exclusion on the size of the chain and predicted the existence of the theta point, at which the effects of volume exclusion vanish. The theta point can easily be identified experimentally, and the properties of chains studied in this state do, indeed, show the expected ideal behavior.

The properties of a polymer chain at the theta point are, then, only a result of the local chemical architecture: the structural geometry, the energies of bond rotations, and the interactions between neighboring atoms. The relationship between the chemical architecture and the properties of polymers was being actively studied by Flory's research group in 1974. He concluded his lecture by presenting the rigorous mathematical theory that was being used to calculate various configuration-dependent properties of long-chain molecules in dilute solutions, in which the chains are so far apart that the interactions between them can be neglected.

Critical reception

Response to the announcement that Paul Flory had been awarded the 1974 Nobel Prize in Chemistry was uniformly enthusiastic. *Chemical and Engineering News* opened its story by pointing out that, in contrast to the 1974 prizewinners in peace and literature, "no one is likely to question the credentials of Dr. Paul J. Flory of Stanford University." The story went on to quote Frank E. Karasz of the University of Massachusetts, who called Flory "*the* man in polymer chemistry."

The articles in the other major scientific news journals were comparable. Leo Mandelkern, writing in *Nature*, said that Flory "stands foremost among those who have devoted themselves to the development of the physical chemistry of high polymers." *Science News* quoted an unnamed Stanford colleague, who said that "the plastics industry could not have developed without Flory's methodological and practical contributions." The popular press also noted the event. *The New York Times* published a brief profile of Flory and a summary of both his prizewinning accomplishments and his current research interests. Flory's own response was modest. In *Science News*, he said he was "overwhelmed, highly honored, and humbled at the same time." He thought it was "a bit unfair for one person to be singled out for recognition" in such a broad field with so many contributors.

A long and thoughtful article was written for the November 22, 1974, issue of *Science* by Walter H. Stockmayer. Stockmayer gave an excellent, though selective, review of Flory's scientific accomplishments; more important, he also gave considerable insight into the distinguishing characteristics of his work that set him apart from the many other practitioners in the field. He quoted Thomas G. Fox, a Flory collaborator, who characterized Flory's work: "I think the secret of his success is an unparalleled intuition for grasping the physical essentials of a problem, for visualizing a phenomenon in terms of simple models amenable to straightforward treatment and productive of results that are valid to the degree required by the original statement of the problem." Stockmayer added that Flory also had the "intuition (faith?)" that his own intuitions were correct and stood by his ideas even when challenged. Flory usually was proved to be correct in the long run.

The overall public reaction of the scientific community can be best summarized by a quotation from Eugene Helfand in *Physics Today*: "Beyond the breadth of his research, Flory's impact is attributable to the fact that he challenged the central problems, provided practical solutions, and verified them with the right experiments."

Biography

Paul J. Flory was born on June 19, 1910, in Sterling, Illinois. His parents were Ezra Flory, a clergyman-educator, and Martha Brumbaugh Flory, a former schoolteacher. He was graduated from Elgin (Illinois) High School in 1927 and entered Manchester College, a liberal arts college in Indiana. After receiving his bachelor's degree in chemistry in 1931, he entered graduate school at Ohio State University, where he received a master's degree in synthetic organic chemistry under the direction of C. E. Boord. He then changed fields and did his doctoral research in physical chemistry with Herrick L. Johnson. Flory's dissertation research was in the areas of photochemistry and spectroscopy.

Upon completion of his Ph.D. at Ohio State in 1934, Flory joined the Central Research Department of the DuPont Company, where he became acquainted with polymers. During this period he met Emily Catherine Tabor, whom he married on March 7, 1936. In 1938, Flory moved to the Basic Science Laboratory at the University of Cincinnati. The urgency of war-related research on the development of synthetic rubber lured him back to industry, first at the Esso (later Exxon) Laboratories (1940-1943) and then at the research laboratories of the Goodyear Tire and Rubber Company (1943-1948).

In 1948, Flory was invited to deliver the George Fisher Baker Lectures at Cornell

University. He subsequently accepted a faculty appointment in the chemistry department at Cornell, moving there permanently in the fall of 1948. Flory left Cornell in 1957 to become executive director of the Mellon Institute in Pittsburgh. In 1961, he moved to the chemistry department at Stanford University. Flory formally retired from Stanford in 1975 but maintained an active research program until his death in 1985.

Scientific Career

Upon completion of his Ph.D., Paul Flory joined the DuPont Company, where he was assigned to the small research group headed by the great Wallace H. Carothers, the inventor of nylon and neoprene, whose name must be placed alongside that of 1953 Nobel laureate Hermann Staudinger as a founder of macromolecular chemistry. Carothers introduced Flory to polymers, long-chain molecules composed of repeating units, and convinced him that they were valid objects of scientific inquiry. Polymer chemistry was a new science in 1934. The work of Staudinger and Carothers had only recently convinced the scientific community that macromolecules were linked by ordinary covalent bonds, the same as those in the small molecules with which organic chemists were accustomed to working, rather than by mysterious "secondary linkages." Carothers' research group was making significant progress in the synthesis of polymers, leading ultimately to the development of neoprene rubber and nylon, the first synthetic fiber. In the process, they were raising a number of important questions concerning the speed, or rate, of the chemical reactions in which the polymers were formed.

Flory had done research on the rates of reactions as a graduate student, so Carothers assigned to him the task of deciphering the rates of formation of condensation polymers. The formation of a simple condensation polymer such as nylon involves the repetition of an elementary chemical reaction to form what is known as an amide linkage. The building blocks of a polymer are small molecules called monomers, each of which contains two different reactive sites (groups of atoms that can undergo a chemical reaction), so that, as the reaction proceeds, larger and larger molecules are formed. The process is the chemical analogue of adding links to a chain. It was assumed at the time that because larger molecules move more slowly in solution, reactions between them would be more sluggish than those between the original small monomers. Flory, however, in a theoretical investigation of the distribution of the sizes of the molecules formed in the polymerization reaction, took the contrary view that reactivity is independent of molecular size. Beginning with this assumption and using straightforward statistical methods, he was able to calculate the distribution of molecular sizes, producing a result known as the "most probable distribution." This result was reported in 1936. The assumption of equal reactivity was controversial, but Flory trusted his insight into the physical and chemical processes that governed the rate of reaction and stood his ground. A few years later, in 1939, he produced the experimental data to support his hypothesis.

While at DuPont, Flory also investigated the rates of the other major type of polymer formation reaction known at the time, vinyl or addition polymerization. This is the reaction that produces such familiar substances as polystyrene, polyethylene, and Teflon. In contrast to a condensation polymerization, where there is a reactive site on each end of the chain, in an addition polymerization there is a single reactive site on each growing chain. The chain will continue to grow until that site is destroyed. Flory pointed out that, along with the termination reactions that were known to destroy this reactive site, another process, which he called "chain transfer," would be important in these polymerizations. In chain transfer, the reactive site is moved from the growing chain to some other, previously unreactive molecule in the system. This process is important in controlling the lengths of the chains formed in the reaction. Flory's hypothesis was controversial but was ultimately shown to be correct by the work of Frank R. Mayo.

In the early 1940's, after a brief stay at the University of Cincinnati, Flory returned to industry to work on the development of synthetic rubber. He turned his attention to nonlinear polymers and the phenomenon of network formation or gelation. To be useful in most practical applications, rubber must be cross-linked. The practical method for cross-linking natural rubber was invented in 1839 by Charles Goodyear and is usually called vulcanization. A cross-linked polymer forms an extensive network or gel, in which each part of the molecule is connected to every other part of the molecule by chemical bonds. Such a network will neither dissolve nor flow and often exhibits the familiar elasticity of a rubber band. The difference between a linear polymer system and a network can be imagined by thinking about the difference between a collection of lengths of string and a fishing net. The collection of strings can easily be separated, but the net cannot be taken apart without cutting.

Flory approached the problem by studying the reactions between monomers having more than two reactive sites. Such a system will ultimately form a single huge network molecule or gel. (This process is essentially familiar to anyone who has made a gelatin dessert; a liquid gradually turns into a solid-like substance.) Flory was able to calculate the number of reactions between monomers needed to form the gel, and this prediction agreed fairly well with the results of experiments.

During this period, Flory developed his version of the lattice theory of polymer solutions. Maurice L. Huggins obtained similar results independently, so this work is generally known as the Flory-Huggins theory. The problem was to calculate the number of configurations or arrangements of a long-chain molecule in the presence of other chains with which it cannot overlap. The lattice model adopted by Flory and Huggins makes this calculation tractable, and the results describe the behavior of solutions and mixtures of polymers. The original Flory-Huggins theory applied only to polymer solutions at high concentrations; the extension of the theory to dilute solutions was accomplished some years later by Flory and William R. Krigbaum.

Flory also began his lifelong interest in the phenomenon of rubber elasticity at this time. His first papers on this subject were done in collaboration with John Rehner, Jr., in 1943. The fundamental problem is to understand the origin of the restoring force when a rubbery substance is stretched. The major contribution to this force comes from the decrease in the entropy of the chains as they are extended. Entropy is a measure of the disorder of a system: The larger the disorder, the larger the entropy. In the undeformed rubber, the long chains can adopt any one of a large number of random coil configurations, resulting in a large entropy. As the sample is stretched, the chains are extended and can adopt fewer configurations. This means it possesses a reduced entropy. The second law of thermodynamics, one of the fundamental laws of nature, states that systems with high entropy are favored relative to those of low entropy. Since the entropy is decreased as the rubber is stretched, a restoring force is generated that tries to pull the rubber back to its undeformed state. Flory was able to translate this idea into mathematical terms and produce a quantitative theory of rubber elasticity. Similar theories were developed independently by Frederick T. Wall and by Hubert M. James and Eugene Guth at about the same time.

In 1948, Flory was invited to deliver the George Fisher Baker Lectures at Cornell University. His stay at Cornell resulted in the offer of a faculty appointment in the chemistry department, where he remained until 1957. While he was preparing the Baker lectures, Flory thought of a way to treat the effects of excluded volume on the configurations of polymer chains. This result, which was published in 1949, is probably his most remarkable contribution to polymer science and was one of the topics treated in detail in his Nobel lecture. The Baker lectures were ultimately expanded into a book, *Principles of Polymer Chemistry* (1953), which was an immense contribution to the pedagogy of polymer science. It was the bible for generations of students, and it still remains a useful reference.

Flory's Cornell years were extremely productive ones. He began to study the problem of polymer crystallization. He showed that crystallization-melting phenomena in crystals of long-chain molecules could be understood in the same way as those in small molecule systems were. These ideas were later applied to oriented systems such as fibers and ultimately to fibrous proteins such as those in ligaments and muscles.

His work on polymer crystallization led Flory into another controversy, this one concerning the morphology of semicrystalline polymers. When long-chain molecules crystallize, they do so by folding back on themselves. An important question in understanding the structure and formation of these crystals is the nature of the folding: Is the folding tight and orderly, so that the molecule looks something like a carpenter's rule, or are the folds loose and random like the wires of an old-fashioned telephone switchboard? Flory was a strong advocate of the latter model, but other respected members of the polymer community were supporters of the first. The experimental data, however, could not unambiguously distinguish between the two alternatives, so the controversy remained unresolved even to the time of Flory's death.

Flory also studied the effect of polymers on the flow properties of solutions. Addition of a small amount of polymer to a solvent makes the solution much more viscous. The difference is even more dramatic than the difference between the viscosities of water and honey. This increase in viscosity is related to the configuration of the polymer molecule in the solvent. Flory made significant contributions, both experimental and theoretical, to the understanding of this phenomenon.

Another important area that he began to investigate while at Cornell was liquid crystalline substances. A liquid crystal is composed of rodlike molecules that, at low temperatures, can line up in the same direction but still remain a fluid. Liquid crystals composed of small molecules are important materials used in display devices for calculators and watches, and polymeric liquid crystals are used to make very strong synthetic fibers. This was a topic that Flory continued to study for the rest of his life.

Flory left Cornell to become executive director of the Mellon Institute in 1957 and then, after four years in that position, moved to Stanford University for the remainder of his career. At Stanford he began to study the configurational statistics of linear polymers, using the sophisticated mathematical techniques of the so-called rotational isomeric state model. This model takes into account the detailed local chemical architecture of the polymer chain in a realistic way and allows one to calculate the configuration-dependent properties of the chain at the theta point. Flory's research group at Stanford did extensive theoretical and experimental research in this area. Some of this work is summarized in Flory's second book, *Statistical Mechanics of Chain Molecules* (1969).

In the mid-1970's, he again turned his attention to the phenomenon of rubber elasticity and produced a more sophisticated theory that took into account the effects of intermolecular interactions on the properties of the network. This work, done partly in collaboration with Burak Erman and known as the Flory-Erman theory, was partly responsible for a general revitalization of interest in this problem throughout the polymer community. As had much of Flory's previous work, his ideas generated controversy. He was preparing a paper on this subject for presentation at the annual meeting of the American Chemical Society at the time of his death in 1985.

Paul Flory was clearly the most important figure in the early development of the physical chemistry of macromolecules. His contributions, in a real sense, defined the field. His tremendous insight, coupled with remarkable theoretical and experimental skills, helped reveal many aspects of the fascinating behavior of macromolecules. In addition, he worked tirelessly to promote the view that polymer science is a legitimate subject for basic scientific research and not only a branch of technology. He also argued that material on macromolecules should be a larger part of the undergraduate chemistry curriculum. He was highly regarded both as a teacher and as a person by his students. His strong sense of honor led him to become a courageous advocate for the cause of human rights all over the world. He used the public status that accompanies the Nobel Prize to fight for the rights of oppressed scientists abroad. Throughout his career, he exerted a powerful influence on the field of polymer science as a teacher, a researcher, and a human being.

Bibliography

Primary

CHEMISTRY: "Molecular Size Distribution in Linear Condensation Polymers," *Journal of the American Chemical Society*, vol. 58, 1936; "Kinetics of Polyesterification: A Study of the Effects of Molecular Weight and Viscosity on Reaction Rate," *Journal of the American Chemical Society*, vol. 61, 1939; "Molecular Size Distribution in Three Dimensional Polymers," *Journal of the American Chemical Society*, vol. 63, 1941; "Thermodynamics of High Polymer Solutions," *Journal of Chemical Physics*, vol. 10, 1942; "Statistical Mechanics of Cross-Linked Polymer Networks: I, Rubberlike Elasticity," *Journal of Chemical Physics*, vol. 11, 1943 (with J. Rehner, Jr.); *Principles of Polymer Chemistry*, 1953; *Statistical Mechanics of Chain Molecules*, 1969.

MISCELLANEOUS: *Selected Works of Paul J. Flory*, 3 vols., 1985 (edited by Leo Mandelkern et al.).

Secondary

Hounsell, David A., and John Kenly Smith, Jr. *Science and Corporate Strategy.* Cambridge, England: Cambridge University Press, 1988. This is a study of research and development in the DuPont Company between 1902 and 1980. The theme of the book is the evolution of research strategy in the company, and it tells the story of the major research developments at DuPont. One of those stories is the development of nylon by the group headed by W. H. Carothers, in which Paul Flory played a major role. The tension between basic research and product development is well illustrated by this incident.

McMillan, Frank M. *The Chain Straighteners.* New York: Macmillan, 1979. A highly readable history of the discovery and commercialization of stereoregular polymers, this book provides a fascinating account of the nature of scientific research. This discovery involved both academic and industrial scientists from Europe and the United States, so the book gives a picture of science on an international scale. Paul Flory had only a minor direct role in this discovery, but the book makes clear his enormous indirect influence on the polymer community.

Mark, Herman. *Giant Molecules.* New York: Time, 1966. This book is part of the Life Science Library and was written for the layperson. It is an overview of polymer science, focusing mainly on the uses of polymers as materials. It provides good nontechnical explanations of polymer chemistry and the processing of polymers into useful products.

Morawetz, Herbert. *Polymers: The Origin and Growth of a Science.* New York: John Wiley & Sons, 1985. This is the first effort at a comprehensive history of polymer science and was written by a major figure in the field. It concentrates on the development of scientific ideas rather than on the people. It is rather technical and may be difficult reading for a nonscientist. It does not place the work of Paul Flory in a broad historical context.

Morris, Peter J. T. *Polymer Pioneers*. Philadelphia, Pa.: Center for the History of Chemistry, 1986. This is a history of polymer science and technology written for a nontechnical audience. It contains a brief historical overview of the field and timelines of the major developments. It also includes biographies of twelve major figures in the history of polymer science, including Paul Flory. It is richly illustrated with photographs.

Stockmayer, Walter H., and Bruno H. Zimm. "When Polymer Science Looked Easy." *Annual Review of Physical Chemistry* 35 (1984): 1-21. This article contains the reminiscences of two important figures in polymer chemistry concerning the way in which they were attracted into the field in the 1940's. Stockmayer describes his work on the problem of gelation, which was inspired by the 1941 papers by Flory. Zimm writes about the early work on the applications of light scattering to polymers. While some of the material is rather technical, the article provides the lay reader with an interesting portrait of the origins of university polymer research in the United States.

Jeffrey Kovac

1975

Chemistry
John Warcup Cornforth, Australia
Vladimir Prelog, Switzerland

Physics
Aage Bohr, Denmark
Ben R. Mottelson, Denmark
L. James Rainwater, United States

Physiology or Medicine
Renato Dulbecco, United States
Howard M. Temin, United States
David Baltimore, United States

Economic Sciences
Leonid V. Kantorovich, Soviet Union
Tjalling C. Koopmans, United States

Literature
Eugenio Montale, Italy

Peace
Andrey D. Sakharov, Soviet Union

JOHN WARCUP CORNFORTH
1975

Born: Sydney, Australia; September 7, 1917

Nationality: Australian
Areas of concentration: Organic synthesis and stereochemistry

Cornforth made dramatic contributions to organic synthesis, particularly concerning steroids, terpenes, and penicillin. Using isotopes, he investigated reactions involving chiral molecules and determined the stereochemical demands of enzyme-catalyzed reactions

The Award

Presentation

On December 10, 1975, Professor Arne Fredga of the Royal Swedish Academy of Sciences presented John Warcup Cornforth for the Nobel Prize in Chemistry. He pointed out that Cornforth and his cowinner, Vladimir Prelog, had studied in great detail the changes that compounds of carbon undergo. Their approach to understanding the exact steps by which one form of matter enters into a new molecular arrangement involved the study of the geometry of the atoms in space. It is as if, Fredga says, one were to leave Stockholm by car for Oslo. Soon one would come to a branch in the road: right to Oslo, left elsewhere. Such decisions of right or left lie at the very heart of the huge array of chemical reactions constantly taking place in living tissue.

These biochemical reactions, so vital to human well-being, are nearly all facilitated by the complex proteins called enzymes. Cornforth's greatest contribution was in showing that each step in an enzyme-controlled reaction sequence involves a choice between geometrically distinct possibilities. For example, a large molecule called squalene plays a key role in the synthesis of steroids such as cholesterol. Squalene itself is formed from six molecules of a much simpler compound known as mevalonic acid. The process of converting one into the other involves fourteen separate chemical reactions, each of which requires a right or left choice between a specific pair of hydrogen atoms. Since each choice depends on the previous history of a given molecule, there are 16,384 different possible routes that must be considered, yet only one of these paths leads from mevalonic acid to squalene.

Cornforth showed which hydrogen the enzyme concerned selects at each of the fourteen steps. To accomplish this nearly inconceivable task, he, "with brilliant mastership, utilized the properties of the hydrogen isotopes." The element hydrogen exists in three forms, which differ only in their mass (the amount of material they contain). This property, which is usually called their atomic weight, is given certain relative values. The most common hydrogen isotope is assigned the value of one; heavy hydrogen, or deuterium, becomes two; and radioactive hydrogen, or tritium, three. While each of these atoms of hydrogen has the same ordinary chemical properties, they are different physically.

These differences, together with modern instrumentation and rare insight, allowed Cornforth to examine the geometric details of enzymic reactions. Even in cases where the structures of the starting chemicals and the product obtained did not reveal that a choice had been made, he was able to give definitive evidence of a unique stereochemical pathway. It is noteworthy that Fredga cites the contributions of Cornforth's wife and collaborator Rita Harradence Cornforth.

Nobel lecture

Cornforth began his December 12, 1975, lecture, entitled "Asymmetry and Enzyme Action," with characteristic modesty in acknowledging the source of his accomplishments—a historic 1948 note by Alexander Ogston in the British scientific magazine *Nature*. Throughout his talk, Cornforth referred to the Ogston effect. Until reading Ogston's note, he said, he had thought of stereochemistry as a motorist thinks of a system of one-way streets—a set of obstacles on the way to a destination.

The term "stereochemistry" is used to denote the study of the exact three-dimensional distribution of the atoms that are bonded together in the conception of what a molecule must look like. Cornforth gave a brief history of the late nineteenth century beginnings of this subtle view of molecular structure. At that time it was becoming clear that a carbon atom can be attached to four atoms or groups of atoms in the form of a nearly regular tetrahedron. If all these attachments are different, there are two forms of the molecular structure, which are related as an object and its mirror image are. Since these two models are non-superimposible in the same sense that one's right and left hands are, they are unique. The word "chiral" (from the Greek word for hand, *cheir*) describes this relationship. Such right- and left-handed molecules form a vital part of the chemistry of living systems such as human bodies. An especially important example is the class of proteins called enzymes, which are made up of many smaller molecules, nearly all of which are themselves chiral.

Cornforth moved at once to the central theme of his greatest contribution: the realization and demonstration that enzymes make specific right- or left-hand choices even in chemical reactions that do not appear to demand such highly regulated chemical discrimination. He considered the important biochemical molecule citric acid, which is constantly being made and used in one of the most important energy-generating systems. Citric acid, the molecules from which it is made, and the molecules that result from its consumption are all achiral. They all involve carbon atoms that have at least two identical atoms or groups attached. Thus it would appear that no interesting stereochemistry is present or is required to understand the detailed steps by which these reactions proceed.

The application of another isotope, that of carbon, showed clearly that reality was less simple and more interesting. When citric acid is synthesized enzymatically from carbon dioxide containing radioactive carbon, it is possible to distinguish between its two chemically identical groups. It should follow that when the citric acid is subsequently taken apart, only half the radioactive carbon will be lost to each of the products, carbon dioxide and succinic acid. When the experiment was carried out, however, the results showed clearly that all of the radioactive carbon is released as carbon dioxide. Obviously the enzyme involved in this particular chemical step chooses one of the two "identical" groups and is therefore stereospecific. He discussed several additional examples of such "hidden asymmetry."

Cornforth recognized that these observations present compelling evidence of the correctness of Ogston's visualization of stereochemistry. Further, he saw in them an important method for studying the mechanisms by which enzymes catalyze chemical reactions. He reasoned that even if the molecules undergoing reaction have no chirality, the enzyme does and will only accept that substrate molecule from one of the two possible spatial presentations. This situation is in striking agreement with the description, presented in 1894 by Emil Fischer, of enzyme catalysis (resembling a lock and key fitting together) of the enzyme and the molecule undergoing reaction.

Along with the biochemist George Popják, Cornforth had been studying the biosynthesis of cholesterol and its precursor squalene. They had found that while squalene appears to result from the joining of two identical fifteen-carbon molecules, called farnesyl pyrophosphate, the process actually required "the exchange of one, and only one, hydrogen atom from one of the carbon atoms that became joined together." This requirement of a nonsymmetrical synthesis of a symmetrical molecule so intrigued Cornforth that he, Popják, and Mrs. Cornforth undertook the task of working out the exact stereochemistry of all fifty hydrogens in the biosynthesis of squalene. The bulk of Cornforth's lecture dealt with the problems encountered on this difficult voyage of exploration and their successful solution of the problem.

Also of importance was his description of the work carried out in collaboration with Hermann Eggerer on the chiral methyl group. This particular structural arrangement involves three identical hydrogen atoms. The difficult task of introducing chirality without substantially changing the chemistry required that all three hydrogen isotopes be used. A still more difficult problem remained, that of determining the absolute configuration of the two possible products—that is, which one was right- and which was left-handed. A brilliant and delicate series of biochemical transformations, in which Mrs. Cornforth played a central role, opened the possibility of productive studies in many additional enzymic reactions.

Cornforth concluded by recognizing the importance of his teacher and friend, Sir Robert Robinson (winner of the Nobel Prize in Chemistry, 1947), in stimulating his "wonder at the chemistry of Nature." On a philosophical note, he summarized the many studies his work had stimulated as showing that "an enzyme must, it seems, catalyze strictly stereospecific reactions even when this specificity is not required by the structural relation of substrate to product."

Critical reception

The announcement of the 1975 chemistry prize seems to have created interest among both the press and the public. A number of fairly detailed reports appeared, including a story in *The New York Times* that ran to nearly half a page. The article included photographs and was largely biographical; scientific details were, however, woven into the article. The author had contacted other chemists and found them to be enthusiastic about the selection of Cornforth and Prelog.

Understandably, the British technical press gave a larger amount of space to Cornforth's research, but it did not neglect the important complementary work of Prelog. An unidentified writer for *Chemistry in Britain* quoted Cornforth at length about his work, the future, and his views on cooperation between academic and industrial scientists, yet presented no information on his scientific accomplishments. Martin Sherwood of *New Scientist* used the minimal space available to produce a fine description of both Cornforth's and Prelog's stereochemical studies.

In a more popular vein, *The Times* of London took justifiable pride in Cornforth's work but still made clear that these accomplishments were built on Prelog's studies of small molecules and synthetic reactions. As always, the letters to *The Times* make interesting reading. On October 22, Professor Sir Ewart Jones, Fellow of the Royal Society, wrote suggesting that since ten British chemists had been honored with the Nobel Prize in the third quarter of the twentieth century, those advising young people on careers in science might take notice. An article in *Science* by two eminent American chemists, Ernest Eliel and Harry Mosher, discussed the work of Cornforth and Prelog in the context of modern stereochemistry. Their article has a warm and personal tone, and they discuss the laureates' work in relation to their own.

Biography

In Sydney, Australia, on September 7, 1917, John Warcup Cornforth was born. He was the second of four children born to his parents, an English-born father and a mother of German descent, who divided their living between the city of Sydney and rural New South Wales.

When Cornforth was about ten, he began to suffer hearing loss from otosclerosis. He was, however, able to obtain a fine education at the Sydney Boys' High School before he became completely deaf. He credits Leonard Basser of that school for guiding him toward a career in chemistry. Sydney University provided an excellent opportunity to continue the laboratory work he had begun at home when he was fourteen, as well as a superb library.

Cornforth continued research work at Sydney after graduating with first-class honors in 1937. At that time, he won a scholarship to study with Robert Robinson at the University of Oxford. As World War II began, he traveled to England with the other scholarship winner that year, Rita H. Harradence. While working toward their doctorates for steroid synthesis, they were married in 1941. They continued during the war in the same laboratory, working on the synthesis of penicillin—work that

Cornforth described in his contribution to *The Chemistry of Penicillin* (1949).

After World War II, Cornforth continued to collaborate with Robinson until 1946, when he joined the staff of the National Institute for Medical Research. At their facilities in Hampstead, and later at Mill Hill, he began a twenty-year collaboration with the biochemist George Popják. In 1962, Cornforth and Popják became codirectors of the Milstead Laboratory of Chemical Enzymology operated by Shell Research Ltd. There Cornforth carried out the work for which he shared the 1975 Nobel Prize with Vladimir Prelog. In that same year, Cornforth became Royal Society Research Professor at the University of Sussex.

Cornforth has been elected to many honor societies, including the Royal Society (England, 1953), National Academy of Sciences (United States, 1978), Australian Academy of Science (1977), and the Royal Netherlands Academy of Arts and Sciences (1978). Among his numerous honors are the Corday-Morgan and Flintoff medals (British Chemical Society, 1953 and 1966), the Ciba Medal (British Biochemical Society, 1966), and the Davy, Royal, and Copley medals (the Royal Society of London, 1968, 1976, and 1982). Honorary degrees have been awarded him by the universities of Oxford, Dublin, Liverpool, Warwick, Aberdeen, and Sydney. In 1972, he became Sir John as a Commander of the British Empire and in 1977, a Knight Bachelor.

Scientific Career

Cornforth describes himself as an organic chemist and has, in fact, accomplished some remarkable results in that field, achieving, for example, the first total synthesis of a nonaromatic steroid. This feat was completed simultaneously with Robert Burns Woodward of Harvard University, who won the Nobel Prize in 1965 for his remarkable skill in the synthesis of complex natural products. It is more accurate and descriptive, however, to classify Cornforth's work as physical or biophysical organic chemistry. This particular subdivision of chemical science has roots deep in the nineteenth century but only began to flourish in the second half of the twentieth. The intention of those working in this area is not only to prepare new compounds or old compounds in new ways but also to understand the details of how the transformations take place. The contrast between the classical organic and the physical organic chemist can be seen clearly in the presentation speech given by Professor Fredga at the Nobel Prize ceremonies. If one were to see only the opening scene of *Hamlet* and the final scene of the last act, he said, one would meet the principal characters and then view the dead bodies and survivors. This is a reasonable approximation of mixing reactants together and then isolating the products and by-products of a reaction. The physical organic chemist seeks to describe the action that takes place during the rest of the drama that leads to the final scene.

Cornforth's earliest work, under the direction of Robert Robinson, was concerned with steroid synthesis, and it led to his doctoral thesis at Oxford. This same general area of research in the same laboratory earned a doctoral degree for his wife, Rita, who continued to be his most constant collaborator. Steroids and their synthesis continued to be one of Cornforth's most compelling scientific interests, and the specific steroid, cholesterol, was to figure prominently in his Nobel Prize-winning work.

During the latter part of World War II, both Cornforths continued in Robinson's Oxford laboratory, where they made important contributions to studies of the synthesis of the life-giving drug penicillin. Also in the 1940's, prior to his move to the National Institute for Medical Research, Cornforth had been studying the work of Konrad Bloch, winner of the Nobel Prize in Physiology or Medicine (1964) on the yeast biosynthesis of cholesterol. Popják was showing at that time that the same chemical pathway occurred in rat livers. They saw that their work, coupled with Ogston's stereochemical insight, offered a wonderful opportunity to study the exact stereochemical demands of enzymic reactions.

Much of the work that Cornforth and Popják carried out on cholesterol has proved to be applicable to other steroids and to terpenes in general. The basic molecule found central to all these chemical transformations is called mevalonic acid and has six carbon atoms in its structure. One of these possesses the most common cause of chirality: being attached to four different atomic groups. Interestingly, this stereochemistry is lost soon after the transformation toward cholesterol begins. Three carbon atoms remain, each with two chemically identical hydrogens. In these pairs, the individual hydrogen atoms become stereochemically distinct in response to the demands of the enzymes that act upon them. This situation represents exactly the sense in which Ogston viewed such reactions.

Using the very latest in synthetic methods, instrumental techniques, and isotope labels, combined with brilliant strategy, Cornforth, his wife, and Popják were able to devise and perform experiments showing that in the stereochemistry, a unique choice was invariably made by the appropriate enzyme for each of the six possibilities.

Even this nearly incredible amount of work did not solve all the problems associated with the biosynthesis of such a complex natural product as cholesterol. There remained the methyl group, in which not two, but three apparently identical hydrogen atoms had to be considered. Using the three chemically identical hydrogen isotopes, which differ in their mass (in the ratios of 1:2:3), Cornforth was able to prepare the first example of a chiral methyl group. More problematic was the task of determining which of the two products (the object or its mirror image) had which exact arrangement in space. This problem was solved using a series of synthetic reactions in which both Cornforth and his wife could take justifiable pride. At first they considered using a stereospecific enzymic reaction that they knew to be stereospecific, but they did not know its absolute direction. In the end, they were able to avoid any assumptions and carry out an unambiguous, purely chemical synthesis: They showed that the popularly held opinion of the enzyme's stereochemistry was incorrect.

The work for which Cornforth was awarded the 1975 Nobel Prize represents one of the highest accomplishments of late twentieth century science from several points of view. He and his collaborators worked with compounds that are of central importance in the healthy operation of the human body. These same compounds and their chemical transformations also tie together—practically and intellectually—a vast area of bioorganic chemical knowledge. Cornforth and his coworkers' use of the most modern theoretical and laboratory methods allowed the design and execution of experiments that reached a previously inaccessible level of understanding of molecular transformations. Finally, the combination of brilliance in design and skill of execution shown in their studies makes one appreciate the beauty and elegance to be discovered in the chemistry of nature. It has been said that, thanks to Cornforth's work, more is known about the biosynthesis of terpenoids than about any other biochemical process of comparable complexity.

Bibliography

Primary
CHEMISTRY: "Oxazoles and Oxazolones," in *The Chemistry of Penicillin*, 1949 (edited by H. T. Clarke et al.); "Absolute Configuration of Cholesterol," *Nature*, vol. 173, 1954 (with I. Youhotsky and G. Popják); "A General Stereoselective Synthesis of Olefins," *Journal of the Chemical Society* (London), 1959 (with R. H. Cornforth and K. K. Mathew); "A Stereoselective Synthesis of Squalene," *Journal of the Chemical Society* (London), 1959 (with R. H. Cornforth and K. K. Mathew); "Studies on the Biosynthesis of Cholesterol-7," *Tetrahedron*, vol. 5, 1959 (with R. H. Cornforth, A. Pelter, M. G. Horning, and G. Popják); "Asymmetric Methyl Groups and the Mechanism of Malate Synthase," *Nature*, vol. 221, 1969; "Exploration of Enzyme Mechanisms by Asymmetric Labelling," *The Chemical Society Quarterly Reviews*, vol. 23, 1969; "Asymmetry and Enzyme Action," in *Les Prix Nobel*, 1975; "Synthesis of Substituted Dibenzophospholes. Part 8: Synthesis and Resolution of Atropisomers of a 4,6-Diaryldibenzophosphole," *Journal of the Chemical Society Perkin Transactions I*, 1987 (with L. M. Huguenin and J. R. H. Wilson).

Secondary
Eliel, Ernest L., and Harry S. Mosher. "The 1975 Nobel Prize for Chemistry." *Science* 190 (1975): 772-774. Written by a world-class stereochemist, Eliel, this article is a rich biography and a sound presentation of stereochemistry. The comments on Cornforth's research interests at the time of winning the Nobel Prize and about him as a person are both important.
McElheny, Victor K. "Chemistry Prize Is Shared by Two." *The New York Times*, October 18, 1975: 15. An accurate description of the two scientists' contributions and personalities. Much longer and more detailed than expected for a newspaper article. Quotes other chemists on the importance of the work.
"Nobel Chemistry Awards, 1975." *Chemistry in Britain* 11 (1975): 432-433. While the treatment of scientific and biographical material is nearly nonexistent, the interviewer does ask some significant questions. Cornforth's responses regarding his

work, the future, and academic-industrial cooperation are of particular interest.

Ramsay, O. Bertrand. *Stereochemistry*. London: Heyden, 1981. The introduction gives a brief history of stereochemistry, centered on the Nobel Prize winners in the field. It places Cornforth's work historically and provides a reprint of one of his most significant papers, on the asymmetric methyl group.

Sherwood, Martin. "Nobel Prizes 1975: Chemistry." *New Scientist* 68 (1975): 220-221. Biographical information is presented, along with an excellent presentation of Cornforth's most important scientific accomplishments. Remarkably clear on very difficult concepts. It also underlines the importance of Prelog's contribution.

"Sir John (Warcup) Cornforth." In *McGraw-Hill Modern Scientists and Engineers*, vol. 2, edited by Jay E. Greene. New York: McGraw-Hill, 1980. A well-written summary of Cornforth's scientific accomplishments and a useful biographical sketch.

Wasson, Tyler, ed. *Nobel Prize Winners*. New York: H. W. Wilson, 1987. Presents a thorough description of Cornforth's scientific work, accompanied by personal views of the man and his philosophy. Clear science writing for the lay reader.

K. Thomas Finley

1975

Chemistry
John Warcup Cornforth, Australia
Vladimir Prelog, Switzerland

Physics
Aage Bohr, Denmark
Ben R. Mottelson, Denmark
L. James Rainwater, United States

Physiology or Medicine
Renato Dulbecco, United States
Howard M. Temin, United States
David Baltimore, United States

Economic Sciences
Leonid V. Kantorovich, Soviet Union
Tjalling C. Koopmans, United States

Literature
Eugenio Montale, Italy

Peace
Andrey D. Sakharov, Soviet Union

VLADIMIR PRELOG
1975

Born: Sarajevo, Bosnia (modern Yugoslavia); July 23, 1906

Nationality: Swiss
Areas of concentration: Organic synthesis and stereochemistry

Prelog expanded the understanding of stereochemistry—the spatial arrangement of atoms and molecules. He developed theories concerning chiral (mirror-image) molecules; he also demonstrated surprising reactions involving medium ring compounds, those with eight to eleven ring members. Later, he described the areas of enzymes active in catalysis

The Award

Presentation

Professor Arne Fredga of the Royal Swedish Academy of Sciences referred to Prelog's beautiful experimental work in his presentation speech on December 10, 1975. He began by offering a telling description of the usual view of a chemical reaction as being somewhat akin to seeing only the opening and closing scenes from *Hamlet*: Between the mixing of the chemicals and the isolation of the products, there are many "to be or not to be" scenes. It was for his efforts to solve these dilemmas through the application of geometric reasoning to chemical problems that Prelog was awarded the 1975 Nobel Prize in Chemistry.

Fredga referred specifically to Prelog's work with medium-size carbon rings and his discovery of their flexibility and the accompanying reactions that take place across the ring. He also singled out the enzymatic studies of oxidation and reduction, saying that some recent X-ray studies confirmed aspects of Prelog's work.

Through all Prelog's studies runs the thread of stereochemistry. Without exaggerating the point, Fredga indicated that Prelog made fundamental contributions to chemists' appreciation of the basic idea of symmetry in molecules. He was able to attack the questions in both the theoretical and practical arenas. Both the penetration of his thoughts and the skill of his synthetic efforts contributed to the utility of the concept of chiral molecules in nature.

Nobel lecture

The title of Prelog's lecture, "Chirality in Chemistry," delivered on December 12, 1975, helped make the enormous range of Prelog's contributions clear. More than any other chemist, he made the application of stereochemical thinking the supreme tool of the workers of the late twentieth century. His lecture began with a discussion of the word "chiral," derived from the Greek *cheir*, meaning "hand," because hands are the most familiar chiral objects. By chiral, the chemist means objects that are mirror images of each other but are entirely lacking in symmetry.

Part of his lecture was given to discussion of tetrahedra, since it is this geometric form upon which much of the world of organic, or carbon-containing, compounds is built. Prelog also discussed the somewhat simpler situation of two-dimensional chirality. In a flat world, the mirror image of an irregular triangle shows the lack of symmetry demanded for chirality. If one thinks about these two triangles and a self-imposed inability to move out of the plane, it becomes clear that the two cannot be superimposed on each other. It is this inability to be brought into congruence that is characteristic of chiral objects such as molecules. Prelog recognized Louis Pasteur for his insight and experimental brilliance in showing that chirality can be related to molecular structure.

At this point, Prelog turned to a discussion of chemistry—in particular, how chirality relates to the ability to comprehend the facts of this scientific discipline. In a more general tone, he referred to Aldous Huxley's suggestion that science is always dealing with symbol systems. For Prelog, it was truly astonishing that a fairly workable system had been created for managing the huge amount of information that chemists have amassed in two hundred years.

Selecting what he referred to as a molecule of medium complexity, an antibiotic called boromycin, Prelog described the information that a chemist needs to understand how its atoms are arranged in space. One must visualize this arrangement before thinking about its synthesis or preparing it from simpler molecules. Prelog showed that this moderately complex molecule contains 136 atoms of five elements. The next question, he said, is trying to understand its constitution—that is, the sequence in which the atoms are held one to another, or bonded. As for the chirality, Prelog pointed out that there are eighteen separate atoms, chiral centers, in boromycin that can exist in right- or left-handed form, thereby making a possible 262,144 structures for boromycin on the basis of stereochemical considerations alone.

This brief introduction to the complexities of the synthesis of naturally occurring molecules demonstrated a central problem in communication. Prelog discussed in general terms the work he undertook with R. S. Cahn and Sir Christopher Ingold to design a system that would describe exactly the stereochemistry of each chiral center in a molecule. While he did not present an introduction to the brilliant system they designed, he did illustrate the great economy it affords. His illustration allowed his audience to appreciate the elegance and utility of the method without getting lost in the unfamiliar details.

At this point, Prelog described some of the greatest successes of these fundamental studies in the nature of stereochemistry. While chemists had used the concept for more than a hundred years, there were still gaps in their appreciation of its consequences. Prelog and his collaborators were able to find entirely new types of stereoisomerism. Most of these new types occur in the less carefully studied molecules of greater size and complexity.

A brief but detailed discussion of several additional known types of stereoisomerism was presented, and Prelog then concluded with a brief hint of the significance of these studies in biochemical, enzymatic reactions. He left this area of interest to be discussed by his cowinner, John W. Cornforth.

Critical reception

The 1975 Nobel Prize in Chemistry, unlike many, seems to have caught the interest of the reading public, and a number of detailed and accurate news reports appeared. For example, *The New York Times* devoted nearly half a page to the story; it quoted the Royal Swedish Academy in noting that "this research is of fundamental importance to an understanding of biological processes." The article, which includes photographs, is largely biographical, although the scientific details are skillfully interwoven. The author took the trouble to contact other scientists and found them enthusiastic about the selection of Prelog and Cornforth.

The technical press in England gave equal billing to Prelog, while devoting more than the usual amount of space to Cornforth's research. Prelog's collaborator, R. S. Cahn, wrote a brief but personal biographical sketch for *Chemistry in Britain*. In *New Scientist*, Martin Sherwood devoted most of his attention to Cornforth but showed how Prelog's work both complemented and differed from Cornforth's. In a more popular vein, *The Times* of London understandably devoted less space to Prelog but mentioned the importance of his work with small molecules and synthetic reactions as making Cornforth's studies of enzymes more meaningful.

Two distinguished American chemists, Ernest Eliel and Harry Mosher, writing in *Science*, placed both Cornforth and Prelog in the context of modern stereochemistry and their own diverse careers. Their well-written article also contains a large amount of invaluable personal insight.

Biography

In the autobiographical notes printed with his Nobel lecture, Prelog tells how, as a boy of eight in his hometown of Sarajevo, he stood near the spot where World War I is said to have begun. Shortly thereafter, his family moved to Zagreb, where he attended the *Gymnasium*.

From 1924 to 1929, he studied chemistry at the Czech Institute of Technology in Prague. Although his doctoral dissertation was supervised by Professor Emil Votoček, it was Rudolf Lukeš whom he considered to be his chief teacher and inspiration. The future direction of his career was shown in his selection of three chemists he admired—his "imaginary" teachers: Robert Robinson, Christopher Ingold, and Leopold Ružička. Later he joined them in more direct ways and made important additions to their illustrious careers.

The worldwide economic crisis of 1929 forced Prelog to seek industrial employment. His five years in the laboratories of the chemical firm of G. J. Dříza in Prague provided him with a set of skills and attitudes unusual in an academic chemist. Prelog has always maintained important ties with the foremost industrial firms.

His first love had always been university life, and in 1935 he became a lecturer at the University of Zagreb. In the period before World War II, Prelog advanced to professor of organic chemistry. In 1941, as so many intellectuals did, he fled the Nazi terror; he joined his idol Ružička at the Eidgenössische Technische Hochschule in Zurich, Switzerland.

In addition to his brilliant scientific career, Prelog has been a successful administrator. Under his direction, the ETH has become one of the few world-class centers for research in organic chemistry. With characteristic modesty, he gives ample credit to his younger colleagues for their roles in accomplishing the nearly impossible task of directing a group of brilliant, creative minds.

Prelog has a long list of honors that includes his election as a foreign member of the most important scientific honor societies in the United States (National Academy of Sciences, American Philosophical Society, and American Academy of Arts and Sciences), England (Royal Society), Ireland (Royal Society), and the Soviet Union (Academy of Sciences). The universities of Paris, Brussels, Manchester, Zagreb, Liverpool, and Cambridge have awarded him honorary doctorates. Medals and awards have come from Germany (Hofmann), Switzerland (Werner), Belgium (Stas), Britian (Davy), and the United States (Adams).

Prelog praises his adopted country, Switzerland, both for giving him citizenship and for allowing him to be a world citizen. He loves swimming, skiing, and traveling. An engaging sense of humor reveals itself in the remark that he has given lectures in more than 150 places in spite of the fact that he does not speak any language properly.

Scientific Career

When one looks carefully over Prelog's lifelong record of chemical accomplishments, it becomes clear why the Nobel Prize was awarded to him for his extraordinary work in stereochemistry. He is unsurpassed in the range and variety of his chemical undertakings. Prelog is thought by some to be a natural product chemist— that is, one interested primarily in the proof of the structure of complex molecules found in living systems. To others, his name is associated with the discovery and explanation of new and unexpected chemical reactions. Still others link his name with nomenclature, naming compounds to indicate their chirality, or relationship to right and left hands.

Much of Prelog's earliest work involved cyclic compounds. Such molecules have their atoms bonded together in a ring structure, and they occur very frequently in nature. Moreover, an extremely important aspect of much of his later studies in all fields has centered on this structural type. The particular rings that he and his research group investigated contained the nitrogen atom as well as the carbon atoms characteristic of organic molecules. Since not all of the atoms in the ring are of the same element, the compounds are usually referred to as heterocycles. No other synthetic area has grown so rapidly and productively in the two-hundred-year history of modern chemistry.

It is in the alkaloids, one particular area of nitrogen heterocyclic chemistry, that Prelog made his greatest contributions. These exceedingly complex molecules, found in vegetable matter, are of vital importance in medicinal applications. He studied the antimalarial drug quinine (along with related compounds that have the same atomic composition but a different structure) and the *Cinchona* alkaloids. The chief difference found in members of these two classes of compounds was the exact, three-dimensional arrangement in space of their atoms. This problem illustrates the importance of stereochemistry in that it refers to two or more molecules whose atoms are exactly the same in every way except their location in space. The sense and difficulty of this problem can best be appreciated by thinking of one's right and left hands. Both hands, under ideal conditions, have identical parts, and these parts are linked together in exactly the same manner. Still, the two cannot be considered identical to each other. They will not fit into each other's gloves. The chemist says they are not "superimposable": One cannot imagine every part of one occupying the corresponding location of the other. In fact, the two hands are related as are an object and its mirror reflection. This simplest and most general case is exactly the situation with chiral molecules.

In studying these alkaloids and many others, such as those related to the poisonous but medically useful strychnine, Prelog was able to show exactly what their detailed atomic spatial arrangements are and to make critical corrections to earlier proposals for their structures. It is certain that until chemists know exactly how a molecular formula is constructed they can have no hope of making the compound in the laboratory or factory or of understanding how it operates in maintaining health or curing disease.

Another naturally occurring chemical is adamantane, which exists only in minute amounts in petroleum from Moravia. This compound, composed of only carbon and hydrogen atoms, consists of four rings, all sharing as many sides as possible. In effect, this molecule of only ten carbon atoms is much like a tiny fragment of a diamond, which consists of only carbon atoms linked as tightly as possible. Prelog's synthesis of this remarkable molecule opened the way for the preparation of a large number of related and theoretically important compounds as well as the useful study and application of adamantane itself.

In the course of his studies of these ring compounds, Prelog was the first to show that nitrogen as well as carbon atoms could be the cause of chirality in organic molecules. In these same years, he also made significant contributions to an appreciation of the ways in which atom pairs held together by two electron pairs might be arranged in positions where rings were also joined together. Since these double bonds are of high reactivity and thus of great interest in determining chemical reactions, questions relating them to structural concerns are also of prime importance in appreciating how chemical change occurs.

Before Prelog arrived in Zurich, Leopold Ružička had been awarded the 1939 Nobel Prize. The part of his work that had the greatest interest to Prelog was the synthesis of large (about twenty atoms) carbon ring compounds. With characteristic energy and talent, he developed a synthetic method which not only greatly improved Ružička's method for making these important perfume substances but also became and remains effectively the only pathway to rings of eight to eleven carbon atoms.

Studies of these medium rings allowed Prelog to describe unique and unexpected new reactions. He suspected, correctly, that the intermediate size of these carbocycles would give them special chemical opportunities to display reactivity and that a detailed knowledge of their exact geometry was of critical importance. This work anticipated by a year the brilliant Nobel Prize-winning efforts of Derek Barton. At the same time as, but independently of, Arthur C. Cope in the United States, Prelog discovered how remote parts of a flexible ring can influence reaction sites. These reactions that occur across the ring, now known as transannular reactions, have proved important in understanding detailed reaction pathways.

Those studying living systems see that in nature, chemical reactions produce only one member of the possible object/mirror image pair, while in the laboratory one almost always finds more or less equal amounts of both. Working with stereoselective synthetic reactions, chemists today have arrived at a closer approximation of the natural environment, but a major share of the credit for the successful launching of this exciting field of study must be given to Prelog and his colleagues.

They approached the problem along several different fronts. For example, in collaboration with the Cornforth husband-wife team, Prelog showed that extremely important naturally occurring alcohols, such as linalool, can have their stereochemical arrangement determined by chemical conversion to a new class of compounds called atrolactates. The general statement of this principle is now known as Prelog's rule. This work has been expanded in several directions, each of which involves the concept of using differences in bulk of groups of atoms to control the direction of chemical reactions.

When, as is often the case, it is not possible to obtain a distinct preference for one of the compounds, the problem of separating materials with nearly identical properties must be faced. Prelog approached this difficult task in a truly imaginative way: He reasoned that if the mixture were allowed to pass through a column of material which was itself chiral, the two stereoisomers might separate. He thus became the first to obtain the compounds involving chiral nitrogen atoms. Shortly after winning the Nobel Prize, he published studies that developed this concept and involved membranes that separate chiral compounds.

By the mid-twentieth century, many chemists realized that all the exciting new knowledge being obtained about the chirality of organic compounds would be much more useful if there were more reasonable ways of presenting and discussing it. Prelog was one of the very few willing to undertake such a difficult task; in 1954 he joined R. S. Cahn and C. K. Ingold "to build up a system for specifying a particular stereoisomer by simple and unambiguous descriptors which could be easily assigned and deciphered." Their proposals have become universally accepted and are currently an essential part of every college sophomore's first course in organic chemistry. Using the most basic of the chemist's models of nature, atomic numbers, and the smallest number of conventions, it is possible to designate each chiral molecule as either right- or left-handed (noted as R or S, from the Latin *rectus* or *sinister*).

In the process of generating the Cahn-Ingold-Prelog system of absolute nomenclature, these scientists were faced with the task of thinking through, more carefully than ever before, exactly what stereochemistry means. Prelog said that "it is somewhat embarrassing to find that one does not actually know what types of stereoisomers are possible." Typically, he took this as an opportunity and has subsequently demonstrated that new and unexpected types of chirality are both possible and synthetically obtainable. As the material in his Nobel Prize lecture clearly demonstrates, he has made important advances in applying group and graph theory to the general field of chemical topology.

The outstanding American stereochemist Ernest Eliel describes stereochemistry as "not a branch of chemistry but rather a point of view which pervades nearly all of chemistry." In the autobiographical notes that accompany his Nobel lecture, Prelog clearly finds this an agreeable way to look at the world. He has made it a central aspect of an exceedingly productive scientific career. The more one attempts to understand the detailed workings of the chemistry of nature, the more one is forced to recognize the critical importance of chirality. Prelog has made central contributions to the definition and exploration of stereochemical questions, and he has used many of the answers to explore other chemical processes. Most important, his influence is certain to endure through succeeding generations in the important additions he has made to the very language of organic chemistry. The humane workings of his mind can be sensed at the conclusion of his Nobel lecture, when he characterizes the question of why nature prefers one stereoisomer over another "as one of the first problems of molecular theology."

Bibliography

Primary

CHEMISTRY: "Zur Kenntnis des Kohlenstoffringes: Ein Herstellungsverfahren für vielgliederig Cyclanone," *Helvetica Chimica Acta*, vol. 30, 1947 (with L. Frenkiel, M. Kobelt, and P. Barman); "Newer Developments of the Chemistry of Many-Membered Ring Compounds," *Journal of the Chemical Society*, 1950; "Specification of Configuration About Quadricovalent Asymmetric Atoms," *Journal of the Chemical Society*, 1951 (with R. S. Cahn and C. K. Ingold); "Specification of Asymmetric Configuration in Organic Chemistry," *Experientia*, vol. 12, 1956 (with R. S. Cahn and C. K. Ingold); "Conformation and Reactivity of Medium-Sized Ring Compounds," *Pure Applied Chemistry*, vol. 6, 1963; "Constitution of Rifamycins," *Pure Applied Chemistry*, vol. 7, 1963; "Problems in Chemical Topology," *Chemistry in Britain*, vol. 4, 1968; "The Role of Certain Microbial Metabolites as Specific Complexing Agents," *Pure Applied Chemistry*, vol. 25, 1971; "Chirality in Chemistry," in *Les Prix Nobel*, 1975; "From Configurational Notation of Stereoisomers to the Conceptual Basis of Stereochemistry," in *Van't Hoff: Le Bel Centennial*, 1975 (edited by O. Bertrand Ramsay).

Secondary

Cahn, R. S. "Nobel Chemistry Awards, 1975." *Chemistry in Britain* 11 (1975): 432-433. An all-too-brief commentary by Prelog's colleague. Especially strong in giving personal insight and an appreciation of their work together on the system of absolute stereochemistry nomenclature.

Eliel, Ernest L., and Harry S. Mosher. "The 1975 Nobel Prize for Chemistry." *Science* 190 (1975): 772-774. An important and human description of the man and his work by a friend, Eliel, who is also distinguished in stereochemistry. Good insight into Prelog as a science administrator.

Finley, K. Thomas. "The Acyloin Condensation as a Cyclization Method." *Chemical Reviews* 64 (1964): 573-589. Treats only one small area of Prelog's work but gives insight into the care and effort he lavished on every aspect of his career.

McElheny, Victor K. "Chemistry Prize Is Shared by Two." *The New York Times*, October 18, 1975: 15. An accurate description of his scientific contribution and his personality. Much longer and more detailed than would be expected for a newspaper item.

Oesper, Ralph E. "Vladimir Prelog." *Journal of Chemical Education* 28 (1951): 575. Written by a knowledgeable chemical historian, but very brief. Interesting, however, in that it was written when Prelog was just beginning to attract international attention.

Ramsay, O. Bertrand. *Stereochemistry*. London: Heyden, 1981. This book is essentially a collection of reprints of papers written by the Nobel Prize winners in the area of stereochemistry. The introduction gives a brief history of the field that centers on these men. Prelog is included, and one of his most significant papers is reprinted.

Sherwood, Martin. "Nobel Prizes 1975: Chemistry." *New Scientist* 68 (1975): 220-221. Major emphasis is placed on Cornforth, but it does show the important dependence he had on Prelog's studies.

"Vladimir Prelog." In *The Biographical Dictionary of Scientists: Chemists*, vol. 2, edited by David Abbott. New York: Peter Bedrick Books, 1984. A standard short biography of Prelog.

"Vladimir Prelog." In *McGraw-Hill Modern Scientists and Engineers*, vol. 3, edited by Jay E. Greene. New York: McGraw-Hill, 1980. This exceptionally well-written and informative article presents an excellent outline of Prelog's varied scientific contributions.

Wasson, Tyler, ed. *Nobel Prize Winners*. New York: H. W. Wilson, 1987. An interesting and well-written biography that presents a good balance between the science and personality of Prelog. Difficult technical points are briefly explained.

K. Thomas Finley

1976

Chemistry
William N. Lipscomb, United States

Physics
Burton Richter, United States
Samuel C. C. Ting, United States

Physiology or Medicine
Baruch S. Blumberg, United States
D. Carleton Gajdusek, United States

Economic Sciences
Milton Friedman, United States

Literature
Saul Bellow, United States

Peace
Mairead Corrigan, Northern Ireland
Betty Williams, Northern Ireland

London   Lotte Meitner-Gra

WILLIAM N. LIPSCOMB
1976

Born: Cleveland, Ohio; December 9, 1919

Nationality: American
Areas of concentration: Borane chemistry and X-ray crystallography

Lipscomb, through skillful experiments and exacting calculations, delineated and organized the chemistry of boron-hydrogen compounds (boranes). His work on boranes is unique in its depth and scope and reveals new aspects of chemical bonding, molecular structure, and chemical reactivity that have general applicability

The Award
Presentation

The Nobel Prize in Chemistry for 1976 was awarded to William Lipscomb by Gunnar Hägg, a chemical crystallographer and member of the Nobel Committee for Chemistry. Hägg first mentioned in his address that for many years the structures and bonding of boranes remained a mystery, since chemists prior to Lipscomb had attempted to apply the conventional ideas of chemical bonding (wherein two electrons are used to hold two adjacent atoms in a chemical bond). Understanding proved very difficult in the case of boron hydrogen compounds, or boranes, because of the inability to rationalize the numbers of boron and hydrogen atoms involved. For example, one boron compound was known to contain two boron and six hydrogen atoms, and another contained ten borons and sixteen hydrogens. The rules for combining atoms, so carefully worked out from studies of carbon compounds and others, did not apply to boranes in any obvious way. Lipscomb, starting in 1954, was able to show that a two-electron, three-atom bond, proposed in 1949 but never seen experimentally before, was able to explain many of the chemical and structural features of this class of compounds. He not only made detailed theoretical calculations but also elaborated the geometry of different boranes experimentally, principally through the use of X-ray crystallography.

Because boranes are very reactive and somewhat unstable, he had to develop special low-temperature techniques for these experiments. Hägg related how Lipscomb extended these lines of research to include not only the electrically neutral borane molecules but also ionic borane species and other types of molecules related to boranes. His work made it possible to predict the stability of boranes and their reactions under different conditions and thus contributed greatly to preparative borane chemistry. This work has many implications beyond the study of boranes, and scientists are finding that the ideas that Lipscomb developed can explain the structures and properties of other compounds, such as those containing carbon metal bonds, as well. Hägg pointed out that rarely does a single investigator have primary responsibility for the development and direction of both theory and experimental knowledge in a large subject field such as borane chemistry. Yet Lipscomb did this, by solving very difficult theoretical and experimental problems, and, in one sense, created the field of borane chemistry. His work has transformed borane chemistry from an arcane laboratory curiosity into a major area for chemical exploration and promise.

Nobel lecture

Lipscomb entitled his lecture "The Boranes and Their Relatives." It was presented December 11, 1976, and it emphasized the strong interplay of theory and experiment that characterizes his research. Throughout the lecture, he talked about the relationships between the three-dimensional atomic and electronic structures of molecules and the chemical transformations they display. He started by remembering Alfred Stock, the great German chemist who established borane chemistry more than sixty years previously by developing the first synthetic techniques for preparing these volatile and very reactive compounds. Their unusual chemical formulas seemed to defy simple classification based on the well-established chemistry of carbon compounds. (Carbon is next to boron in the periodic table, hence the attempts.) Early work by several groups (notably William Price's, which discovered the shape of the diborane molecule in 1947, and John Kasper's, which discovered the basketlike shape of $B_{10}H_{14}$ in 1948) gave experimental evidence for the polyhedral arrangement of atoms in boranes and the existence of the three-atom, two-electron bond involving a bridging hydrogen atom between two boron atoms (B-H-B), which was a very novel concept. These polyhedral molecules could be thought of as fragments of the geometric solids known as the octahedron and icosahedron. Lipscomb explained how, starting in 1946, he developed techniques, similar to those of Isidor Fankuchen, for conducting X-ray crystallographic studies at the low temperatures necessary to work with the very volatile and hazardous boranes and related compounds.

In the 1950's, he formulated the three-center bonds found in several of these fragmentlike, or open-structure-type, boranes in terms of molecular orbital theory. They included molecules such as B_4H_{10}, B_5H_9, and B_5H_{11}. The mathematical capabilities of this theoretical approach provided a theoretical framework for describing the bonding in boranes, which could not only explain the experimentally observed structures but also predict new possibilities. This approach was continued and refined over the next two decades by Lipscomb and coworkers. These studies resulted in a series of generalized simple algebraic formulas, called valence rules, that could be used to predict the correct number of hydrogen atoms, bonding electrons, and three-center bonds in a given borane. Lipscomb's insightful studies into the three-center bond showed that there were actually two types: an open center bond wherein the atoms can be visualized as occupying the corners of a triangle with the electrons (or molecular orbitals, called MOs) meeting at the center, and a "curved" one in which the atoms can be placed on the perimeter of an arc of a circle, with the electrons between them on the circumference. These bonding ideas were quite novel, and much simpler than the well-established but more cumbersome valence bond theory, which required as many as twenty-four different resonance structures for a molecule such as $B_{10}H_{14}$. Lipscomb insightfully realized that his valence rules implied the existence of many boranes and a quite varied chemistry for boron compounds, and, in 1957, with Richard Dickerson formalized the general bonding scheme into a set of bonding patterns. He updated this in 1971 with Irving Epstein into the form chemists now use for these molecules.

Sufficient computational power became available in the computers made in the 1960's to allow Roald Hoffmann and Lawrence Lohr, working with Lipscomb, to program larger and more complex models for the chemical bonding in compounds of carbon, boron, and hydrogen, called carboranes. Some simple rules emerged from this work, which predicted the exact positions within these molecules where certain types of chemical reactions would occur. These predictions were verified experimentally. The computations, called the extended Hückel theory, were widely used, and applied by Robert Woodward and Hoffmann (developers of the Woodward-Hoffmann rules) and many others who studied the bonding in complex organic and inorganic molecules.

Lipscomb completed his lecture with a discussion of localized molecular orbitals and the bonding found in the transient species which exist during the course of a chemical reaction. Localized MOs offer a convenient, useful, and computationally less demanding model for the behavior of bonding electrons in a small area of a molecule. Lipscomb closed with some speculations and applications of his ideas and acknowledged the great influence of Linus Pauling on his whole scientific career.

Critical reception

Reaction of the daily newspapers to the award announcement on October 14, 1976, was complimentary and usually centered on the announcement by the Royal Swedish Academy of Sciences, which bestows the Nobel Prizes each year. This reception was attributable partly to the noncontroversial nature of the award and partly to the general obscurity of boranes, which have made relatively little news over the years, except as rocket fuels. A Swedish newspaper ran a cartoon showing a couple sitting by their television set with the legend: "Can you remember ever having seen a borane, Gustav?" This same mood was reflected in the American press, which tended to devote relatively more space to other laureates' works in areas better understood by the general readership. The *Los Angeles Times* noted that for the first time in the seventy-six-year history of the prizes for science, literature, and economics, one country (the United States) had won them all, and that it happened in the year that it celebrated its bicentennial. Seven Americans won five prizes. Lipscomb's work was said to provide science with a "brilliant white light on the subject of chemical bonding."

The *New York Times* noted that his work started in one of the most esoteric areas of inorganic chemistry and that the award was the first in a long time to be awarded for a discovery in the field of pure inorganic chemistry. It quoted Ingvar Lindqvist of the University of Uppsala, Sweden, as saying that there have been few single fields of inorganic chemistry in which one person has dominated so clearly as Lipscomb has in borane chemistry. It went on to mention that potential applications for boranes existed in the fields of cancer therapy and strong fiber materials. *The Washington Post* quoted Dr. Roald Hoffmann, a well-known chemist at Cornell University and peer of Lipscomb, as saying that he was surprised that Lipscomb was recognized for his work on boranes rather than for his important X-ray studies on the structures of proteins, which he had been performing for the previous nine years. This work is just as interesting as that which led to understanding the double helix (referring to the DNA molecule, which carries the chemical information of the genetic code). The article lauded Lipscomb's boron work as leading to new drugs, plastics, and treatments for cancer and inoperable brain tumors.

The journal *Science* put Lipscomb's achievements in perspective in a very laudatory article by Russel Grimes, a chemistry professor and colleague, which outlined the course of his efforts over twenty years and described in detail the importance of his work on boranes. It complimented him as one of the extraordinary scientific innovators of the time and honored him as a dominant figure in the study of boranes, in major part responsible for the dramatic metamorphosis of boron chemistry from a highly esoteric one into an area having major impact on other fields, especially organic, organometallic, and polymer chemistry. He was lauded for his high achievements in advancing the understanding of the nature of the chemical bond, and his impact on chemists about molecular stability was called his greatest achievement. The weekly *Chemical and Engineering News* not only discussed his work but also tried to show some of the diverse facets of the man in the article "Lipscomb: A Chemist for All Seasons." It devoted some time to the human side of his life, mentioning his love of tennis and chamber music as a performing clarinetist. His philosophy and attitudes about chemistry, his research, and his career were also explored to give some insight into this man who won the Nobel Prize. The article also pointed out that roughly two-thirds of his current research efforts (in 1976) dealt with the structure and function of enzymes, a subject rather removed from boron chemistry but one that challenged Lipscomb's formidable expertise as an X-ray crystallographer.

Biography

William Nunn Lipscomb was born in Cleveland, Ohio, to William Nunn, Sr., and Edna Patterson (née Porter), but moved to Lexington, Kentucky, the following year. His father was a physician who encouraged him with chemicals purchased from the local drug store, and before the boy reached high school, he had a basement laboratory. He obtained his bachelor's degree from the University of Kentucky in 1941, and that same year entered the California Institute of Technology for graduate study, intending to study physics. During World War II, he interrupted his studies and worked on projects there for the Office of Scientific Research and Development for a three-year period from 1942 to 1945, during which time he wed Mary Adele Sargent. He then switched to chemistry, mainly in response to the influence of Linus Pauling, and received his Ph.D. working under Pauling, Edward Hughes, and Verner Shoemaker. Upon completion of his Ph.D., he took a position at the University of Minnesota in 1946, and he became chief of the physical chemistry division there in 1954. He moved to Harvard University in 1959, later becoming the Abbott and James Lawrence Professor of Chemistry. He was the chairman of the chemistry department from 1962 to 1965, remaining active in teaching and research and devoting much of his time to the study of the structure of enzymes. He once said that his original intention in 1949 was to spend a few years understanding the boranes and then to seek to discover a systematic description of bonding for the vast numbers of electron-deficient intermetallic compounds (compounds between two or more metals). This latter objective has not been reached, but the field of boron chemistry has grown and benefited greatly from his efforts. He is an accomplished clarinetist who once considered a musical career, performs in several concerts yearly, and has performed on television. His interests include chamber music (his daughter plays the cello, his son the French horn), tennis, and membership in the Baker Street Irregulars (devotees of Sherlock Holmes).

Scientific Career

The primary theme in Lipscomb's work has been the relationship between the geometric and electronic structures of molecules and their behavior, both chemical and physical. Before Lipscomb's work, the bonding in electron-deficient molecules was poorly understood. These molecules are unlike most others in that they have fewer than two electrons bonding a pair of atoms together somewhere in the molecule, and may have several such pairs. The deficiency of electrons raises many questions about the bonding, structure, and properties of these molecules, because much of the ideas about chemical bonds are based on the concept that two atoms employ two electrons to form a mutual bond. The element boron has a strong tendency to form a wide variety of these electron-deficient compounds containing hydrogen, called boranes, and it has occupied a dominant place in his researches. Early X-ray structural studies in the late 1940's and early 1950's showed Lipscomb that the ideas about bonding in boranes had been developed using incorrect geometrical structures. He developed low-temperature X-ray techniques that allowed him to keep the volatile and sometimes explosively unstable compounds in crystalline form long enough to obtain the necessary data to determine their structures. Much current knowledge about these structures is attributable to work that he and his students have done. A common structure seen in boranes is based on an icosahedron, which is a symmetrical solid with twenty sides composed of equilateral triangles. (Geometrical solids that have triangular faces are called deltahedrons and were known to the ancient Greeks.) Examples of this structure are found in the dodecaborane anion, $B_{12}H_{12}^{-2}$, and in $C_2B_{10}H_{12}$, a carborane. There are several smaller molecules, such as $B_{10}H_{14}$ and B_6H_{10}, that are fragments of the dodecaborane structure. As larger and larger molecules were analyzed, it became obvious that they could generally be thought of as polyhedral geometric solids or fragments thereof. Lipscomb devised some simple algebraic rules to enable the prediction of how many boron and hydrogen atoms are needed for a given geometric structure that is a complete or fragmentary deltahedron. These rules not only brought a sense of order to boron structural chemistry but also contributed greatly to the understanding of their other chemical properties. It opened the door to a rich and varied chemistry for boron, which had been anticipated by comparison with its neighbor in the periodic table, carbon, but never before realized. (Carbon has perhaps the most diverse and complicated chemistry of any element.) Lipscomb was recognized for this work with the Harrison Howe Award in 1958.

X-ray diffraction work on boranes prior to 1940 was interpreted to give more open structures than the octahedron, icosahedron, and other polyhedra later found by Lipscomb. Linus Pauling described these structures theoretically as using resonating one-electron bonds. The works of Frank Stitt and of William Price confirmed the physical existence of the boron-hydrogen-boron bridged structure (BHB) in the simplest borane molecule, diborane, B_2H_6. The unique characteristics of this three-center bond are that hydrogen is bonded to more than one atom and that only three bonding electrons are used by the three atoms, instead of the expected four. The theory of this bridging structure was clearly formulated by Hugh Longuet-Higgins. Lipscomb, in a seminal 1954 paper with Bryce Crawford and William Eberhardt, made the crucial extension of the BHB bond to a similar BBB bond. Then, by devising a proper combination of three-center, two-electron BBB bonds and two-center, two-electron BB bonds, he showed that the rather bewildering array of structures known for boron hydrides at that time could be rationalized. More important, new structures could be predicted with this topological bonding approach and then sought experimentally by synthetic chemists. During the succeeding twenty-five years, Lipscomb and his collaborators produced elegant researches into the bonding, structure, and reactivity of these compounds, always correlating predictions with available data. One can make a simple comparison to show the impact of this work. Next to hydrocarbons (carbon hydrides), boron hydrides have become the largest known family of molecular hydrides. Unlike hydrocarbons, however, much of the general theory that explains their behavior and structure comes from one source: Lipscomb and his coworkers. He views his work as studying structure and function, meaning that it should not be thought of as being primarily theoretical chemistry or inorganic chemistry; instead, it cuts across the usual fields of chemistry and applies what is needed from each. His method of research has always been to take a variety of approaches to solve any given problem, which leads him into theoretical, structural, kinetic, synthetic, and spectroscopic studies, among others.

By the late 1960's, Lipscomb had developed some of the first computer-based methods for describing bonding in larger molecules. These methods are based on molecular orbital theory and are computationally very intensive. Without computers, such a study of boranes or carboranes would be very limited, if not impossible. One result of these studies was the development of the concept of a central three-center bond for the BBB and BCB groups of atoms. The common method of constructing a chemical bond is to place the bonding electrons directly between the bound atoms. The regions of space occupied by the electrons are called orbitals and have both an orientation and a shape relative to the bound atoms. For three triangularly arranged atoms, the electrons would be placed along the sides of the triangle in orbitals shaped similarly to fat sausages. Lipscomb calls this an open three-center bond to signify that the center of the triangle is open, or has no electrons in it. He has developed another class of three-center bonds, however, which he describes in a different manner, called the closed three-center bond. In this bond, the electrons are placed in orbitals directed toward the center of the triangle, rather than between pairs of atoms along the sides. This view of bonding in certain boranes and carboranes was consistent with their chemical properties, bond strengths, and structures.

Other results of the computer studies were also important. The bonding electrons in boranes were described as delocalized—some of these electrons could travel from atom to atom throughout the molecule rather than be localized between any specific pair of atoms. This process helps to explain the unusual chemical and thermal stability of the framework, and the ability of electron-deficient (in the Lewis sense of two electrons per bond) molecules to form strong bonds. The basic tenet is that if more electrons are shared between atoms, the bonding becomes stronger. Thus, a double bond with four electrons is stronger than a single bond with two electrons. By delocalizing the electrons, this in effect puts more electrons between all the involved atoms and increases the strength of all the bonds in the framework. This in turn stabilizes the molecule to heat or chemical attack. In a sense, that is also what happens in a closed three-center bond, for the electrons are holding three atoms together, rather than two. The most delocalized systems known are metals, but there delocalization has given them totally different properties from those of the boranes. Another new bonding description was developed to describe molecules typified by B_8H_{13} and B_8H_{14}, called a fractional three-center bond. Rather than follow the usual practice of writing two resonance structures, which use two-center, two-electron bonds, a single structure is used that has two partial bonds to the atoms involved. Chemists frequently write what are called resonance structures, which are simply versions of the same atomic structure with different distributions of electrons, arranged in pairs between atoms to form bonds. Molecules with many atoms can have large numbers of resonance structures. The bonds in the actual molecule are considered to be a combination of all these versions, called a resonance hybrid. Resonance can be thought of as another theoretical technique to delocalize the electrons and increase the bond strength.

Lipscomb's ideas about the fractional three-center bond have been incorporated into the thinking of many other chemists who study the "nonclassical" carbonium ions ($C_5H_5^+$ is one example of these positively charged ions whose bonding is different from that found classically in carbon compounds), metallocenes (compounds containing metal atoms and several carbon atoms with double bonds), metal clusters (compounds having from four to twenty or more metal atoms), organometallics, and metal carbonyls (compounds with metals attached to carbon monoxide). These compounds all have assemblages of atoms, or clusters, which can formally be thought of as borane analogues and whose bonding can be described with the ideas developed for the boranes. Importantly, the ideas developed for bonding in the simpler boranes also work to describe the larger molecules and molecular ions of the group. Their structures, although more complex polyhedrons, can still be explained and predicted using localized two- and three-center bonds.

When industrial researchers synthesized the first borane compounds in which several of the boron atoms were replaced by carbon to form carboranes, they immediately attracted attention because of their unusual structures and properties. Some of these compounds have great thermal stability and can withstand long periods at 700 degrees Celsius. Lipscomb studied these compounds and made important predictions, proved by experiment, about their bonding, shapes, and chemical reactivities. Some of the carborane molecules (such as the icosahedral $C_2H_{10}B_{12}$ or the pentagonal bipyramidal $C_2B_5H_7$) were quite novel and helped to dispel another long-standing idea about carbon, namely, that it can connect to four · other atoms at the maximum. In these compounds, carbon often bonds to five or six adjacent atoms, and Lipscomb has provided basic insights into the theory and application of carborane chemistry.

Lipscomb's hand is seen in many areas of boron chemistry, as noted in his book *Boron Hydrides*, published in 1963. As one example, he applied the technique of nuclear magnetic resonance (NMR) to the study of boron compounds because NMR provides structural information about the number and types of neighbors that each boron has in a molecule. This was particularly helpful in the study of the structures of the polyhedral boranes. He developed both empirical and theoretical approaches to the interpretation of NMR spectra for simple boron hydrides, and his work led to a second book in 1969, with Gareth Eaton, *NMR Studies of Boron Hydrides and Related Compounds*. In his own words, however, the technique is somewhat limited, and the application to the more complex boranes is still in the future.

He has also worked in another area of boron chemistry, one that deals with the bonding in reaction intermediates. These are the transient, or short-lived, chemical species, which are formed as molecules are transformed from reactants to products during a chemical reaction. They rarely exist as stable compounds that can be isolated and so must be studied theoretically or by inference from experimental data. Although chemists studying carbon compounds have successfully examined many reaction intermediates, very little is known about boron compounds. Lipscomb has made a variety of theoretical studies, predicting how various boron compounds would be likely to break apart or add extra atoms during chemical reactions. This involves prediciting not only which bonds are weakest, that is, most likely to undergo chemical change, but also the preferred spatial orientation of all species during the course of the reaction. Such studies are helpful for predicting products when new synthetic reagents or methods are to be explored and for explaining the presence of unexpected products.

Although he has remained active in boron chemistry, Lipscomb has turned increasingly in the 1970's and 1980's to the study of enzyme-substrate complexes using X-ray crystallography. The low-temperature techniques he pioneered with the boron work are applicable there, and computerized methods for data collection and interpretation make these challenging studies feasible. He is an excellent X-ray crystallographer and has studied the enzymes concanavalin A, glucagon, carboxypeptidase A (his work led to a proposed mechanism for its action), carbonic anhydrase, and aspartate *trans*-carbamylase. This work challenges the limits of instrumentation and of computers, because of the large number of atoms found in an enzyme molecule; it requires the collection of large amounts of very precise data and sufficient computational power to convert it into a three-dimensional structure.

Lipscomb has won numerous scientific awards during his career, including the Peter Debye Award in Physical Chemistry and the American Chemical Society Award for Distinguished Service in the Advancement of Inorganic Chemistry. He is a member of the U.S. National Academy of Sciences and the American Academy of Arts and Sciences, and he holds honorary doctorates from the University of Kentucky and the University of Munich.

Lipscomb's work with the boranes has revealed an extremely important message: The Lewis concept of a chemical bond as a pair of atoms held together by a pair of electrons is a useful guide, but it can only extend so far. Lipscomb has shown that there are ways to describe the bonding in atoms that are innovative, powerful, and extremely useful. The impact of these ideas on theories and experiments is profound and leads to new discoveries. He has shown that there exists a rich and varied chemistry for molecular frameworks or clusters that might encompass almost half of the elements in the periodic table and that remains to be explored.

Bibliography

Primary
CHEMISTRY: *Boron Hydrides*, 1963; *NMR Studies of Boron Hydrides and Related Compounds*, 1969 (with Gareth Eaton); "Structural Aspects of the Tetrahedral Intermediate in the Carboxypeptidase A Intermediate," in John Stezowski, Jin-Ling Huang, and Mei-Cheng Shao, eds., *Molecular Structure*, 1988 (with Dwane Christianson).

Secondary
Brown, Herbert. *Boranes in Organic Chemistry*. Ithaca, N.Y.: Cornell University Press, 1972. An extremely well-written introduction to the world of organoboron chemistry, it gives many reactions and properties of these compounds, which

have many uses for modern structural materials, synthetic reagents, and catalysts. Important chemical properties are pointed out, and reactions of commercial utility are given. The various classes of reactions that boron undergoes are given, and examples are shown.

Cotton, Albert, and Geoffrey Wilkinson. *Advanced Inorganic Chemistry.* 5th ed. New York: Wiley-Interscience, 1988. Many aspects of general inorganic chemistry are covered, and an overview of the chemistry of boron covers the major features and places boron in perspective with the other elements. This book is highly regarded as an informative and detailed textbook, using many illustrations to show the structural features of molecules.

Huheey, James. *Inorganic Chemistry.* 2d ed. New York: Harper & Row, 1978. Structure and chemical reactivity are emphasized throughout this textbook, which covers the main groups of elements in the periodic table. A full chapter is devoted to boron hydrides. Many illustrations are used to enhance the explanations of different kinds of bonding and molecular structures. Written for the second-year chemistry student.

Liebman, Joel, Arthur Greenberg, and Richard Williams, eds. *Advances in Boron and the Boranes: A Volume in Honor of Anton B. Burg.* New York: VCH Publishers, 1988. The book is a collection of essays that overlays work from different areas of chemistry to honor Burg, a pioneer of modern inorganic chemistry. Two essays by Nobel laureates Lipscomb and Pauling are included. A wide variety of different approaches and techniques in the study of boron chemistry are shown.

Mutterties, Earl. *Boron Hydride Chemistry.* New York: Academic Press, 1975. This book is written by one of the foremost experts in boron chemistry and describes many of the structural and chemical features of this class of chemical compound. Detailed discussions of the geometries and bonding found in boranes are given. Boranes, from the simplest to the largest, are described, and methods for their preparation and study are given. Their reactions and some of the unique features of their behavior are shown and compared with those of other compounds.

Steinberg, Howard. *Organoboron Chemistry.* New York: Wiley-Interscience, 1964. This three-volume set covers the range of boron chemistry. Volume 3 deals with boron carbon compounds and gives many details of their history, methods of preparation, and properties. A large amount of information is compiled from many different sources, and the book provides a convenient single reference for boron chemistry to that time.

Stock, Albert. *Hydrides of Boron and Silicon.* Ithaca, N.Y.: Cornell University Press, 1933. This work is by the father of boron chemistry, who describes the experimental techniques he developed as needed to prepare these volatile and potentially dangerous compounds. His work is regarded as the first to place boron chemistry on its correct foundation.

Wade, Kenneth. *Electron Deficient Compounds.* New York: Appleton-Century-Crofts, 1971. An introductory book that covers boranes, carboranes, boron polyhedra, and other kinds of electron-deficient compounds, such as metal hydrides.

It outlines preparative methods and instrumental methods for their study. Each type of compound is given a chapter, which includes a discussion of their structures and the chemical bonding with many illustrations of apparatus and molecules.

William Van Willis

1977

Chemistry
Ilya Prigogine, Belgium

Physics
John H. Van Vleck, United States
Sir Nevill Mott, Great Britain
Philip W. Anderson, United States

Physiology or Medicine
Rosalyn S. Yalow, United States
Roger Guillemin, United States
Andrew Schally, United States

Economic Sciences
Bertil Ohlin, Sweden
James Meade, Great Britain

Literature
Vicente Aleixandre, Spain

Peace
Amnesty International

ILYA PRIGOGINE
1977

Born: Moscow, Russia; January 25, 1917

Nationality: Belgian
Areas of concentration: Statistical mechanics and thermodynamics

Prigogine developed a theoretical framework for analyzing the behavior of systems in nonlinear states, far removed from equilibrium. He focused on so-called open systems such as living cells, finding that such systems, under the influence of fluctuations, can spontaneously undergo transitions to systems of increased order

The Award

Presentation

Professor Stig Clæsson presented Ilya Prigogine for the 1977 Nobel Prize in Chemistry. In his address, Clæsson, a physical chemist and a member of the Nobel Committee for Chemistry, initially reviewed the history of classical thermodynamics, starting with John Dalton's notion of heat as a consequence of atomic motion and leading toward the elucidation of the basic laws of thermodynamics, which were brilliantly applied to physical and chemical systems by Hermann von Helmholtz, Rudolf Clausis, and Josiah Willard Gibbs. Despite the wide range of applications of this discipline, it was clear that "classical" thermodynamic methods could be applied only to a so-called reversible process—that is, a process that reverses its direction if a system variable (such as temperature) is changed even slightly.

In the 1930's, Lars Onsager (winner of the Nobel Prize in Chemistry in 1968) extended classical thermodynamic concepts to treat systems "close" to equilibrium, in domains where the flow of a thermodynamic quantity (such as heat) is directly proportional (or in a linear relation) to its driving force (temperature gradient). Prigogine expanded the range of thermodynamic application to include systems "far" from equilibrium, characterized by nonlinear kinetic laws, and "open" to their surroundings with respect to transfer of energy and mass. He and his associates found that such systems can spontaneously change their entire set of characteristics, with the new systems, termed dissipative structures, displaying greater order than the old.

The approaches developed by Prigogine and his colleagues (principally Paul Glansdorff, René Lefever, and Grégoire Nicolis) have relevance to a very wide range of complex biological and sociological problems, including cell development, structures of biological communities, and even city traffic congestion. Prigogine's contributions, Clæsson said, have revitalized thermodynamics and provided a framework of unification for the biological, physical, and social sciences. Prigogine stands as "the poet of thermodynamics."

Nobel lecture

Professor Prigogine delivered his Nobel address, "Time, Structure, and Fluctuations," on December 8, 1977. To comprehend the general thrust of his talk, one must be generally familiar with several concepts. Thermodynamics, the central discipline for his work, is the study of energy changes in natural processes. Such processes are usually irreversible, in that they proceed in a definite direction with time. Reversible or equilibrium processes can be nudged to go either forward or backward with even minuscule changes in the system's variables. The observed, or macroscopic, properties of a substance reflect an average behavior of all its components, each of which (for example, a water molecule that is part of an ice cube) has its own individual microscopic properties.

Initially in his presentation, Prigogine reviewed the second law, the cornerstone principle of thermodynamics, noting that for isolated systems all irreversible processes are accompanied by increases in entropy, a macroscopic measure of the system's disorder. According to classical interpretations, the second law points the arrow of time toward increasing randomness; the universe is "running down."

If a system at equilibrium (and thus at maximum entropy) is subjected to macroscopic stress (such as the introduction of an energy pulse) the system will pass into a nonequilibrium or irreversible condition. If the displacement is relatively small, the system will proceed back toward its initial equilibrium. Such irreversible states—those located "close" to equilibrium—show rates for their processes (such as heat flows and diffusions) that are linearly related to their driving forces (temperature gradients, concentration gradients). This "near-equilibrium" domain was first probed quantitatively by Lars Onsager; Prigogine himself studied this "linear" range extensively and showed that steady states may be obtained here which are characterized by the production of entropy at small, steady rates.

The major portion of Prigogine's address is devoted to both macroscopic and microscopic aspects of processes occurring "far" from equilibrium, in the so-called nonlinear range, where Onsager's relations do not hold. Together with Glansdorff, Prigogine showed in 1971 that systems far from equilibrium, depending on the kinetic laws controlling the specific case, may reach a point of instability (a "bifurcation") and undergo a transition to an entirely new state of organization. The resulting "dissipative" structures are maintained by energy and/or mass flow with its surroundings. Prigogine describes in detail how certain patterns of sequential chemical reactions, when subjected to certain restraints in the nonlinear region, can suddenly change direction. These examples explain both the striking phenomena of visually "oscillating" chemical reactions and the functioning of key biochemical cycles. In addition, his theory helps to rationalize biological evolution, wherein the creation of increased order seems to be in conflict with interpretations of the second law or isolated systems.

Prigogine then turned to microscopic aspects of his findings. He discussed how bifurcations that produce dissipative structures can be the result of microscopic fluctuations amplified to macroscopic size in systems distant from equilibrium. In his final, highly mathematical development, Prigogine summarized his group's most recent theoretical approaches, aimed at describing and analyzing irreversibility on the microscopic level. His concluding remarks, touching upon concepts of time, were highly philosophical and raised many more profound questions to be addressed.

Critical reception

The announcement of Dr. Prigogine as the chemistry Nobel Prize winner in 1977 met with relatively restrained reactions. He himself possessed none of the controversial political aura surrounding some earlier recipients such as Linus Pauling, nor did his field of endeavor, chemical thermodynamics, have the popular recognition of those of prior recipients who had solved medical questions or invented devices such as transistors. Despite efforts to convey the broad relevance of his "dissipative structures," Prigogine's work was basically abstract and mathematical.

The New York Times described him in a headline as a "Chemist [who] Told How Life Could Defy Physics Laws." It was a misleading but eye-catching headline, and one which the honoree would have rejected. The reference in the headline was to the "conflict" between the increased-disorder aspect of the second law for closed systems and Prigogine's successful thermodynamic theory explaining evolution in terms of dissipative structure formation in open systems. The recipient was characterized as "an outgoing Renaissance man," an accomplished pianist who often "dreams of finding common mathematical principles unifying all sociocultural evolution."

A very brief article in *Chemical and Engineering News* endorsed his contributions "that extend the laws of thermodynamics to dissipative structures." This journal quoted Prigogine as indicating he was "really surprised" to win the award, but *The New York Times* cited an unnamed Brussels colleague's remarks to the effect that "the professor more or less expected this award—it was in the normal course of things." It was more than a year after the award that *Chemical and Engineering News* had a comprehensive article explaining in some detail the importance of Dr. Prigogine's work.

Science reported Professor Prigogine's award with a two-page technical article, including a background on Lars Onsager's preceding work. It is interesting that Onsager's Nobel award came almost forty years after his pioneering papers, whereas Prigogine's work was recognized within a decade of its development. The *Science* article (by MIT scientists Itamar Procaccis and John Ross) concludes with the comments, "It is gratifying that the Nobel Prize has been awarded to the man who set an important and promising field in motion. With extraordinary enthusiasm and drive, Prigogine has established a school of thermodynamics that has stimulated and influenced scientists in many fields around the world."

Biography

Ilya Prigogine was born in Moscow, Russia, on January 25, 1917, the younger of two sons of Roman Prigogine, a chemical engineer, and Julia (née Wichman). When he was only four, his family fled from the Soviet Union in reaction to the new revolutionary government. For the next eight years (1921-1929), the Prigogine family migrated through Lithuania and Germany, in search of an economically secure and politically stable location. In 1929, the family finally settled in Brussels, Belgium, a location that Prigogine would identify as his home for the rest of his life. He received a classical college-preparatory education at the Atheneum of Ixelles. His entire college education was obtained at the Free University of Brussels: He completed his doctorate there in 1941 and was appointed professor in 1947, a position he held for his entire career.

As his reputation grew, so did his list of academic appointments. In 1959, he became director of the Brussels International Institute of Physics and Chemistry, a prestigious institution founded by Ernest Solvay. Increased collaboration with American scientists led to his appointment in 1962 to the faculty of the Enrico Fermi Institute for Nuclear Studies and the Institute for the Study of Metals. In 1967, he founded the Center for Statistical Mechanics and Thermodynamics at the Austin Campus of the University of Texas; for the next two decades, he spent nine months at his job in Brussels and three months at "his" institute in Texas.

Prigogine married engineer Maria Prokopowicz in 1961, and they had two sons. His colleagues regarded him as a Renaissance man—an accomplished pianist, an avid student of the arts and archaeology, a philosopher of science, and an internationalist deeply concerned with finding the common principles underlying all sociocultural evolution. In addition to the Nobel Prize, Dr. Prigogine received numerous awards and honors, including the Solvay Prize in 1965, the Swedish Academy's Arrhenius Gold Medal in 1969, the Rumford Medal in 1976, and many honorary doctoral degrees.

Scientific Career

Ilya Prigogine always had a deep interest in two interrelated concepts: the nature of time and the dynamics of change in natural processes. As a youth he became fascinated by French philosopher Henri Bergson's comments on "duration" in his book *Creative Evolution*. Bergson perceived that real duration is more than a sequence of instantaneous states connected by physical law. In his view, duration "means invention, creation of forms, continued development of what is new. Pure change, real duration, is something spiritual." Grounded in philosophies such as Bergson's, it is no great wonder that Prigogine has been called "the poet of thermodynamics."

The Free University of Brussels was the site of Prigogine's entire formal college education, as well as his principal academic home beginning in the 1930's. His family had settled in Brussels when he was ten, after fleeing the Russian revolution in 1921. Despite a strong pull toward music and the arts, Prigogine pursued studies in physics and chemistry, following the general path of his father and older brother. He received his doctorate in 1941. His early career was dominated by work on classical thermodynamics, a branch of both physics and chemistry dealing with energy changes in natural processes. His thinking had been strongly shaped by two Brussels faculty mentors: Theophile deDonder and Jean Timmermans. DeDonder had startled the systematic world of chemical thermodynamics by introducing into his formalism two new functions, which he called "affinity" and "degree of reaction." Using these functions, deDonder was able to formulate descriptions of systems not directly at equilibrium and to predict the direction of change for such systems. This very preliminary treatment of nonequilibrium processes was nevertheless revolutionary.

Timmermans was an active experimentalist who applied thermodynamic methods to matter in condensed states, that is, liquids and solids wherein the subunits (atoms, molecules) are in close contact. Prigogine was very intrigued by a phenomenon observed in Timmermans' laboratory in which a mixture of liquids spontaneously separated into separate components, an apparent reversal of ordinary mixing tendencies. These solution studies later led to a book, *The Molecular Theory of Solutions*, coauthored with André Bellemans and Victor Mathot in 1957. His association with Timmermans explains his later conviction that even a theorist must always be in close touch with applications.

Prigogine also felt a deep kinship with the great physicists Ludwig Boltzmann, Max Planck, and Albert Einstein, all of whom had probed deeply into thermodynamics, especially its famous second law. In Prigogine's view, the second law, which predicts the direction of processes, "brought an original and unexpected element into descriptions of the evolving physical world," because it introduced time with an arrow pointing to the future. He stated that "a large part of my scientific career would be spent elucidating the many macro- and micro- aspects of the second law." Prigogine intuitively believed that in some context, the second law must have a "constructive or ordering" influence, an apparent conflict with the law's usual interpretation, for closed systems, which suggests a universe "running down." "As living beings ourselves," he has stated, "we provide striking examples of systems of high organization, totally dependent on nonequilibrium (or irreversible) phenomena."

Following his doctoral work, Prigogine focused his thinking entirely on the workings of thermodynamics outside its time-independent equilibrium points. In 1945, he produced his theorem of minimum entropy production, which predicted that systems close to equilibrium could also settle into time-independent, or "stationary," states characterized by less disorder than the true equilibrium state. This "close-to-equilibrium" domain was precisely the region investigated some fifteen years earlier by Lars Onsager, who found that flow processes in this range were linearly related to their driving forces.

For approximately the next twenty years (from the mid-1940's to the mid-1960's) Prigogine and his collaborators—notably Glansdorff, Lefever, and Nicolis—investigated the "nonlinear" range of processes far from equilibrium, the actual domain of most natural events. During this period, Prigogine's reputation as a creative scientist grew rapidly. In 1967, following numerous collaborations with scientists who would be on its faculty, he founded and became director of the Ilya Prigogine Center for Statistical Mechanics and Thermodynamics at the University of Texas in Austin. He also held faculty rank at the University of Chicago in the 1960's.

The major theoretical finding of Prigogine and his colleagues, and the basis of his Nobel award, was that open systems either displaced or initially created far from equilibrium do not necessarily proceed to a state of maximum entropy. Instead, time-dependent "bifurcation" points appear, which may "branch" in entirely new directions, toward states of greater order. These new systems, referred to as "dissipative structures," are maintained in more ordered states by flows of energy and/or matter to and from the surroundings.

In the late 1960's and the early 1970's, the newly discovered nonlinear thermodynamic techniques were successfully applied both to chemical reaction sequences and to flow processes such as viscosity and diffusion. Prigogine has acknowledged the assistance of chemical engineer Robert Schecter of the University of Texas in the applications to hydrodynamic processes. Especially striking examples of a successful application of Prigogine's theories are the "oscillating reactions" first reported in the 1960's. In these mixtures, precise geometric patterns of color appear periodically in solutions which are initially uniform. Nonlinear thermodynamics is also applicable to the analysis of fast reaction kinetics, work first described by Manfred Eigen (winner of the Nobel Prize in Chemistry, 1967).

As they worked on the observed (or macro-) scale behavior of nonequilibrium processes, Prigogine and his coworkers concurrently were investigating the implications of their formulations at the molecular (or micro-) scale. The connection between the macroscopic properties of a system of particles and the behavior of individual subunits is statistical mechanics, a mathematical discipline originally developed by the physicists Ludwig Boltzmann, James Clerk Maxwell, and Josiah Willard Gibbs. Prigogine was convinced that statistical fluctuations that were quickly "dampened" close to equilibrium could become amplified in systems far from equilibrium, leading to the bifurcations arising in his thermodynamic theory. With the assistance of mathematicians, notably Gerard Klein, Prigogine was able to produce a rigorous development of nonequilibrium thermodynamics, free of certain probabilistic assumptions that had characterized Boltzmann's earlier efforts. The finished product emerged as a text in 1962, a complement to his book on irreversible thermodynamics (published initially in the middle 1950's).

During the 1970's, encouraged by his associates Leon Rosenfeld of Copenhagen and Gregor Wentzel of the University of Chicago, and assisted by many of his students, Prigogine succeeded in developing a generalized theory of irreversibility that facilitates connections between rate processes and thermodynamic behavior at the microscopic level.

Throughout his career, Prigogine has always had an eye for varied practical applications of his abstract formulations. Thus, in 1971, he collaborated with American Robert Herman on a theory relating his nonequilibrium mechanics to municipal traffic congestion. Following his Nobel award, he focused his attention on diverse questions, including biological evolution, cosmological theories, and a general philosophy of nature. His book *La Nouvelle Alliance* (coauthored with Isabelle Stengers), published in French in 1979 and translated into English in 1984 as *Order out of Chaos*, stands as a monument to the breadth and depth of his thinking. According to futurist Alvin Toffler, *Order out of Chaos* "is a lever for changing science itself, compelling us to reexamine its goal, its method, its epistemology—its world view."

Bibliography

Primary

CHEMISTRY: *Thermodynamique Chimique conformément aux méthodes de Gibbs et de Donder*, 1945 (with Raymond Defay); *Étude thermodynamique des phénomènes irréversibles*, 1947; *The Molecular Theory of Solutions*, 1957 (with André Bellemans and Victor Mathot); *Introduction to Thermodynamics of Irreversible Processes*, 1957; *Non-Equilibrium Statistical Mechanics*, 1962; *Non-Equilibrium Thermodynamics, Variational Techniques, and Stability*, 1966 (with Russell J. Donnelly and Robert Herman); *Surface Tension and Adsorption*, 1966 (with Defay); *Thermodynamic Theory of Structure, Stability, and Fluctuations*, 1971 (with Paul Glansdorff); *Self-Organization in Non-Equilibrium Systems*, 1977 (with Grégoire Nicolis); "Non-Equilibrium Thermodynamics and Chemical Evolution: An Overview and Review," *Advances in Chemical Physics*, vol. 55, 1984.

BIOPHYSICS: *Structure, Dissipation, and Life*, 1969; "Life and Physics: New Perspectives," *Cell Biophysics*, vol. 1, 1986.

COSMOLOGY: "Thermodynamics of Cosmological Matter Creation," *Proceedings of the National Academy of Sciences, USA*, vol. 85, 1988.

PHILOSOPHY OF SCIENCE: *From Being to Becoming: Time and Complexity in the Physical Sciences*, 1980; *Order out of Chaos: Man's New Dialogue with Nature*, 1984 (with Isabelle Stengers); *Exploring Complexity*, 1987 (with Nicolis).

SOCIOLOGY: *Kinetic Theory of Vehicular Traffic*, 1971 (with Herman).

Secondary

Eddington, Sir Arthur. *The Nature of the Physical World*. Cambridge, England: Macmillan, 1929. Reprint. Ann Arbor: University of Michigan Press, 1958. This classic is the philosophic primer on key concepts developed by Prigogine, including time and its "arrow," entropy, macroscopic versus microscopic behavior, and the nature of reality.

Griffin, David Ray, ed. *Physics and the Ultimate Significance of Time*. Albany: State University of New York Press, 1986. A collection of presentations given at a conference in Claremont, California, on the nature of time. The concepts of Prigogine and of physicist David Bohm are the primary concerns of the book; Prigogine summarizes his work on irreversibility and time and receives "feedback."

Lepkowski, Will. "The Social Thermodynamics of Ilya Prigogine." *Chemical and*

Engineering News 57 (April 16, 1979). A short but informative plain-language summary of Prigogine's work, especially its generalized applications to social structures. This article also contains a bibliography of books described as "relevant to entropy and social issues."

Toffler, Alvin. "Science and Change," foreword to *Order out of Chaos*, by Ilya Prigogine. Boulder, Colo.: Shambhala Press, 1984. Toffler offers a very flattering evaluation of the importance of Prigogine's concepts, which he describes collectively as a "comprehensive theory of change."

Weintraub, Pamela, ed. *Omni Interviews*. New York: Ticknor and Fields, 1984. This is a relatively lengthy interview with Prigogine, entitled "Wizard of Time," originally published in *Omni* magazine. Prigogine responds to queries about time, "classical" views of nature versus his own views, the second law, and bifurcation theory and its applications to society.

Winfree, Arthur T. "Rotating Chemical Reactions." *Scientific American* 230 (June, 1974): 82-95. This paper gives a clear descriptive account of the so-called Belousov-Zhabotinsky reactions, in which chemical reactions suddenly "organize themselves" to produce colorful spiral wave patterns in an oscillating fashion. These reactions are widely cited as proof of Prigogine's bifurcation theory.

Roger W. Armstrong

1978

Chemistry
Peter D. Mitchell, Great Britain

Physics
Pyotr Leonidovich Kapitsa, Soviet Union
Arno A. Penzias, Germany and United States
Robert W. Wilson, United States

Physiology or Medicine
Werner Arber, Switzerland
Daniel Nathans, United States
Hamilton O. Smith, United States

Economic Sciences
Herbert A. Simon, United States

Literature
Isaac Bashevis Singer, United States

Peace
Menachem Begin, Israel
Anwar el-Sadat, Egypt

PETER D. MITCHELL
1978

Born: Mitcham, Surrey, England; September 29, 1920

Nationality: British
Areas of concentration: Biochemistry and bioenergetics

Mitchell developed a unifying theory to explain how organisms utilize energy derived from the oxidation of organic molecules to synthesize adenosine triphosphate (ATP), the universal currency of chemical energy required to perform work in all living systems

The Award

Presentation
The Nobel Prize in Chemistry was presented to Peter Mitchell on December 10, 1978; the presentation address was delivered by Lars Ernster of the Royal Swedish Academy of Sciences and professor of biochemistry at the University of Stockholm. In the presentation address, Ernster, an authority on biological energy acquisition and utilization, described the ubiquitous requirement for living organisms to derive energy from their environment and then to transform that energy into a form that can be used to carry out the specialized functions of each cell within the organism. Ernster discussed the existence of a "universal energy currency" in organisms, the molecule adenosine triphosphate (ATP). Energy, in the form of ATP, is derived either from the absorption of light in photosynthesis or (during the process of respiration) from the degradation of organic molecules to carbon dioxide and water using atmospheric oxygen. The energy stored within the chemical bonds of the ATP molecule is utilized for numerous energy-requiring cellular reactions. Of special significance to Mitchell's work is the fact that the reactions responsible for ATP production are membrane-associated processes that take place within special membrane-bound cellular structures, as in chloroplasts during photosynthesis, in mitochondria during respiration, or in the outer cellular membranes of bacteria.

Ernster then explained Mitchell's contribution to the field of bioenergetics, the study of how energy is transformed and utilized by biological organisms. Mitchell's scheme, known as the chemiosmotic hypothesis, envisioned that positively charged hydrogen ions (protons) were transferred from one side of the membrane to the other, and that this process was associated with electron transfer reactions and ATP synthesis.

In concluding remarks, Ernster mentioned the skepticism that Mitchell's proposals initially received from the scientific community. Because of research by Mitchell and others, however, the chemiosmotic hypothesis, which explains how cells are able to generate different concentrations of protons on opposite sides of a membrane (a protonic potential) and how this potential can then be utilized to provide energy for cellular processes, has become accepted as the chemiosmotic theory.

Nobel lecture

Peter Mitchell delivered his Nobel address, entitled "David Keilin's Respiratory Chain Concept and Its Chemiosmotic Consequences," on December 8, 1978. Mitchell's lecture was clearly presented as a tribute to the scientific career and personal friendship that Mitchell had enjoyed with Professor David Keilin at the University of Cambridge. Mitchell began by noting Keilin's discovery of the cytochromes, membrane-associated proteins involved in biological electron transfer reactions, and his concept of a "respiratory chain," a series of reactions in which electrons are passed sequentially from one electron carrier molecule to the next, releasing useful energy in the process.

As a preface to the presentation of his chemiosmotic hypothesis and his research supporting it, Mitchell noted historically significant studies in the field of bioenergetics which stimulated the development of his hypothesis. The "chemical coupling" hypothesis, which stated that the energy from electron-transfer reactions was coupled to ATP synthesis via chemical intermediates, was actively investigated by many of the leading scientists in bioenergetics prior to and during Mitchell's development of the chemiosmotic hypothesis.

Mitchell outlined his hypothesis essentially as he had initially proposed it in 1961. He explained how the generation of a difference in the concentration of protons on opposing sides of a biological membrane, a consequence of the orientation of the sites of the electron transfer reactions in the membrane, might be utilized to provide the energy to synthesize ATP. His concept of "proticity," by analogy with electricity, involves a flow of protons through a closed circuit, such as that existing in biological membranes, which could be used to perform work.

After presenting his hypothesis, Mitchell discussed some of the principal biological effects that he had predicted and experimentally verified to test his proposed model. The most critical studies were those that compared the numbers of protons and electrons being transferred to the numbers of ATP molecules synthesized during operation of the respiratory chain. Also important was the demonstration of the involvement of the "proticity" in the movement of molecules across membranes, and the requirement for an intact membrane for the overall process.

Mitchell presented the concepts of vectorial metabolism, that is, how some membrane-associated processes are attributable to the fact that certain enzyme-catalyzed reactions cause the net unidirectional movement of molecules across membrane barriers. An interesting sidelight was his analogy between the principles of his chemiosmotic hypothesis and those involved in explaining the functioning of the hydrogen-burning fuel cell, originally described in 1839.

The wide applicability of the principles of his hypothesis to numerous important biological processes was briefly noted by Mitchell, and he presented hypotheses to explain some of the fine details of the mechanisms involved in the movement of protons across membranes and of electron transfer reactions in membranes.

Mitchell assessed his chemiosmotic hypothesis as one which has achieved almost complete acceptance within his lifetime, and he concluded with a final and fitting tribute to David Keilin for his influence and insight into the fundamental processes of bioenergetics.

Critical reception

Following the announcement that Mitchell had been awarded the 1978 Nobel Prize in Chemistry, several articles appeared that praised the innovative nature of Mitchell's work, which had led to a novel concept of energy transduction in living systems. In an article in *Science*, Franklin M. Harold of the University of Colorado referred to Mitchell's hypothesis and its implications as "nothing less than a scientific revolution. . . . [I]n time it may transmute our perception of how living cells function." An article in *Chemical and Engineering News* referred to the perceived impact of Mitchell's ideas as "revolutionary."

Nevertheless, the awarding of the prize to Mitchell was not without controversy. When Mitchell first introduced the chemiosmotic hypothesis in 1961, his ideas were so radically different from those in the mainstream of bioenergetics research that most scientists were skeptical. Harold noted in his article in *Science* that Mitchell's hypothesis was not widely welcomed by biochemists, but added that "his theory came under severe attack, much of it based on the failure of critics to understand the postulates." Ronald Kaback of the Roche Institute was quoted in *The New York Times*: "When he first made this hypothesis nobody believed him."

The skepticism with which Mitchell's ideas were received by the scientific community had not fully abated by the time the Nobel Prize was awarded in 1978. An article in *Science News* noted research by Britton Chance of the University of Pennsylvania, a leading proponent of the chemical coupling hypothesis, and other scientists, that disputed some of Mitchell's findings. The controversy was emphasized in a *Chemical and Engineering News* article which considered the choice of Mitchell as the Nobel laureate in chemistry as surprising, because many believed that the theory had not yet been fully proved experimentally. In that article, Britton Chance noted, "The chemist's mind boggles at the incompleteness of it." Although he was uncertain whether Mitchell was correct, Chance did have great praise for Mitchell as a scientist and for the attention that the prize had brought to the area of bioenergetics. Despite the unanswered questions, Efraim Racker of Cornell University noted that there remained little controversy over the major points of the chemiosmotic theory but said that disagreement remained regarding the details of how a proton differential is generated. Some of these controversial points have remained an area of healthy scientific dispute.

A point commonly noted in many of the articles appearing after Mitchell's receipt of the Nobel Prize was the unorthodox laboratory setting in which he worked. The conversion of the Glynn House mansion into a laboratory, Mitchell's small research group, and the limited financial resources for his research all drew attention. A *Newsweek* article captioned Mitchell's photograph with the words: "Mitchell: Small is good." Harold wrote in his article in *Science* that "Mitchell's unconventional laboratory is almost as celebrated as his scientific contributions." Despite the controversies, Mitchell's hypotheses have received nearly universal acceptance, and few would disagree that the chemiosmotic hypothesis has revolutionized the way in which scientists look at energy transformation in biological systems.

Biography

Peter Dennis Mitchell was born in Mitcham, Surrey, England, on September 29, 1920, to Christopher Gibbs Mitchell, a civil servant, and Kate Beatrice Dorothy (née) Taplin. Mitchell's mother was an independent, practical, and atheistic woman, whose philosophies had great impact on him. Mitchell obtained his secondary education at Queens College, a public school in Taunton, England, and despite difficulties with his entrance examinations, was admitted in 1939 to Jesus College at the University of Cambridge. His studies at Cambridge emphasized the physical and natural sciences and, in particular, the chemistry of biological processes. In 1942, Mitchell began graduate studies in the department of biochemistry at Cambridge with Professor James F. Danielli. After receiving his Ph.D. in 1951, he remained at Cambridge from 1950 to 1955 in the position of demonstrator in the department of biochemistry.

Mitchell moved to Edinburgh University in 1955 to organize the chemical biology unit in the department of zoology. He became a senior lecturer in 1961, and in 1962 was appointed to the position of readership. A year later, however, Mitchell found it necessary to resign his position because of acute gastric ulcers. Mitchell married Patricia Mary Helen Ffrench in 1958 and was the father of six children—four sons and two daughters.

For two years after leaving Edinburgh, Mitchell was not directly involved in scientific research. During this period, he and Jennifer Moyle, a former colleague and collaborator at Cambridge, founded Glynn Research Limited. This nonprofit organization, funded by substantial contributions from Mitchell and his older brother Christopher, was created both to promote fundamental biological research and to finance the restoration of the Glynn House, a mansion near Bodmin, Cornwall, England, part of which was to house the Glynn Research Laboratories. At Glynn House, Mitchell resumed his research career and occupied the position of research director. Despite financial limitations, Mitchell and his small staff undertook the task of experimentally verifying many of the predictions of the chemiosmotic hypothesis which he had proposed while at Edinburgh. In the years following his receipt of the Nobel Prize, Mitchell continued an active research program at the Glynn Research Laboratories.

Scientific Career

Mitchell's interest in the properties and functions of biological membranes began as a graduate student at the University of Cambridge, where he was the first doctoral student of Professor James Danielli. It was Danielli who introduced Mitchell to the study of membrane structure and permeability properties. Specifically, Mitchell's graduate research included the study of the mode of action of penicillin on bacterial cells and the development of a novel antidote to arsenic poisoning. These two research interests led to studies of the exchange of arsenate and phosphate ions across the bacterial cell membrane, which, in turn, contributed to his understanding the processes involved in the exchange, or countertransport, of ions across membranes. The scientific interests developed while in Danielli's laboratory were clearly expanded upon in Mitchell's research in the following years, and the process of countertransport was an important conceptual component of what was to become Mitchell's chemiosmotic hypothesis.

While at Cambridge, Danielli introduced Mitchell to David Keilin, director of the Moltento Institute of Biology and Parasitology at Cambridge. Keilin's friendship, scientific accomplishments, and philosophies strongly influenced the direction of Mitchell's research interests. Mitchell has described Danielli as his "official teacher" and Keilin as his "unofficial benefactor." The pioneering studies by Keilin and others provided a stimulus and a framework for Mitchell's landmark hypothesis.

In the 1920's, Keilin had begun experiments that demonstrated the existence of a series of water-insoluble protein electron carriers, which he called cytochromes. He found that oxidation-reduction (electron-transfer) reactions occur at an inorganic metal center within the cytochrome protein molecule. Complementary work in Germany by both Otto Warburg and Heinrich Wieland on soluble enzymes catalyzing electron transfer reactions led to the formulation in the 1960's of the idea of a respiratory chain.

The respiratory chain hypothesis described the removal of hydrogen atoms from molecules in the cell derived from the breakdown of foodstuffs, the transfer of an electron taken from the hydrogen atom to the membrane-bound cytochrome system, and eventually to molecular oxygen. The work of Herman Kalckar and others demonstrated that the energy released as a result of the transfer of electrons to and from the components of the respiratory chain was conserved and coupled to the formation of ATP, the central chemical energy source required for many metabolic reactions in biological systems. These basic principles were eventually demonstrated in a variety of experimental membrane systems, including the inner mitochondrial membrane of animals, the thylakoid membrane within the chlorplasts of plants, and the outer plasma membrane of bacteria. Mitchell's work described the biophysical basis for how the energy obtained from Keilin's respiratory chain could be conserved in a chemical form useful for enabling biological systems to perform work.

Prior to the acceptance of Mitchell's chemiosmotic hypothesis, there was considerable controversy among those working in the discipline of bioenergetics concerning the mechanism by which respiratory electron transfer was energetically coupled to the synthesis of ATP. The prevailing hypothesis was that there were several sites along the respiratory chain in which sufficient energy was released as a result of the oxidation-reduction reactions to promote the formation of energy-rich chemical intermediates. The energy derived from these high-energy intermediates was believed to promote the formation of ATP by combining a molecule of adenosine diphosphate (ADP) and a molecule of inorganic phosphate. Through the late 1950's and the 1960's, a major emphasis of research in this area was the search for reputed energy-rich chemical intermediates whose existence was critical to the verification of this chemical coupling hypothesis. These attempts were unsuccessful, however, leading some insightful scientists to suggest that the energy derived from the electron-transfer reactions might not be coupled to ATP synthesis via a high-energy chemical intermediate; rather, the energy might be obtained from some other type of physical or chemical interaction, perhaps caused by high-energy-containing three-dimensional conformation of a protein molecule, a phenomenon of an electrical nature, or an osmotic imbalance resulting from a differential in the concentrations of some chemical on the opposite sides of the membrane. In fact, these latter considerations were most appropriate to the model that Mitchell was to propose.

Mitchell's chemiosmotic hypothesis was originally outlined in an article in *Nature* in 1961, published while he was at Edinburgh University. The hypothesis provided an alternative explanation of how the transfer of the energy derived from the oxidation-reduction reactions of the respiratory chain is coupled to ATP formation. Among the concepts that were essential for the formulation of this hypothesis was Mitchell's recognition of the potential role of the membrane-bound components of the respiratory and photosynthetic oxidation-reduction systems. An intact biological membrane system was also necessary, to function as a barrier to the movement of electrically charged molecules; further, there must be a controlled, directional, facilitated movement of molecules across this membrane barrier.

Mitchell's hypothesis incorporated most of the important concepts that had been firmly established by his distinguished predecessors. As foods are broken down by enzyme-catalyzed reactions within cells, some molecules undergo specific enzyme-catalyzed oxidation-reduction reactions. Electrons derived from the oxidation of these molecules are specifically transferred to a component of the respiratory chain existing within the inner membrane of a double-membrane bounded subcellular compartment (organelle) known as the mitochondrion, or in the outer membrane of a bacterium. In the special case of photosynthesis in plants, electrons are energized by the absorption of light by a chlorophyll molecule within the thylakoid membrane system of the chloroplasts. In each of these cases, electrons are transferred from one component of an electron transport chain in the membrane to the next. During this process, energy is released, which is conserved by promoting the vectorial movement of protons from one side of the membrane to the other. This unidirectional (one-way) movement of protons across the membrane results in a difference in the concentrations of protons on the two sides of the membrane. This concentration difference (protonic potential) has both an electrical component (caused by the asymmetric distribution of the positively charged protons) and a chemical activity component (caused by the difference in the concentration of protons on the two sides of the membrane).

Inherent within this asymmetric distribution of protons is the energy necessary to promote the formation of ATP from ADP and inorganic phosphate. This reaction is catalyzed by an enzyme called ATP synthase embedded in the membrane, which directly uses the energy released when protons flow back across the membrane from the regions of high concentration to low through a proton pore within the ATP synthase molecule.

Mitchell made the analogy between the movement of electrons through an electrical conductor (electricity) and what he called "proticity," the movement of protons from a region of high proton concentration on one side of a membrane to a region of low concentration on the other. This "proticity" can be used to perform work (ATP synthesis) as the protons pass through the enzyme ATP synthase, analogous in many respects to the way in which the movement of electrons through a wire from a region of high concentration to low can be utilized to perform work in an electrical appliance.

The critical experiments in support of the chemiosmotic hypothesis were carried out in the 1960's by Mitchell and his colleague Jennifer Moyle at Glynn Research Laboratories and in other laboratories throughout the world. Such experiments determined the number of protons moving across the membrane per pair of electrons passing through the series of electron carriers in the respiratory electron transport chain; they also determined the number of protons that move across a membrane per molecule of ATP formed by the ATP synthase-catalyzed reaction. The identification of the membrane proteins that link the movement of protons to the movement of other molecules across membranes, as well as the recognition of the critical role the membrane serves as a barrier to many molecules, particularly protons and hydroxide ions, was essential in supporting Mitchell's hypothesis.

In the years following the receipt of the Nobel Prize, Mitchell and his coworkers have sought to explain some of the fine details of the biochemical mechanisms involved in cellular energy transfer. Some of this research has involved the investigation of the mechanisms involved in proton translocation and the electron transfer reactions in membranes. These studies have included the possibility of complex and varied paths for electrons through the different electron carriers in the electron transfer chains and an investigation of the significance of the way that complexes of the electron carrier proteins are arranged in the membrane.

The broad implications of Mitchell's work provided a framework within which many diverse biological and physiological phenomena could be explained, including the functional mechanisms of the light receptor systems of halophilic bacteria, the relationship of proton generation to heat production in the fat cells of hibernating animals, and the chemical mechanisms involved in flagellar motion of bacteria. Mitchell's contributions have had dramatic impact and far-reaching implications concerning how scientists perceive the ways in which cells are able to utilize, transform, and generate energy.

Bibliography

Primary

CHEMISTRY: "Coupling of Phosphorylation to Electron and Hydrogen Transfer by a Chemi-Osmotic Type of Mechanism," *Nature*, vol. 191, 1961; *Chemiosmotic Coupling in Oxidative and Photosynthetic Proton Circuits*, 1966; "Chemiosmotic Coupling in Oxidative and Photosynthetic Phosphorylation," *Biological Reviews*, vol. 41, 1966; "Vectorial Chemistry and the Molecular Mechanics of Chemiosmotic Coupling: Power Transmission by Proticity," *Transactions of the Biochemical Society*, vol. 4, 1976; "Vectorial Chemiosmotic Processes," *Annual Review of Biochemistry*, vol. 46, 1977; "David Keilin's Respiratory Chain Concept and Its Chemiosmotic Consequences," in *Les Prix Nobel, 1978*, 1979, and *Science*, vol. 206, 1979; "Compartmentation and Communication in Living Systems. Ligand Conduction: A General Catalytic Principle in Chemical, Osmotic, and Chemiosmotic Reaction Systems," *European Journal of Biochemistry*, vol. 95, 1979.

Secondary

Boyer, Paul D., Britton Chance, Lars Ernster, Peter Mitchell, Efraim Racker, and E. C. Slater. "Oxidative Phosphorylation and Photophosphorylation." *Annual Review of Biochemistry* 46 (1977): 955-1026. This article is a compilation of individual reviews by each of the authors, leading authorities in aspects of cellular bioenergetics. The reviews emphasize the status of the field of bioenergetics at the time, focus on points of agreement and disagreement among the authors, and provide suggestions for the direction of future research.

Harold, Franklin M. *The Vital Force: A Study of Bioenergetics*. San Francisco: W. H. Freeman, 1986. This book provides an easily read introduction to all aspects of bioenergetics, including the chemiosmotic theory, and is appropriate for readers with an elementary chemistry background.

Hinkle, Peter C., and Richard E. McCarty. "How Cells Make ATP." *Scientific American* 238 (March, 1978): 104-123. This article provides a lucid introduction to the history and principles of cellular bioenergetics and the chemiosmotic theory. The article presents a rather in-depth examination of these principles, yet it is appropriate reading for one with little background in either chemistry or biochemistry.

Nicholls, David G. *Bioenergetics: An Introduction to the Chemiosmotic Theory*. New York: Academic Press, 1982. This book offers a clear and complete presentation of the chemical and physiological aspects of energy transduction in biological systems; it emphasizes the role of Mitchell's chemiosmotic theory in these mechanisms.

Oldeberg, W., ed. "Peter Mitchell." *Les Prix Nobel, 1978*. Stockholm: The Nobel Foundation, 1979. This includes the short biography of Peter Mitchell that accompanied the official publication of Mitchell's Nobel Prize lecture.

Racker, Efraim. "From Pasteur to Mitchell: A Hundred Years of Bioenergetics."

Federation Proceedings 39 (1980): 210-215. This article provides an interesting account of the history of bioenergetics, written by one of the leading scientists in the field. In addition to providing a historical perspective, Racker discusses the important scientific questions that had not yet been clarified at the time.

Skalachev, V. P., and Peter C. Hinkle, eds. *Chemiosmotic Proton Circuits in Biological Membranes*. Reading, Mass.: Addison-Wesley, 1981. This volume is a compilation of assessments and speculation regarding aspects of the chemiosmotic theory. Each of the individual thirty-five articles was written by scientists active in the field of bioenergetics, and the volume was published in honor of Peter Mitchell on the occasion of his sixtieth birthday.

Slayman, Clifford L. "Proton Chemistry and the Ubiquity of Proton Pumps." *Bioscience* 35 (January, 1985): 16-17. This article offers a brief introduction to the importance of proton pumps in divergent biological systems; it is a preface to a full issue of this journal devoted to the discussion of the role of proton pumps in a variety of organisms.

H. David Husic
Diane W. Husic

1979

Chemistry
Herbert C. Brown, United States
Georg Wittig, West Germany

Physics
Sheldon L. Glashow, United States
Abdus Salam, Pakistan
Steven Weinberg, United States

Physiology or Medicine
Allan M. Cormack, United States
Godfrey N. Hounsfield, Great Britain

Economic Sciences
W. Arthur Lewis, Great Britain
Theodore W. Schultz, United States

Literature
Odysseus Elýtis, Greece

Peace
Mother Teresa of Calcutta, India

HERBERT C. BROWN
1979

Born: London, England; May 22, 1912

Nationality: American
Areas of concentration: Boron compounds and organic synthesis

Studying boron compounds and the multiplicity of their chemical reactions, Brown made practical their use as reagents in organic syntheses. The discovery and use of the organoboranes and the development of a technique for synthesizing sodium borohydride have contributed significantly to bonding rearrangements and modifications within and between carbon atoms

The Award

Presentation

Professor Bengt Lindberg of the Royal Swedish Academy of Sciences, on December 10, 1979, presented to those assembled Herbert C. Brown and Georg Wittig, joint recipients of the Nobel Prize in Chemistry. In his address, Lindberg surveyed the general field of organic chemistry, concerned as it is with carbon compounds. Recognizing the importance of synthesizing compounds in a field of more than two million synthesized organic compounds, Lindberg stressed the importance of efforts to facilitate such processes of synthesis. The practical consequences of effective methods of synthesis have included the development of pharmaceuticals, vitamins, pesticides, an alleviation of world famine, and the hope for future practical and environmentally safe synthetic products.

Lindberg pointed out that one of the important keys to chemical synthesis involves developing methods for bonding and linking carbon atoms. In some cases, such as the work of Brown and Wittig, the methods developed have been so significant that they have merited the Nobel Prize. This is clearly the case, Lindberg said, regarding Brown's development of boron compounds and Wittig's development of phosphorus compounds. The result of the work of both researchers has been the generation of reagents that have had an important impact on organic synthesis.

The work of Brown, Lindberg noted, has been with boron compounds, borohydrides and the organoboranes. The study and development of these compounds and their use as reagents have resulted in new methods and approaches for molecular rearrangements, for doubling bonding additions, and for the linking of carbon atoms. The work of Georg Wittig has involved the Wittig reaction, which bears his name. As the result of reaction between a phosphorus compound that he discovered and carbonyl compounds, a compound is formed in which two carbon atoms are joined by a double bond. This method has had wide use in industry and elsewhere. Lindberg concluded by congratulating Brown for developing "new and powerful tools" and Wittig for discovering a reaction that was "one of the most important reactions in organic chemistry." Both recipients of the Nobel Prize, Lindberg noted, have contributed much to organic synthesis.

Nobel lecture

On December 8, 1979, Herbert C. Brown presented his Nobel lecture, entitled "From Little Acorns to Tall Oaks: From Boranes Through Organoboranes." The lecture surveyed, with grace and elegance, Brown's forty-three years of research into compounds of boron. He started with his earliest understanding of the field, Alfred Stock's *The Hydrides of Boron and Silicon* (1933), and then discussed his work at the University of Chicago, completing the Ph.D. in 1938 and working in various capacities at that institution until 1943. In the fall of 1940, Brown's laboratory, directed by H. I. Schlesinger, was assigned by the National Defense Research Committee the task of developing low-molecular-weight compounds of uranium. This was accomplished, but a practical method of synthesizing diborane was needed, which Brown supplied. It involved the reaction of lithium hydride with boron trifluoride in ethyl ether solution. Finding a substitute for lithium hydride expanded the area of discovery. Through work for the Army Signal Corps, the basis for the present industrial process for the manufacture of sodium borohydride was discovered in 1942. In 1945, lithium aluminum hydride was synthesized. This and the sodium borohydride discovery represented major changes "in procedures for the reduction of functional groups of organic molecules."

Coming to Purdue University in 1947, Brown indicated, he was given opportunities for greatly expanded research. His initial effort involved increasing the reducing properties in sodium borohydride (reduction involves the gain of electrons or hydrogen atoms or the ability of an agent to add electrons or hydrogen atoms), while decreasing those in lithium aluminum hydride to provide a whole range of reducing agents. This was accomplished, and Brown moved on to develop standardized procedures for hydroboration (the process of adding diborane to an unsaturated hydrocarbon or organic molecule) and for using organoborane products of organic syntheses. All this involved a meticulous analysis of the field and a growth of understanding of what was possible. The consequence was that methods were developed to use boron to "stitch" together individual molecules or complex structures or to "rivet" temporary structures into carbon structures. Three separate procedures were developed for these purposes; this clearly enhanced methodology.

In addition, Brown succeeded in developing methods and procedures for the hydroboration of acetylenes, developing from these vinyl boranes, and then synthesizing pheromones through the use of organoborane chemistry. The latter synthesis was especially important for the production of insecticides.

Having surveyed the field for which he received the Nobel Prize, Brown then offered gentle advice to young chemists. Brown said that when he had come to chemistry in the 1930's, he believed that "organic chemistry was a relatively mature science" and most of the subject was already known. "There appeared to be little new to be done." More than forty years of research had proved this view wrong and showed that the future lay open and potentially "fruitful." Rejecting pessimism, Brown urged that young chemists be the "enthusiastic" and "optimistic" explorers of new "continents" of discovery in the world of chemistry.

Critical reception

The faculty and staff of Purdue University had been very supportive of the work of Herbert C. Brown. The Department of Chemistry and the School of Science had honored him with a symposium on May 5 and 6, 1978, and had prepared, on the occasion of that symposium, a 277-page document entitled *Remembering HCB: Memoirs of Colleagues and Students of Herbert C. Brown*. Viewing Brown with fondness, respect, and enthusiastic praise, this document reflected the atmosphere at Purdue University and among its chemistry alumni that greeted Brown on his receipt of the Nobel Prize. As Purdue University had not produced a Nobel laureate before, the award was perceived as a unique mark of distinction for Purdue and for this truly outstanding faculty member.

The scientific world found Brown's work very praiseworthy. *Science News* (October 20) spoke of Brown's research as facilitating the manufacture of chemicals and materials and as requiring a generation of chemists to explore fully. Because of Brown's efforts, various drugs, such as cortisone, and a wide range of pesticides could more easily be manufactured. The *Science News* article, in addition to noting Brown's significant work in the chemistry of boron, noted the importance of Brown's investigations of the steric strain, a force arising from the particular arrangement of atoms in a molecule. Proper utilization of the steric strain could aid reactions.

On January 4, 1980, a lengthy article on Brown's Nobel award appeared in *Science*, written by James H. Brewster and Ei-Ichi Negishi. The article, entitled "Brown: Passes Through the Mountains," was especially laudatory. Speaking of Brown's research as "systematic" and "unusually logical," Brewster and Negishi pointed to Brown's scrupulous commitment to careful research and objectivity. Brown's approach was summarized in his own words: "The main thing is to find out exactly what is going on."

Starting with the discovery of the hydroboration reaction (the process of adding diborane to an unsaturated hydrocarbon or organic molecule), Brown and his co-workers discovered that the hydroboration reaction permitted the use as chemical intermediaries of the organoboranes. The article then surveyed how monoalkylboranes, dialkylboranes, or trialkylboranes are formed, how these substances are synthetically useful and may be used for reductions, and the chemical results of substitutions of boron atoms by hydrogen, amino groups, deuterium, or other atoms. All such important reactions may be exceeded in significance by the use of organoboranes for carbon-carbon bond formation. The result has been an "exponential-increase" in the possibilities for synthesis and the opening of "whole new areas of organometallic chemistry to explore." The article contended that, "for this, the

Nobel Prize is richly deserved" and concluded with a brief biography of Brown.

A third description of Brown's winning of the Nobel Prize in Chemistry appeared in the December, 1979, issue of *Scientific American*. Quoting the Nobel Committee, this article stated that, "thanks to the work of Brown and his co-workers the organoboranes have become the most versatile reagents ever created in organic chemistry." The article indicated that Brown had been specifically cited for his synthesis of sodium borohydride, for his conversion of borohydrides into useful reagents, and for his discovery and development of the organoboranes. All these activities had opened enormous possibilities for expanding research in organic chemistry.

The New York Times reported, in its October 16, 1979, issue, on the significance of the work of Brown and Wittig for the development of processes that have made possible and feasible the mass production of important chemicals and pharmaceuticals. The response of the scientific world and the public to Herbert C. Brown's receipt of the Nobel Prize was very favorable and noncontroversial. It seemed an appropriate acknowledgment for a lifetime of dedicated, conscientious, meticulous, and intelligent research that produced very important results for the field of organic chemistry and chemical synthesis and manufacturing.

Biography

Herbert Charles Brown, the son of Charles Brovarnik and Pearl Gorinstein Brovarnik, was born on May 22, 1912, in London, England. His parents had emigrated to England in 1908 and thence to the United States in 1914, where they settled in Chicago. The family name was changed to Brown. The father supported the family as a cabinetmaker and, in the United States, as a carpenter. In addition to Herbert C. Brown, the family included a sister, Ann, and two younger sisters, Sophie and Riva.

In 1920, Brown's father opened a hardware store in a black neighborhood of Chicago, and the family lived above the store. Brown attended school, dropping out of high school after his father's death in 1926 to help support the family. Returning to high school in 1929, he was graduated in 1930. Crane Junior College, which Brown entered in 1933, closed after Brown's first semester there, so he took some classes at Lewis Institute. He began working at the home laboratory of a former Crane instructor, Nicholas Cheronis, where he fell in love with his future bride-to-be, Sarah Baylen. Brown and Baylen attended Wright Junior College in 1934 and were graduated in 1935. Brown then took a competitive examination and received a small scholarship to the University of Chicago in 1935. He received the baccalaureate degree in 1936, and, as a graduation present, Sarah presented him with all that she could afford: a two-dollar copy of Alfred Stock's *The Hydrides of Boron and Silicon* (1933), on the subject that became Herbert's lifework and the research area for which he would receive the Nobel Prize.

Entering the University of Chicago as a graduate student, Brown received the Ph.D. in 1938, followed by a postdoctoral fellowship, and in 1939 became a research assistant and instructor under his former research director, H. I. Schlesinger. Brown remained at the University of Chicago until 1943, when he went to Wayne State University in Detroit. Brown established the chemistry laboratory at Wayne, was promoted to associate professor, and in 1947 was invited to Purdue University as a full professor. Accepting that assignment, Brown became Witherall Distinguished Professor in 1959 and became Witherall Research Professor in 1960. He became a professor emeritus in 1978 and received the Nobel Prize in 1979. In 1987, Purdue University named its new chemistry building in honor of Herbert C. Brown. Additional honors, awards, and citations have been numerous.

Scientific Career

Herbert C. Brown has sought to make science students aware of his scientific career so that they will be encouraged to persist in science and will feel "optimistic about the future possibilities for chemistry." Entering college in the darkest days of the Great Depression, February, 1933, Brown soon found himself out of school when Crane Junior College closed its doors after he had attended for only one semester. Brown, however, met two remarkable people at Crane: his wife-to-be, Sarah Baylen, who at first "hated him"; and Nicholas Cheronis, a Crane chemistry professor. Soon, Herbert and Sarah became inseparable, attending classes together, working together to support their educational objectives, and eventually becoming lifetime partners. When Crane closed, Cheronis invited Brown and Baylen to work in a consulting laboratory in his home and helped teach them organic chemistry and qualitative analysis. Brown also studied quantitative analysis on his own.

When, in September of 1934, Wright Junior College opened, Herbert and Sarah both attended, studying science; there Cheronis had become head of the Department of Physical Sciences. Brown was graduated in 1935 and then attempted to enter the University of Chicago on a competitive scholarship. Brown was very surprised to have won the scholarship, but it made possible his attending the University of Chicago. Because tuition at college was one hundred dollars per quarter regardless of the number of classes taken, Brown overloaded himself with courses in order to reduce the cost of his education. This permitted him to graduate as a bachelor of science in 1936. Although seeking work rather than graduate school, Brown let himself be persuaded by Julius Stigliz to attend the graduate school of the University of Chicago on a four-hundred-dollar assistantship (of which Brown paid three hundred dollars for tuition and expenses). Because Brown had become interested in boron hydrides, he did his research under H. I. Schlesinger. Brown had undertaken a study of the reaction of diborane with aldehydes and ketones to determine whether the result was a simple addition product or involved the movement of the hydride from boron to carbon. Brown, therefore, explored the reactions of diboranes with various substances. He was awarded the Ph.D. in 1938, and his dissertation was published in 1939 as *Hydrides of Boron XI: The Reaction of Diborane with Organic Compounds Containing a Carbonyl Group*.

Having completed the Ph.D., Brown attempted to find employment in private industry but failed. Fortunately, Morris S. Kharasch of the University of Chicago gave Brown a sixteen-hundred-dollar postdoctoral fellowship to do research in the area of free-radical chemistry, chlorination, and sulforation. In 1939, Brown became assistant to Schlesinger, with the rank of instructor of chemistry. Anton B. Burg, Schlesinger's assistant, had accepted a position at the University of Southern California, thereby leaving open the position at the University of Chicago for Brown. Burg had synthesized beryllium borohydride, and R. T. Sanderson had synthesized aluminum borohydride, so Brown synthesized lithium borohydride, studied its chemistry, and began work on the synthesis of gallium borohydrides.

At this critical juncture, in 1940, Schlesinger was asked by the National Defense Research Committee to undertake a war research effort to obtain volatile compounds of uranium, needed because of difficulties in dealing with uranium hexafluoride, which was being used for nuclear experiments. Brown was given major responsibility in the organization and direction of the research team. Initially preparing a bistrifluoromethyl compound of uranium, with a molecular weight of 1066, the research team was informed that the requirement was for low-molecular-weight compounds of uranium, not to exceed 238. Consequently, Brown was asked to develop uranium borohydride, which could meet both the requirements of volatility and low molecular weight.

Combining aluminum borohydride and uranium fluoride in a sealed vacuum tube, Brown discovered that, upon warming, green crystals were produced. This discovery was made just as Harold C. Urey of Columbia University, the director of the University of Chicago research project, was visiting. Urey was very interested, asked for an analysis of the green crystals, and was subsequently told that they were uranium borohydride and met the volatility and molecular weight requirements. Given this success, the University of Chicago team was asked to expand its research to make the uranium borohydride in quantity. The key to this effort was developing approaches to the quantity production of diborane and metal borohydrides. Rather than diverting Brown from his research interest, then, the war effort permitted a great expansion of research into his area of interest: To Brown's laboratories were added researchers and equipment. Because Schlesinger was increasingly occupied with academic and departmental matters, much of the expansion and organization of the research became Brown's responsibility, along with a very heavy teaching burden and the need to direct the research of Ph.D. candidates, who assisted with Brown's research. In spite of Brown's many duties, his research effort was greatly facilitated.

The major inhibition to the production of uranium borohydride in large quantities was the synthesis of diborane, a substance that Brown's laboratories could produce only in small amounts. After some experimentation, a new route was developed, and synthesis in quantity became realizable. This, in turn, made possible quantity production of uranium borohydride. When, however, lithium hydride, a constituent in the process, became unavailable, it became necessary to develop the means of using sodium trimethoxyborohydride instead. After some experimentation, Brown's research team was successful in making the substitution that permitted quantity production of diborane and uranium borohydride. Having developed new synthetic processes and explored the field of boranes, Brown and his researchers were now told that the U.S. government no longer needed uranium borohydride, because the difficulties with uranium hexafluoride had been solved.

The frustration over this news was only partly eased by the satisfaction of the discovery of so many effective synthetic processes. As Brown prepared to dismantle his research effort, the Army Signal Corps hired the laboratory to develop an inexpensive means of supplying large quantities of sodium borohydrides, discovered in 1942. Such a process was soon developed and has since become the means of the present industrial production of this chemical, essential to the manufacture of pharmaceuticals.

Brown's work at the University of Chicago was meticulous, highly creative, and significant. His compensation was negligible. In spite of his formidable teaching assignment, his direction of Ph.D. candidates, and the productivity of his laboratory, his annual salary was low and he remained untenured, since tenure was achieved only after an appointment of ten years. Brown, therefore, resolved to secure his status at the University of Chicago. When he requested of Schlesinger a departmental decision on tenure in 1943, the Department of Chemistry refused to decide, and Brown made the determination to go elsewhere.

Seeking the assistance of M. S. Kharasch, Brown was directed to Professor Neil Gordon, department head at Wayne University (later to become Wayne State University) in Detroit. Brown was subsequently hired at a higher salary, a teaching load of twelve hours per week, and a requirement to develop a research laboratory. The establishment and outfitting of a research laboratory proved to be a considerable challenge, but Brown was successful in organizing his laboratory and publishing seven papers in his first year at Wayne.

One important area of research at Wayne, and the subject of five articles during Brown's first year there, was the topic of steric strains (deviation of the bond angles of a given molecule—that is, the angles formed between its constituent atoms— from their normal angles). Having begun research on this topic at Chicago, Brown proved to be as important a theoretical chemist as he was a practical chemist. He forced recognition of the fact that steric strains within the bond angles of compounds could have as important a qualitative or quantitative effect on reactions as did electron charge. He identified the roles of front strain, internal strain (especially important in ring compounds, or organic compounds with more than two atoms that are oriented in cyclic patterns, or rings), and back strain, in the transition states of reactions. These studies led Brown into an analysis of the classical carbonium ion problem, resulting in his challenge of the nonclassical view and the necessity of recognizing that some of the differences between the classical and the nonclassical views of the ion may be purely definitional.

In 1946, Brown was promoted to associate professor of chemistry, and in 1947 he was invited to go to Purdue University at the rank of full professor of inorganic chemistry, where he remained. The opportunities at Purdue were considerable, and

Brown began to experiment with controlling the reducing characteristics of sodium borohydride and lithium borohydride (that is, the ability of these molecules to donate electrons or hydrogen atoms to other molecules), which would expand the range of utilization of these reducing agents. The experiments were successful and significantly contributed to the effective use of these chemicals. Yet another area of development at Purdue concerned hydroboration. Working with B. C. Subba Rao, Brown discovered hydroboration (the process of adding diborane to an unsaturated hydrocarbon or organic molecule). In 1956, Rao discovered that diborane could be added to alkenes or unsaturated hydrocarbons in ether solution at room temperature. This extended the use of organoboranes and contributed much to new approaches to the synthesis of complex molecules. Brown's book *Hydroboration* (1962), part of the McGraw-Hill *Encyclopedia of Science and Technology*, is a comprehensive analysis of the many different approaches and reactions made possible by hydroboration. These reactions were developed in the decade following Rao's discovery of the consequences of the addition of diborane to alkenes and alkynes.

Hydroboration made possible the use and study of the organoboranes, which Brown's research laboratory then investigated and on which Brown reported in *Boranes in Organic Chemistry* (1972). The Brown studies revealed an exceptionally rich and varied field of chemistry in the exploration of the organoboranes. The opportunities and paths open for organic synthesis have been immensely expanded. In fact, as the result of research by some of Brown's coworkers, organoboranes were demonstrated to be some of the most useful intermediaries in organic chemistry, contributing to enhancing carbon-to-carbon bonding and to the development of organometallic compounds. Many of his reactions have yielded new synthetic structures.

In turn, the hydroboration of acetylenes did not proceed beyond monohydroboration (addition of a single borohydride unit to the acetylenes), and this, in turn, contributed to the development of vinyl boranes which could be converted into organomercurials and other organometallics. Some of the important work in these areas was undertaken by such coworkers as James B. Campbell, Jr., Gary Molander, George Zweifel, Ei-ichi Negishi, and others, some of whom (including K. K. Wang) were also significantly involved in the development of pheromones, useful in limiting insect numbers.

Some of these activities have gone beyond the scope of Brown's comprehensive account in *Boranes in Organic Chemistry* and *Organic Syntheses via Boranes* (1975) and illustrate how much fruitful research in the field remains. For these reasons, Brown has received many awards, honors, and prizes, becoming Purdue's Wetherill Distinguished Professor in 1959 and Wetherill Research Professor in 1960; being elected to the National Academy of Sciences in 1957, to the American Academy of Arts and Sciences in 1966, and to the Chemical Society in 1978; and receiving the Nichols Medal in 1959, the ACS Award for Creative Research in 1960, the Linus Pauling Medal in 1968, the National Medal for Science in 1969, the Roger Adams Medal in 1971, the Ingold Memorial Medal in 1978, the Nobel Prize in 1979, and honorary doctorates from the University of Chicago in 1968, from Wayne State in 1980, and from Hebrew University in 1980.

Following the Nobel award and as a professor emeritus at Purdue, Brown continued his research, publishing hundreds of additional articles that document his ongoing efforts. The scientific career of Herbert C. Brown has been exceptionally extensive and fruitful. His effectiveness as a researcher has depended on his enormous capability as a leader, as an effective director of human resources, and as a visionary who has been able, with kindness, to instill that vision in his coworkers and colleagues.

Bibliography

Primary
CHEMISTRY: "Hydrides of Boron XI: The Reaction of Diborane with Organic Compounds Containing a Carbonyl Group," *Journal of the American Chemical Society*, vol. 61, 1939 (with H. I. Schlesinger and A. Burg); "Studies in Steric Strains," *American Philosophical Society Year Book*, vol. 113, 1946; "The Present Problem in Inorganic Chemistry," *Journal of Chemical Education*, vol. 27, 1950 (with C. L. Rulfs); "The Borohydrides: A Case History of Academic Exploratory Research," *Chemical and Engineering News*, vol. 29, 1951; "The F-, B-, I-Strains," *Record of Chemical Progress*, vol. 14, 1953; "Chemical Effects of Steric Strains," *Journal of the Chemical Society*, vol. 1248, 1956; "The Chemistry of Molecular Shapes," *Journal of Chemical Education*, vol. 36, 1959; *Hydroboration*, 1962; *Boranes in Organic Chemistry*, 1972; *Organic Syntheses via Boranes*, 1975; "Pioneering in Borane Chemistry," *The Chemist*, vol. 53, 1976; *The Nonclassical Ion Problem*, 1977.

Secondary
Bank, Shelton, ed. *Remembering HCB: Memoirs of Colleagues and Students of Herbert C. Brown*. West Lafayette, Ind.: Purdue University, 1978. Prepared on the occasion of a symposium held on May 5 and 6, 1978, to honor Brown upon his assuming emeritus status at Purdue, this is an extensive collection of letters and reminiscences, 277 pages in length. Written by associates, coworkers, and friends, it provides valuable insights into Brown's interaction with his colleagues, his research techniques, and the charm of the man himself. Especially interesting is the extended letter of his wife, Sarah Baylen Brown. Contains an extensive bibliography of all Brown's writings to 1978. Invaluable to researchers.
Brewster, James. H. "Herbert C. Brown: A Biographical Note." In *Aspects of Mechanism and Organometallic Chemistry*, edited by Brewster. New York: Plenum Press, 1978. An excellent overview of the scientific career of Brown, this study provides a brief biography and elaborates on Brown's involvement with steric strains, aromatic substitution, classical and nonclassical carbonium ions, and organoboranes. The analysis is especially useful in its description of Brown's contributions to theoretical chemistry, especially in its description of the classi-

cal/nonclassical carbonium ion problem. It is clear that Brewster is Brown's major biographer (he also contributed a fourteen-page article in the above-listed memorial volume published by Purdue University), and this article is essential to a balanced understanding of Brown's theoretical as well as his practical work in organic chemistry.

Brewster, James H., and Ei-ichi Negishi. "Brown: Passes Through the Mountains." *Science* 207 (January 4, 1980): 44-46. A fine analysis of the practical organic chemistry for which Brown received the Nobel Prize in 1979. Focusing less on Brown's theoretical studies, this article describes the hydroboration reaction that made the organoboranes feasible in chemical reactions. Brewster and Negishi make clear the great versatility of the organoboranes. The article also offers an excellent and useful biography of Brown. Tracing his scientific career, it particularly elucidates Brown's experiences prior to coming to Purdue.

Brown, Herbert C. "Autobiographical Introduction." In his *Boranes in Organic Chemistry*. Ithaca, N.Y.: Cornell University Press, 1972. Brown traces his career from his entering Crane Junior College in the Depression year 1933 to his award by Purdue University of the R. B. Wetherill Research Professorship in 1960. Summarizes the status of organic chemistry in the United States in the 1930's and attempts to provide encouragement for young chemists. Invaluable for its personal details.

_____. "From Little Acorns to Tall Oaks: From Boranes Through Organo-boranes." In *Les Prix Nobel, 1979*. Stockholm: The Nobel Foundation, 1980. Brown's Nobel lecture focuses on the chemistry that won for him the Nobel Prize in Chemistry in 1979. Starting with an autobiographical sketch, the lecture describes his work with diborane and borohydrides, the development of methods for reductions with complex hydrides, the discovery and development of hydroboration, and utilization of organoboranes. This utilization has made possible two very important practical developments: vinyl boranes and pheromones, both of which have significant industrial applications. Finally, the lecture urges chemists not to become discouraged about the future of chemistry and science.

Purdue University, Department of Chemistry. *H. C. Brown: A Celebration*. West Lafayette, Ind.: Author, 1980. A 140-page account that collects a number of articles describing the background, biography, and scientific career of Brown, this is the most comprehensive treatment of Brown's life and career. Among other items reprinted here are Brown's Nobel lecture, along with several of his articles on hydroboration, borane chemistry, and organoboranes. The bibliography is extensive. Essential for an understanding of the man's life and work.

Saul Lerner

1979

Chemistry
Herbert C. Brown, United States
Georg Wittig, West Germany

Physics
Sheldon L. Glashow, United States
Abdus Salam, Pakistan
Steven Weinberg, United States

Physiology or Medicine
Allan M. Cormack, United States
Godfrey N. Hounsfield, Great Britain

Economic Sciences
W. Arthur Lewis, Great Britain
Theodore W. Schultz, United States

Literature
Odysseus Elýtis, Greece

Peace
Mother Teresa of Calcutta, India

GEORG WITTIG
1979

Born: Berlin, Germany; June 16, 1897

Nationality: German
Areas of concentration: Reaction mechanisms and organic synthesis

Wittig made significant contributions to methodology used to synthesize biologically active materials by the discovery and development of the transformation that bears his name, the Wittig reaction

The Award

Presentation

Bengt Lindberg, an organic chemist and member of the Royal Swedish Academy of Sciences, presented the Nobel Prize in Chemistry to Herbert C. Brown and Georg Wittig on December 10, 1979. Lindberg noted that chemistry is not only the study of natural objects but also that of unnatural materials. Thus, the ability to synthesize a variety of compounds is a necessity. He noted that the complex structural nature of the chemistry of carbon compounds presents a considerable challenge to those wishing to synthesize these molecules. The challenge is worthy, however, since synthetic pharmaceuticals, vitamins, and pesticides have done much to improve the quality of human life. The application of these chemicals has saved millions of lives and greatly reduced suffering. Lindberg noted that significant progress in areas of chemistry related to these materials was expected in years to come. In addition, he expressed the hope that the development of pesticides that would be less harmful to the environment than those currently used would be an important goal for the future.

Lindberg's address acknowledged the many contributions of Georg Wittig to organic chemistry and emphasized the methodology known as the Wittig reaction. This transformation employs a class of phosophorus compounds, phosphorus ylides, which Wittig discovered. On reaction with a carbonyl compound, there is a coupling that produces a double bond between two carbon atoms. This means of linking two atoms is commonly found in biologically active compounds. Thus, the methodology is a significant contribution to the arsenal of reactions available to chemists wishing to synthesize these compounds. The Wittig reaction has been extensively employed in the preparation of a wide variety of compounds in both academic and industrial laboratories.

Nobel lecture

Georg Wittig's Nobel lecture, "From Diyls over Ylides to My Idyll," began by comparing chemical research with mountain climbing. Both are subjects of interest to Wittig, as he has spent considerable time pursuing both activities. He noted that initiative, perseverance, and determination were required for either endeavor. Hard work is rewarded with great joy either at reaching the mountain peak or at attaining a research goal. He also acknowledged the fact that the results of chemical research may be disappointing. His lecture, delivered in Stockholm on December 8, 1979, emphasized the more rewarding areas of his life's work. Wittig summarized fifty years of research, describing how his interests had developed to encompass a number of theoretical problems and their practical implications. He noted that many contributions to the field of preparative organic chemistry resulted from theoretical studies that yielded unexpected results. This was the case during his work on diradicals, the diyls in the presentation's title. An exchange reaction was observed that changed the fundamental characteristics of the molecule involved in the reaction. This manipulation of the nature of the molecule has proven invaluable to chemists devising approaches to complex molecules.

This area of research also gave Wittig the opportunity to study a new type of molecule which had been predicted theoretically but was so unstable that it had never been formed experimentally. The exchange reaction that Wittig found was performed on similar but not identical molecules. A different reaction pathway occurred, and instead of a straightforward exchange, the highly unstable molecule dehydrobenzene was formed. This finding promoted a reevaluation of aspects of the theory of the way in which atoms are linked (bonded) in organic molecules.

The contribution for which Wittig is best known is the Wittig reaction. This reaction provides a means of linking two different molecules in a way commonly seen in naturally occurring compounds. Wittig described the reaction leading to this discovery as "absurd" in retrospect: Chemical principles dictated that the experiment would fail. Indeed, the result was not the intended molecule but a new class of compound that Wittig named "ylides." During a systematic study of the properties of this type of compound, the new transformation, the Wittig reaction, was discovered. Wittig described how his reaction had been applied to the industrial preparation of vitamin A by BASF. It allowed large quantities of the vitamin to be produced for research purposes as well as for pharmaceutical uses.

Wittig concluded his lecture noting that his excursion from "diyls over ylides" had led him to his idyll. By this he meant that on attaining emeritus status in 1967, he was freed from administrative and teaching duties at Heidelberg, allowing him to devote himself fully to research. This also allowed time for another interest of his, the fine arts.

Critical reception

The twenty-fourth German to win a Nobel Prize in Chemistry, Wittig was somewhat surprised to hear that he was the cowinner (with Herbert C. Brown of Purdue University) in 1979. At age eighty-two, Wittig was awarded the prize for research accomplished in the early 1950's, three decades before the contribution was recognized by the academy. Some observers, such as Robert Shaw in the November 15, 1979, issue of the British journal *Nature*, regarded the award as long overdue.

The chemical research selected by the Nobel Committee in 1979 had several common themes. Both Wittig and Brown had worked on their prizewinning research many years prior to the award. The related but independent research of the two chemists used atoms not usually associated with organic chemistry: phosphorus and boron respectively. Another similarity regarding the work says more about the scientists than their science. The major breakthrough in both Wittig's and Brown's research came as a result of an unexpected reaction. Chance and the ability to recognize the significance of surprise results coupled with a systematic and logical approach to the investigation of these results proved a powerful combination and provided the success which both chemists enjoyed.

In the late 1970's, the United States was in the midst of a recession. Economic and international problems had caused national self-confidence to dwindle. American dominance in science, however, continued. Americans were only too pleased to celebrate the presentation of five Nobel prizes for science to United States citizens. This brought the number to one hundred since 1946. In 1979 the prizes for chemistry, medicine, physics, and economics were all shared with nationals of other countries. *U.S. News & World Report* reported the suggestion that splitting prizes between Americans (Brown, born in England, is a United States citizen) and other nationals (Wittig is German) was a conscious effort on the part of the award committee to lessen the American domination of the awards. Other scientists believed that a more likely explanation for the increase in shared prizes reflects the fact that scientific advances could not be easily attributed to only one nation. There is a perception in Europe, particularly in non-English-speaking countries, that Americans too often emphasize research being carried out in their own country and are less interested in research from other nations, particularly if that work is not published in English. The media in the United States does little to minimize this view: *The New York Times* printed an article discussing the 1979 prizes in chemistry and physics with the subheadline "Americans at Harvard and Purdue Win— German and Pakistani Cited."

Another consequence of the economic woes of the United States in 1979 was that fundamental research was becoming increasingly difficult to fund from federal sources. Edwin Vedejs of the University of Wisconsin noted in *Science* that Wittig's research provided "an eminently practical discovery made in the course of fundamental research lacking any preconceived practical objective." Thus, the move toward funding applied science at the expense of fundamental research may be shortsighted.

It would be difficult to suggest two methodologies that had greater impact, in a practical sense, on the synthesis of organic compounds than the contributions of Wittig and Brown. *Chemical and Engineering News*, in October, 1979, described the work of Wittig and Brown as the "cultivation of a fertile continent," as contrasted with the "conquering of high mountains" where the research has little practical consequence. Chemists all over the world use these reactions and their variants every day.

Biography

Georg Wittig was born in Berlin on June 16, 1897. The son of a professor of fine arts, his interest in music began at an early age. In fact, the choice to study chemistry rather than music, in particular piano, was a difficult one. He attended school (the Wilhelms Gymnasium) in Kasel. In 1923, he was graduated from Philipps University in Marburg after an interruption occasioned by military service in World War I, part of which was spent as a prisoner of war in Great Britain. His doctoral adviser was Karl von Auwers. He was appointed *Dozent* at Marburg in 1926. A colleague of Wittig in Marburg was Karl Ziegler, who was to be the corecipient of the Nobel Prize in 1963. He and Wittig became friends and shared an interest in many activities, including mountaineering.

In 1932, Wittig became associate professor at the Technical University of Braunschweig, and in 1937 he moved to Freiburg as special professor. In 1944, he became Institute Director at Tübingen, where the pioneering work on the Wittig reaction was performed. In 1956, Wittig moved to the beautiful city of Heidelberg. He succeeded Karl Freudenberg as director of the Chemical Institute in 1965. He served for two years before retiring in 1967. Wittig's wife of many years, Waltraut, herself a Ph.D. in chemistry, died in January, 1978.

Wittig has honorary degrees from the Universities of the Sorbonne (Paris), Tübingen, and Hamburg; he is an honorary member of a number of international chemical societies. He has won numerous awards in Germany and internationally: the Adolf von Baeyer Medal of the Society of German Chemists (1953), the Silver Medal of the City of Paris (1967), the Roger Adams Award of the American Chemical Society (1973), and the Karl Ziegler Prize of the Society of German Chemists (1975).

Scientific Career

Georg Wittig's early research focused on theory and mechanisms—that is, the way in which reactions occur. He was interested in the highly unstable molecules that often occur during reactions, through which the molecule must pass to become the product, or resulting chemical. In the late 1950's, Wittig was interested in how the chemistry of atoms connected in a ring differed from that of atoms in a open arrangement. In an experiment designed to form a ring compound, Wittig encountered unexpected results. He noted that he could exchange certain atoms (chlorine, bromine, and iodine, collectively known as halogens) for a lithium atom, thus changing the characteristics of the compound. Henry Gilman, working independently in England, noted the same phenomenon. Wittig classified this type of exchange as *Umpolung*, or reversal of polarity. This manipulation of the natural properties of carbon compounds has proved to be of vital importance to chemists developing routes to complex chemicals. This was not, however, the only feature of note with this area of research. When the same reaction was carried out on an aromatic (benzenelike) compound containing a fluorine atom (also a halogen), a different reaction pathway occurred, and the formation of the highly unstable molecule dehydrobenzene was proposed as the initial product. Because of its instability, it reacted further to give different products. The experimental finding was an interesting one, as the molecule had been predicted theoretically but had not been observed experimentally.

The carbon atoms that made up this molecule were linked in a way that is not seen in natural chemicals and therefore was important to chemists' understanding of bonding. The existence of this intriguing molecule was proved by a "trapping" experiment. The dehydrobenzene was produced, and it reacted immediately with another compound, giving a product which could be explained only by the existence, however fleeting, of dehydrobenzene. This molecule was independently formed by the American chemist John Roberts at the California Institute of Technology. He named the molecule benzyne. Despite the unstable nature of the dehydrobenzene, Wittig was able to study its chemistry and succeeded in measuring its lifetime, which was found to be 0.02 second. That is, under the conditions used for this measurement, dehydrobenzene is produced and within 0.02 second reacts to give another product.

In the 1940's, an unexpected reaction and the systematic investigation of the chemistry involved gave Wittig the reaction which now bears his name, the contribution for which he is most famous. In the quest to produce compounds with five atoms attached to a phosphorus atom, Wittig undertook an experiment that was expected to give the required phosphorus compound. In terms of the intended reaction, the experiment failed. The product was not the expected one but a new class of compounds that Wittig named ylides. These new chemicals reacted with carbonyl compounds, readily available organic compounds. To Wittig's astonishment, a product was formed that contained no phosphorus and that linked the two constituent molecules via a double bond, a means of joining two carbon atoms that is often seen in naturally occurring compounds. In addition, the link was formed in a predictable manner. Methods to produce double bonds prior to this work often gave unexpected products or a mixture of more than one compound. This methodology has considerable importance in the synthesis of naturally occurring molecules.

The Wittig reaction indicates the degree to which important discoveries hinge on the recognition of the significance of unexpected experimental results. The first phosphorus ylide was described by Hermann Staudinger in 1919, and although he conceived the possibility of use of the ylide to form double bonds, as in the Wittig reaction, much of his work was published only in thesis form and was not widely known. Wittig and Staudinger served on the same faculty for a time; when Wittig moved to Freiburg in 1937, Staudinger was the Institute Director. By this time, however, Staudinger had ceased work on phosphorus compounds and was actively engaged in a different field of study—for which he won a Nobel Prize in 1953.

In 1944, Wittig moved to Tübingen as Institute Director. It was there that the Wittig reaction was discovered. In 1956, Wittig moved to Heidelberg, where most of the developmental work on the reaction was completed. During this period, the reaction was extended to cover a range of different compounds. Industrial application of the reaction was achieved with BASF. Wittig was a consultant for this large company when the transformation was used in an industrial-scale preparation of vitamin A. A number of other eminent scientists became involved in studies of this reaction and its variants, to a degree that, years after the original work, the reaction may be applied to a host of different materials, producing a wide range of different compounds with double bonds. Much is also known about the way the reaction proceeds and how this pathway may be manipulated to change the outcome.

Another area of interest to Wittig, which was initiated as a theoretical study but which resulted in practical applications, was a study of compounds containing boron. In fact, the result of the research was a commercial product useful to the chemical industry. It was found that a particular boron compound had an unexpected reaction with sodium ions (positively charged sodium atoms). This reaction was so predictable and complete that it could be used to measure how many sodium ions are present in a mixture. This was also found to be true for a number of other, similar ions. The boron compound used in this reaction is now marketed under the trade name Kalignost and is used widely for determination of these ions. This work was completed in 1949; in 1974, Wittig noted that the original project to study the boron compounds had been sidetracked by its practical application and had not yet been reexamined.

When Wittig retired in 1967, he entered his "idyllic" time when he devoted himself entirely to research. This period was very productive. In the ten years after he retired, Wittig was the author of more than fifty publications. One of the major research areas during this time was the result of another chance observation. When nitrogen-containing compounds were reacted with a common class of molecules, followed by reaction with acid, a transformation occurred which, although known, had an unexpected pathway. The reaction, known as an aldol reaction, had given only one product. Previously, problems had arisen using this reaction, as it gave a number of possible products. Wittig's methodology gave only one product, and the transformation was classified as a directed aldol reaction. This modification of a known reaction allowed more flexibility in its use, as the result was predictable and yielded only one compound.

Another avenue pursued during the late 1960's and into the 1970's was the synthesis of three-dimensional compounds. Using methodology developed in the 1940's, Wittig was able to prepare one of the first propellanes. This is a molecule made up of several rings of atoms, arranged with three "arms" that resemble an airplane propeller (hence the name). Wittig and coworkers were obviously pleased with the preparation of this interesting molecule. In describing the molecule, Wittig noted that "the mere appearance causes, I think, a certain feeling of well being." Although chance findings are exciting, Wittig commented that a successful research project such as the propellane synthesis, "dictated by intention," gives considerable satisfaction.

In the 1960's, Wittig's research interests emphasized molecules that, because of their structures, were under some strain. This resulted in their unusually high willingness to react with other chemicals. This line of research continued into Wittig's retirement. One of the developments of this period was molecules containing zinc, which under appropriate conditions formed rings containing three atoms. Wittig's research interests encompass all areas of organic chemistry, and the industrial applications of his work reach many other fields. He is responsible for the development of a number of important technical terms, necessitated by his pioneering work in so many areas. Additions to the chemical vocabulary such as *Umpolung*, "valence tautomerism," "ylide," "halogen-metal exchange," and "dehydrobenzene" are now taken for granted and used without reference to the original work.

One of Wittig's greatest interests, mentioned in his Nobel address, is fine arts. The son of a professor of fine arts, Wittig was well known for his mastery of the piano, and former students often mention his love of music. Indeed, his interest in chemistry and music are well illustrated in his 1964 publication "Variations on a Theme by Staudinger," in which he acknowledges early work in the area of phosphorus chemistry leading up to the discovery of the Wittig reaction. Parallels are drawn between this field and music; Wittig discusses themes and influences in the work of Joseph Haydn, Johannes Brahms, Richard Wagner, Niccolò Paganini, and others.

Wittig's work illustrates very clearly that scientists must always be alert for the unexpected: His most significant contributions were the result of unexpected results and the subsequent investigation and explanation of them. It is most heartening to experimental chemists to know that the annoying failure of their experiment may hold the potential to be a Nobel Prize-winning discovery.

Bibliography

Primary

CHEMISTRY: "Exchange of Aliphatically Bound Bromine for Lithium by Phenyllithium," *Chemische Berichte*, vol. 72B, 1939; "Mode of Reaction of Halogen Containing Hydrocarbons," *Naturwissenschaften*, vol. 130, 1942 (with H. Witts); "Metal Organic Complex Compounds," *Justus Liebigs Annalen der Chemie*, vol. 563, 1949 (with G. Keicher, A. Ruckert, and P. Raff); "Reactions of Pentaphenylphosphorus and Derivatives," *Justus Liebigs Annalen der Chemie*, vol. 580, 1953 (with G. Geissler); "Use of Triphenylphosphinemethylene to Prepare Olefins," *Chemische Berichte*, vol. 57, 1954 (with Ulrich Schöllkopf); "Variations on a Theme by Staudinger," *Pure and Applied Chemistry*, 1964; "Propellanes of the Dihydrobenzo[g,p]chrysene System," *Justus Liebigs Annalen der Chemie*, vol. 749, 1971 (with U. Pockets and H. Dröge); "Old and New in the Field of Directed Aldol Condensations," *Topics in Current Chemistry*, vol. 67, 1976; "From Diyls to Ylides to My Idyll," *Science*, vol. 110, 1980.

Secondary

"Science and the Citizen: The Nobel Prizes." *Scientific American*, December, 1979:

84. A general discussion of the prizes awarded in 1979 in science. The article includes a brief discussion of Wittig's contributions.

Shaw, Robert. "Georg Wittig: Virtuoso of Chemical Synthesis." *Nature* 282 (1979): 231. This is a brief discussion of Wittig's work, written using technical terms. Despite this, however, the general reader will find the personal insights into both Wittig and his wife Waltraut interesting. The author knows Wittig personally and obviously has great affection for him.

"Two Organic Chemists Share Nobel Prize." *Chemical and Engineering News*, October 22, 1979: 6. A brief report of the award-winning research of the corecipients Wittig and Brown written for chemists. Includes a number of direct quotes from the chemists.

Vedejs, E. "Wittig: Fortune Favors the Prepared Mind." *Science* 207 (1980): 42. Appearing just after the Nobel Prize was awarded, this article describes Wittig's work in technical detail, but it also includes some interesting historical perspective.

"Wittig Chemistry." In *Topics in Current Chemistry*, vol. 109. Berlin: Springer-Verlag, 1983. This volume was published to honor Wittig on his birthday. It contains chapters written by former students and coworkers covering many of the areas of chemistry which interested Wittig during his career. The discussion is not, however, limited to Wittig's work but brings the reader up to date in that particular field.

Susan J. Mole

1980

Chemistry
Paul Berg, United States
Walter Gilbert, United States
Frederick Sanger, Great Britain

Physics
James W. Cronin, United States
Val L. Fitch, United States

Physiology or Medicine
Baruj Benacerraf, United States
George D. Snell, United States
Jean Dausset, France

Economic Sciences
Lawrence R. Klein, United States

Literature
Czesław Miłosz, United States

Peace
Adolfo Pérez Esquivel, Argentina

PAUL BERG
1980

Born: Brooklyn, New York; June 30, 1926

Nationality: American
Areas of concentration: Microbiology and biochemistry

Berg devised methods for combining genetic material from one species with another, inventing a method of genetic splicing and formulating the first recombinant-DNA molecule. In the process, he developed techniques for analyzing in elaborate detail the chromosomal structure of viral organisms

The Award

Presentation

Bo G. Malmström of the Royal Swedish Academy of Sciences presented the Nobel Prize in Chemistry to Paul Berg on December 10, 1980. In his address, Malmström expressed modern biology's belief that there is no vital force animating organic life forms, but rather that life is a delicate interplay of chemicals on a molecular level, the basic components being nucleic acids and complex proteins. He identified deoxyribonucleic acid (DNA) as the necessary material in the chromosomes that controls the biochemical ingredients of life, particularly the formation of enzymes. Paul Berg's role in the continuing development in understanding how DNA's chemical structure relates to the biological function of this genetic material was as the first biochemist to construct a molecule using parts of genes from different, totally unrelated species, such as humans and bacteria. Such recombinant-DNA molecules have enormously important potential for modern society, particularly in the production of human hormones via bacterial assistance, a method revolutionizing the medical treatment of numerous diseases. In addition, Berg's work, notably his development of analytic techniques, makes possible the detailed delineation of chromosomal structures in viruses, a step that, combined with the technique for determining the exact sequence of nucleotides in DNA, Malmström believed, may become of great significance to the understanding of the nature of cancer as a malfunction of genetics.

Nobel lecture

Berg's December 8, 1980, Nobel lecture was entitled "Dissections and Reconstructions of Genes and Chromosomes." He began by acknowledging the work of numerous students and colleagues; his research assistants, Marianne Dieckmann and June Hoshi; and his Stanford University associates, particularly Arthur Kornberg and Charles Yanofsky. Berg mentioned dramatic early developments, principally G. W. Beadle and E. L. Tatum's evidence for genes controlling the production of protein; O. T. Avery, A. D. Hershey, and M. J. Chase's work, showing that genes are found in the chain structure of DNA; and James Watson and Francis

Crick's solution of the molecular structure of DNA itself.

Berg began in the late 1960's to study tumor virus systems as a key to understanding mammalian genetic chemistry. At Stanford, he began work on the SV40 virus, discovering its physical and genetic organization by the use of restrictive endonucleases. By the 1970's, he had determined the viral genetic map, even to the presence of the specific nucleotide sequence in the genes, and revealed how the SV40 genes function on the DNA of host organisms during the virus' life cycle. The deliberate use of such organisms led to the development of recombinant-DNA research and the ability to locate recombinant genes into suitable animal cells. Berg and his coworkers devised a procedure to synthesize active nucleotide terminals on the ends of DNA molecules, allowing for DNA to be recombined in vitro.

In the mid-1970's, Berg and Janet Mertz developed the procedure for propagating SV40 deletion mutants using SV40 temperature-sensitive mutants as helpers. In the process, he devised a new group of transducing vectors usable to introduce new genetic information into a variety of types of mammalian cells. Three marker sequences of DNA were formulated, including Ecogpt, a sequence codifying for DHFR (dihydrofolate reductase), and a bacterial plasmid gene, neo[R], specifying an aminoglycoside phosphotransferase. Berg also summarized recent findings with Ecogpt as the marker gene, including R. C. Mulligan's work on isolating the Ecogpt gene itself. Work with human Lesch-Nyhan cells, lacking an enzyme for cellular HGPRT, showed that genetic material derived from *Escherichia coli* could be used to rectify defects caused by the absence of specific enzymes in a cell's makeup. Similar work was also performed on purine nucleotides.

Berg ended by offering his views on recombinant DNA and molecular cloning and their future roles in medicine, such as the removal of crippling genetic defects. He specified the problems with the approach, including the need for more knowledge of human genetic organization, formation, and regulation. The need to confront ethical questions was also raised, but he concluded that the study of recombinant DNA is a field that, despite perhaps tampering with the nature of life itself, should not be ignored but explored, not only to aid humanity but also to provide information on the nature of the universe itself.

Critical reception

The recognition of Paul Berg as the recipient of the Nobel Prize in Chemistry, although noted generally with approval both in the United States and in foreign presses, was not greeted totally without comment. Some disapproved of the Swedish Academy of Sciences' again awarding the prize in chemistry for studies more suited to the realm of molecular biology (*New Scientist*, October 23, 1980) than specifically to the field of chemistry. The larger outpouring of sentiment, however, was in agreement with awarding the prize for Berg's fundamental studies of the biochemistry of nucleic acids, with particular regard to recombinant DNA. Berg was noted for pioneering gene splicing, for transplanting DNA from one organism to another, formulating essentially a molecular gene-copying machine capable of producing such valuable commodities as insulin and interferon (*Newsweek*, October 27, 1980). His work, in essence, made possible the birth of an entirely new industry, one of genetic engineering (*Chemical and Engineering News*, October 20, 1980).

Much was made of the "Berg letter," which, in the early 1970's, asked scientists to suspend different types of genetic research voluntarily. Berg's idea had been to isolate the gene from one organism, the monkey animal virus SV40, which causes tumorous growths in the cells of animals, and transfer it into a totally different organism, allowing him to investigate the gene's workings in isolation from all the other genes of the original organism. Using a bacteriophage and *Escherichia coli*, he was able to recombine DNA from different species by ingenious use of enzymes that can cut, patch, and join nucleic acids. That was the first time that scientists were able to link genes from two different species, creating the prospect of producing entirely new life forms. Berg began to be extremely apprehensive, however, when he realized the vistas of genetic engineering that he had opened up, and he wondered whether recombinant-DNA research could result in modified creatures escaping into environmental situations and becoming detrimental to humans or other organisms on the planet. Consequently, in 1971, he did not execute the last step of his experiment out of concern for the biohazard he saw. Only later, after a conference that he called (1975) to deal with the possible hazards, did he change his initial concerns and do the experiments (*Time*, October 27, 1980). Berg helped draw up the federal guidelines for such types of research, guides making the control of recombinant DNA much more realistic and ensuring that no new genetic "constructs" would be released on the world.

Biography

Paul Berg was born on June 30, 1926, in Brooklyn, New York, to Harry and Sarah (née Brodsky) Berg. He was reared there with his two brothers, Jack and Irving. Paul attended public grade schools and was graduated from the Abraham Lincoln High School in 1943. He credits a Mrs. Wolf, the stockroom clerk at Lincoln High, with inspiring him to enter scientific research. In 1943, he decided on attending Pennsylvania State University, because it had a microbiology department; he was graduated in 1948 with a bachelor's degree in biochemistry. His studies were interrupted by his serving in the U.S. Navy from 1944 to 1946. He was married to Mildred Levy on September 13, 1947. They would have one son, John Alexander, born September 30, 1958.

Berg went to Western Reserve University to do graduate studies in biochemistry, receiving his doctorate degree in 1952. As an American Cancer Society Research Fellow, he went to do postdoctoral training with Herman Kalckar at the Institute of Cytophysiology in Copenhagen, Denmark, working there from 1952 to 1953, and then with Arthur Kornberg at Washington University in St. Louis, Missouri, from 1953 to 1954. He continued work there as a Scholar in Cancer Research from 1954 to 1957.

He became an assistant professor of microbiology at Washington University School of Medicine in 1955, teaching and doing research there until 1959. He then moved to the Stanford University School of Medicine, starting as an associate professor and working to full professor. In 1970, he was named the Willson Professor of Biochemistry. He was chairman of the Department of Biochemistry from 1969 to 1974, and he was appointed a nonresident Fellow of the Salk Institute in 1973, a continuing position.

Scientific Career

As a result of his fundamental biochemical and microbiological training in college, Paul Berg's early research work, principally along biochemical lines, dealt with the basic molecular mechanisms involved with intracellular protein synthesis, an interest arising from his knowledge of the importance of proteins and enzymes in the body. In early 1955, Francis Crick, who shared the 1962 Nobel Prize in Physiology or Medicine for his own work on DNA structure, had proposed an adaptor hypothesis in which amino acids, the basic constituents of proteins, were shown not to interact with the RNA (ribonucleic acid) template directly but instead were fastened together by an adaptor, or joiner, molecule. Not knowing of this theory, Berg set up his own experiments and was able, in 1956, to delineate such a molecule that was specific to the amino acid methionine, the adaptor molecule now known as a transfer-RNA molecule. Such studies led him to become extremely interested in elucidating the structure of genes in organisms and in the possibility of blending characteristics from two or more species in order to study the functioning of individual genetic units.

Immediately after finding the adaptor molecule, Berg began the research for which he would obtain the Nobel Prize in Chemistry in 1980. Understanding how genes were strung on the DNA molecule, he decided to attempt to isolate a single gene from one organism, then transfer it to an entirely different creature, thus allowing him to study the actions of one gene isolated from other genetic interactions of the contributing organism. It had already been established that the hereditary information of a DNA molecule was not embedded in the phosphate or sugar groups, but rather in the order in which four bases—adenine (A), thymine (T), cytosine (C), and guanine (G)—were arranged, with paired bases, A to T and C to G, being hooked on the spiral staircase of the DNA molecule on adjacent arms. A particular code of three bases, taken in order of appearance, acted as an instruction code for the cell, causing the insertion of a specific amino acid into the chain during protein formation. This model apparently works for all life on earth, using the same bases, with the same base sequence relating to the identical amino acid characterization. At the same time that he was working on this protein synthesis problem, Berg was also interested in trying to understand why normal cells in living tissue would turn cancerous, apparently without any ouside influence. Early in his research, he decided that these two problems could be approached in a similar manner.

To work concurrently on isolating a gene and dealing with cancerous cells, which he hypothesized were caused by genetic interaction with the cellular machinery, Berg planned to insert a monkey virus, called SV40, which was known to cause tumors in other animals and in laboratory cultures and human cells, into the common intestinal bacterium *Escherichia coli*. Determining that it was impossible to insert such material directly, he believed that it was possible to use an intermediary tool, called a bacteriophage, a minute virus that attacks bacteria. When the virus finds a possible host bacterium, it injects its own DNA into the cell, where the viral material takes over all the cell's machinery commands by an as-yet-unknown means, but one that involves the virus inserting its own genetic material into the genetic sequence of the bacterium.

Berg proceeded by cutting the donor DNA into small pieces, reacting these parts with a single type of base at a time, and an enzyme called terminal transferase. The enzyme acted to add one base at a time to the clipped end of the DNA molecule. Simultaneously, in another test tube, he did the same to the phage DNA, only adding a complimentary base to the molecule using the same enzyme transferase. Since the two bases were complementary (A-T, C-G), the sticky ends had a tendency to stick together to make a new molecule, one using sections of both the donor and the bacteriophage organisms. The reconstructed phage then injected the recombinant DNA into the *E. coli* when the virus gained admittance into the cell. This method effectively isolated the gene from the donor organism, forming a single closed loop in the *E. coli*. It was the first time that anyone was able to link together genes from two separate species, making the possibility of new life forms feasible.

Before he reached the final steps of the experiment, inserting the new DNA into the bacterium, Berg became aware of the potential danger of implanting a mammalian tumor gene into the ubiquitous *E. coli*, perhaps even creating a new, highly virulent pathogenic microorganism by accident, one detrimental to some species, such as humans. It was this concern that led Berg and several colleagues to draft what became known as the "Berg letter." Yet, after the new safeguards he imposed, and new techniques, in 1971 Berg and his Stanford colleagues David Jackson and Robert Symons succeeded in splicing the five-gene DNA molecule of the mammalian tumor virus SV40 into a DNA loop controlling bacterial genes from *E. coli* and viral genes from bacteriophage lambda. The important paper was published as "A Biochemical Method for Inserting New Genetic Information into SV40 DNA: Circular SV40 DNA Molecules Containing Lambda Phage Genes and the Galactose Operon of *E. coli*." This epoch-making work detailed the fulfillment of the dream of combining the basic material of two separate species into one in such a fashion that the inherent genes and the derived ones still continued to function.

Paul Berg's name became well known both to the scientific community and to the general public as a result of his work and the letter explaining his concerns with possible ramifications of recombinant-DNA research. Much coverage of the issue was given by the press when the letter was published in *Science* (July 24, 1974), in which he outlined clearly the possible dangers inherent in allowing uncontrolled practice of recombinant-DNA experiments without any form of suitable safeguards. For example, if the *E. coli* impregnated with SV40, capable of causing cancerous tumors, were able to escape into the wild and reproduce, existing in rivers and streams, it could perhaps cause a worldwide problem in a very brief period of time, since *E. coli* is found conceivably in all the world's freshwater drinking supply. Consequently, from his study, Berg proposed an absolutely voluntary moratorium on certain types of experiments, and strong controls on a wide range of a number of other types of studies using "created" animals. Two years later, when new and improved techniques made such gene implantations relatively easy to carry out, Berg argued for a temporary moratorium and a conference to formulate safety guidelines for renewed recombinant-DNA research.

As a result of his activities, an international conference was held in Asilomar, California, with a hundred scientists from sixteen countries attending. Following the conference, the National Institutes of Health published, in 1976, a strict set of guidelines to restrict genetic engineering research. That such agreement could be reached and maintained was primarily a result of the integrity and authority of Paul Berg. In that view, it became perhaps ironic that Berg was awarded the Nobel Prize in Chemistry in 1980 for the huge part that he played in developing the splicing techniques that made recombinant DNA possible. Among his later research, after the conference, Berg also studied how viral and cellular genes interact to regulate growth and reproduction. This is being carried along in investigations of the machinery of gene expression in higher organisms, the next interest in his scientific life.

Paul Berg has been awarded many honors and prizes, including the Eli Lilly Prize in Biochemistry (1959), California Scientist of the Year (1963), election to the U.S. National Academy of Sciences and American Academy of Sciences (1966), Distinguished Alumnus Award from Pennsylvania State University (1972), V. D. Mattia Award of the Roche Institute for Molecular Biology (1974), presidency of the American Society of Biological Chemists (1975), honorary D.Sc. from Yale University and the University of Rochester (1978), membership in the Japan Biochemical Society (1978), Sarasota Medical Award (1979), Gairdner Foundation Annual Award (1980), Albert Lasker Medical Research Award (1980), and the New York Academy of Sciences Award (1980).

Throughout his career, Berg liked to work on the edge of biochemical knowledge, combining his expertise in chemistry, molecular biology, and microbiology into investigations of the fundamental features of life. By pushing the frontiers of molecular science, he has become known as the "father of recombinant DNA," allowing other scientists to perceive more clearly the nature of the unseen living world.

Bibliography

Primary

CHEMISTRY: "A Biochemical Method for Inserting New Genetic Information into

SV40 DNA: Circular SV40 DNA Molecules Containing Lambda Phage Genes and the Galactose Operon of *E. coli*," *Proceedings of the National Academy of Sciences*, vol. 69, 1972; "Physical and Genetic Characterization of Deletion Mutants of Simian Virus 40 Constructed In Vitro," *Journal of Virology*, vol. 24, 1977.

Secondary

Bainbridge, B. *Genetics of Microbes*. New York: John Wiley & Sons, 1980. This reference provides a basic description of genetics on the microbe level. The means of formulating gene maps and translating genetic codes are presented. The formation of recombinant DNA for bacteria, fungi, and bacteriophages such as Berg used are described, along with a study of genetic manipulation. Extensive references, diagrams.

Chakrabarty, A., ed. *Genetic Engineering*. Boca Raton, Fla.: CRC Press, 1979. This is a collection of articles detailing the various current methods of genetic manipulation, including the formation of recombinant DNAs. Details Berg's use of lambda bacteriophages, plasmids as cloning vectors. Shows the applications of genetic work, including various social issues. Easy to understand.

Glover, D. *Gene Cloning: The Mechanisms of DNA Manipulation*. New York: Chapman & Hall, 1984. This work shows the principles and strategies associated with genetic experiments. Among the topics covered are recombinant DNA, in vitro experiments, use of phage lambda, and vectors for *E. coli* experiments. Cloning is illustrated in fungi, plants, and animals, with viruses such as SV40. Extensive references, drawings. Well written.

Grell, R., ed. *Mechanisms in Recombination*. New York: Plenum, 1974. This work represents a conference on methods for doing recombinant-DNA studies. Research reported includes phage lambda studies and genetic manipulation of fungi and higher eucaryotics. Models of recombinant-DNA action are presented. Extensive references, difficult reading.

Howard, T. *Who Should Play God?* New York: Delacorte Press, 1977. This is a critique of the biological revolution of the late twentieth century, including genetic developments. It covers recombinant DNA, elimination of "bad" genes, and possible biofutures. Takes a decidedly negative slant on approaches of medicine healing using genetic constructs. Easy reading, providing one viewpoint of the genetic debate.

Mertens, T. *Human Genetics: Readings on the Implications of Genetic Engineering*. New York: John Wiley & Sons, 1975. This is a collection of readings dealing with all aspects of human genetics, from chromosomes to genetic engineering techniques and gene therapy. Covers ethics, genetic counseling, Berg's problem of temporary moratorium of research. Numerous references, fairly easy reading.

Old, R. *Principles of Gene Manipulation*. Berkeley: University of California Press, 1980. This work provides the basic methods of doing genetic recombinations, including cutting and joining of materials, use of plasmids and bacteriophages, various cloning strategies, and implantation methods. Extensive recombinant-

DNA section. Good diagrams, detailed reading.

Wade, N. *The Ultimate Experiment*. New York: Walker, 1977. This very readable work deals with the problems of genetic recombination. Starting with the methods of gene splicing, it discusses the moratorium proposed by Berg, and the Asilomar conference. Good overview of the original work done by Berg and the controversies associated with recombinant-DNA experiments.

Watson, J. *Recombinant DNA*. New York: W. H. Freeman, 1983. This work deals exclusively with genetic manipulation, from the role of genes and the genetic code to the creation of new DNA materials. Covers mutagenesis in organisms as Berg did it, tumor viruses such as SV40. Provides a good DNA research dataline of history, with pictures of contributors. Well written.

Arthur L. Alt

1980

Chemistry
Paul Berg, United States
Walter Gilbert, United States
Frederick Sanger, Great Britain

Physics
James W. Cronin, United States
Val L. Fitch, United States

Physiology or Medicine
Baruj Benacerraf, United States
George D. Snell, United States
Jean Dausset, France

Economic Sciences
Lawrence R. Klein, United States

Literature
Czesław Miłosz, United States

Peace
Adolfo Pérez Esquivel, Argentina

WALTER GILBERT
1980

Born: Boston, Massachusetts; March 21, 1932

Nationality: American
Areas of concentration: Biophysics and molecular biology

Gilbert analyzed how cells construct deoxyribonucleic acid (DNA) molecules and store their genetic messages. His work on determining the precise sequencing of nucleotides that form DNA has been of great importance in biology and medicine

The Award

Presentation
Professor Bo G. Malmström of the Royal Swedish Academy of Sciences presented the 1980 Nobel Prize in Chemistry to Walter Gilbert, Frederick Sanger, and Paul Berg. In his address, given on December 10, 1980, Malmström reflected upon the intimate relationship between biochemistry and medical progress in the twentieth century, claiming that not only for the sake of intellectual curiosity do scientists try to reach a description of life processes in chemical, molecular terms.

Pointing out that the machinery of life is made possible by the unique interplay of nucleic acids and proteins in the form of enzymes, Malmström identified the DNA molecule, which determines the enzymes that a cell manufactures, as a basic mechanism that scientists must understand. Malmström therefore praised Walter Gilbert for developing methods to determine the precise sequencing of the nucleotides that form DNA and for his separate research into those elements of DNA in bacterial chromosomes that control the transcription of the genetic message in the cell.

Malmström mentioned the early fears concerning DNA research, especially the production of recombinant-DNA molecules, those which combine parts of DNA from different species—for example, genes from a human being with part of a bacterial chromosome. Researchers had warned of dangers with the new techniques, sparking public worry that scientists might unleash destructive hybrid chromosomes. Malmström insisted that further research has allayed such fears and that discoveries about how DNA operates, such as Gilbert's, enrich understanding of the basic machinery of the cell and also have significant technical applications, such as the production of human hormones with the aid of bacteria—all to the benefit of humankind.

Nobel lecture
On December 8, 1980, Gilbert presented his Nobel lecture, "DNA Sequencing and Gene Structure," in which he summarized the history and the purpose of his

research in molecular biology. All of it had centered upon two problems: how an organism translates its genetic information into metabolic action and how it controls the process of genetic communication.

Gilbert began by emphasizing that DNA, present in the nucleus of each cell of an organism, stores the information that ultimately delineates every part of the entire organism. This information lies encoded in patterns of linked nucleic acids, the genes. The actual coding in a gene involves small molecular building blocks, called bases, bound in pairs of various combinations along the double-stranded, helical DNA molecule. The order of the bases, through transcription to ribonucleic acid (RNA) and subsequent translation to proteins, determines the productions of proteins, combinations of amino acids that perform most metabolic work. Knowing the sequence of bases—that is, the genetic instructions—allows determination of which protein a gene will produce and, therefore, its function. Unfortunately, Gilbert said, scientists did not yet know how to interpret genetic instructions and so were like children who know the alphabet but are unable to sound out more than a few written words. The task was to learn the vocabulary.

During the late 1960's, research in the genetic control of lactose (milk sugar) digestion in bacteria taught Gilbert how to separate clusters of genes from DNA at predictable points. By the early 1970's, he and Allan Maxam had used what they had learned to read short clusters of bases as part of research into the ribonucleic (RNA) polymerase enzymes that control the transcription of genetic information in DNA. In 1975, Soviet scientist Andrei Mirzabekov had given Gilbert an idea that promised further accuracy in sequencing methods, using chemical reagents to break the DNA at the junctions of two of the four bases. It remained only to find a complementary procedure for breaking the junctions between the remaining two bases. This Gilbert and Maxam did, so that, after further refinements in techniques, they and their graduate student assistants were able to identify the sequence of increasingly large strings of base pairs.

They first used the sequencing method on bacterial DNA and found no ambiguity in the patterns of bases of genes; identical transcription occurred every time. Yet, the greater an organism's complexity, the greater was the potentiality for subtle alteration in genetic patterns and consequent ambiguity in how RNA transcribes the genetic code. In large mammals such as humans, the ambiguities could lead to small mutations in genes and the production of novel protein forms, an evolutionary process not perceived before. Gilbert commented wryly that, just as rapid sequencing methods and genetic cloning (the artificial replication of DNA) were promising a means to spell out the structure of any gene, Nature revealed greater complexity than anyone had imagined, and the critical mechanism of control in multicelled organisms remained elusive.

To this end, Gilbert looked forward to further research. His remarks placed him in the mainstream of contemporary molecular biologists, who assume that reading the "library" of information genetically encoded in DNA not only will provide hitherto unimaginable practical applications of biology but also will lead to understanding the most basic underlying structure of life itself, the sort of fundamental problem for which scientific research exists.

Gilbert concluded by thanking his assistants and teachers, especially James D. Watson, codiscoverer of the double helical structure of DNA.

Critical reception

Walter Gilbert's investigations into the structure of DNA won for him high praise in the press because it furthered a methodological revolution in the study of genes, but, for the most part, the commentators were more interested in the importance of such research to the infant genetic engineering industry—or "recombinant-DNA technology"—that was beginning to promise major breakthroughs in medicine. Gilbert had helped develop the industry as a founder and part owner of the Swiss company Biogen, and the company's announcement that it had won the race to be the first producer of human interferon with recombinant DNA was made only eight months before he received the Nobel Prize. This success fresh in their memories, commentators dwelled on Gilbert's role in it.

At a news conference held shortly after the Nobel Committee's announcement, Gilbert said that he viewed the prize as a tribute to the practical consequences of basic research, and *Science News* and *The New York Times* agreed, enthusiastically mentioning interferon production as especially valuable. Medical researchers were hoping that interferon would provide a powerful weapon against a wide variety of viral diseases and cancers. A spate of subsequent research lowered the high expectations, but at the time it looked as if inscrutable diseases could finally be cured.

Gilbert, however, also considered research such as his to touch upon fundamental, purely scientific issues. "DNA sequences are the basic, underlying structures [of molecular biology]. There is nothing more primitive. Your questions are ultimately answered there," he has stated. This interest in basic research had led him into a great variety of projects in the twenty years before he won the prize and earned for him renown as a scientist, a fact recognized by Gina Bari Kolata in her article on the 1980 laureates for *Science*.

Calling Gilbert much more flamboyant than Frederick Sanger, with whom Gilbert shared half the prize for an independently developed method of DNA sequencing, Kolata also contrasted their methods and results. Sanger had set out single-mindedly to sequence DNA, but Gilbert came to it indirectly, as a consequence of experiments in other aspects of molecular biology. Sanger built DNA segments by synthesizing them with enzyme reactions, and Gilbert produced segments by breaking up native DNA at specific base sequences. Other scientists quickly adopted both methods. Use of one or the other depends in part upon the length of DNA to be analyzed and in part upon individual preferences. For shorter sequences, the two methods require about the same amount of time to perform, but the Gilbert-Maxam method has the advantage of a thoroughly established protocol, so those who use it are likely to be successful.

As *The New York Times* noted, Gilbert's award extended the long series of awards that the Nobel Committee had presented to recognize the crucial contributions by researchers in the chemistry of genetics. Reporter Harold M. Schmeck, Jr., remarked that work such as Gilbert's made it possible to modify genes almost at will and to reproduce them in large quantity; Pearce Wright, science editor for *The Times* of London, credited such work with laying the foundation for genetic engineering. Others were more restrained. Kolata, for example, concluded by observing that the full implications of recombinant-DNA technology and DNA sequencing were unclear, even though the techniques were expanding the biologist's perception of what can be learned through genetics.

Biography

On March 21, 1932, Walter Gilbert was born in the center of American academia, Boston, Massachusetts, and, apart from a long interruption during his boyhood, he has stayed there. His father, Richard V. Gilbert, a leading Keynesian economist at Harvard University, worked for the Office of Price Administration during World War II and afterward became an adviser to the Pakistani government. Emma Cohen Gilbert, Walter's mother, was a Radcliffe-educated child psychologist, who began her son's education with lessons at home.

In 1939, the family moved from Boston to Washington, D.C., where Gilbert attended public schools and later Sidwell Friends High School. His intense curiosity about science bloomed early, earning for him memberships as a child in adult mineralogical and astronomical societies; fascinated with nuclear physics in high school, he often skipped classes in order to read about nuclear technology at the Library of Congress. He was graduated summa cum laude from Harvard in 1953, with a bachelor's degree in chemistry and physics, the same year in which he and poet Celia Gilbert were married; the couple would have two children. He spent his first year of graduate school at Harvard, studying theoretical physics, which particularly attracted him, and then moved to the University of Cambridge to continue his studies with Abdus Salam (in 1979 a Nobel laureate in physics). Gilbert took his doctorate in mathematics in 1957, but the shift from physics to biology already had subtly begun. He had met James Watson at a party in Cambridge and admired him; when Gilbert and Watson found themselves colleagues at Harvard in 1960, Gilbert teaching physics and Watson, biology, Watson was able to intrigue him with the mysteries of molecular biology. Gilbert was soon helping in Watson's laboratory work. In 1965, Gilbert officially became a tenured biophysicist and later taught biochemistry and molecular biology as well. In 1974, he was named American Cancer Society Professor of Molecular Biology.

Four years later, he was looking beyond academia to the business world as a member of Biogen's board of directors. In 1981, he took a leave of absence from Harvard to become the company's chief executive officer, a position that he held until 1984. He returned to Harvard as Carl M. Loeb University Professor but in 1987 launched a new, controversial venture with Genome Corporation, formed to sequence human DNA and market the information.

Scientific Career

Among other scientists, Walter Gilbert is known not only for his brilliance in theoretical and experimental matters but also for his arrogance and daring. Throughout his career, the big problems of science have attracted him, and if he found it necessary, he willingly flouted the traditions of academic science to solve those problems and apply the results.

In 1965, after Watson had interested him in molecular biology, Gilbert addressed one of the biggest mysteries in the field at that time: How is the cell able to turn off genes periodically so that the genetic instructions for protein production remain latent? François Jacob and Jacques Monod postulated one influential model, involving the presence of unknown repressors. This was a crucial theory, because it could explain why different types of cells specialized in different products even though the complete genetic code is present in every cell—why, for example, the pancreatic cells make insulin but muscle cells do not.

Working with Benno Müller-Hill, Gilbert attacked the problem by analyzing a specific enzyme in a simple one-celled organism, the bacterium *Escherichia coli*. *E. coli* feeds on lactose, but in order to digest it, the organism must manufacture the beta-galactosidase enzyme, which it does only when lactose is present. How does *E. coli* know when to start and stop the process? Gilbert and Müller-Hill found that the enzyme repressor (lac repressor) is a protein that binds to the portion of DNA carrying the code for enzyme production (lac operon) but not to other parts of the DNA, thus stopping enzyme production until the presence of lactose alters the chemical environment and causes the repressor to dislodge.

Gilbert examined the problem of DNA replication in 1968. He developed the "rolling-circle model" (also called the "toilet paper model") for DNA replication, a proposal made independently by Jacob. The model was intended to explain the replication of circular DNA, such as that present in the genome of some viruses. So far, however, researchers have found few data to support the model.

Gilbert's discovery of the lac repressor led—accidentally, he claims—to his search for a method to sequence DNA. In 1975, Andrei Mirzabekov visited him in his Harvard office and urged him to use a new method to analyze how proteins recognize specific segments of DNA. Mirzabekov and his colleagues at the Soviet Academy of Sciences had been investigating how DNA interacts with protein in the presence of the reagent dimethyl sulfate. Upon reacting with dimethyl sulfate, the DNA separates at adenine and guanine bases. Gilbert used dimethyl sulfate on the lac operon in order to break up *E. coli* DNA, and then he bound lac repressor to the operon and repeated the experiment for comparison. The repressor protected the lac operon's adenines and guanines from the chemical cutting, while the remainder of those two bases along the DNA separated. The sequence of the lac operon was already known, and so Gilbert learned exactly where the lac repressor binds on *E. coli* DNA. Next, Gilbert tried the same pair of procedures on another lac operon, one in which the sequence was not known. He and Maxam realized that they had a rudimentary DNA sequencing method when they saw the results. With dimethyl sulfate (and by tailoring reaction conditions), they could break any DNA molecule at guanines and adenines.

Yet, that method solved only half the problem, because along the double strands of DNA, adenine (A) always pairs with thymine (T) and guanine (G) pairs with cytosine (C). There is great variety in the ordering: For example, the enzyme Eco RI recognizes the portion of DNA reading G-A-A-T-T-C on one strand and C-T-T-A-A-G on the other, while another enzyme, Hha I, recognizes G-C-G-C paired to C-G-C-G. It is not enough to identify only the guanines and adenines to determine the sequence of bases; Maxam set out to find an agent that would break off cytosines and thymines. He succeeded with hydrazine, a chemical reduction agent. The success meant that any section of DNA could be divided into its smallest units and the sequence of units could be read first by methylating the guanines and adenines and then by exposing the cytosines and thymines to hydrazine. Gilbert immediately recognized the enormous implications of the sequencing method, and so did the Nobel Committee, which therefore named him a prize recipient.

Even before the 1980 award, Gilbert was exploring ways to exploit the new tool to decipher DNA. In 1978, a group of investors persuaded him (despite his initial skepticism) and a handful of leading molecular biologists to help form the genetic engineering company Biogen. He assumed the leadership of the scientific contingent of the company at once, intending to confine himself to the research operations. He had high expectations that genetic research could produce valuable products, and his faith was vindicated in 1980, when Charles Weissmann successfully made the human antiviral substance alpha interferon by inserting human DNA into bacterial DNA and reproducing the bacteria in a culture. Human cells produce interferon very slowly, and so it is very expensive to extract for use in medical treatment, but bacteria can produce it quickly and much more cheaply. The discovery made Biogen famous overnight. It also supported Gilbert's aggressive and expensive research policies.

Gilbert became increasingly fascinated with and involved in the business side of the company. In 1981, while serving as cochairman of the board of directors, he was promoted to chief executive officer. He took a year's leave of absence from Harvard to assume the expanded duties. When the job lasted beyond the year, Harvard asked him to choose between the university and the company; Gilbert stayed at Biogen. Development and marketing had eclipsed the thrill of pure science.

During the next three years, he directed the company into further research while trying to capitalize on alpha interferon by leasing the rights to the gene-splicing to another company, which fabricated it. The arrangement earned money for Biogen but not enough to offset investments in buildings, equipment, and research. Additionally, Gilbert was not satisfied to develop processes for other companies to apply; he wanted to produce and market pharmaceuticals directly. He banked on yet another variety of interferon, gamma interferon, and the immunological protein interleukin-2 to make the company profitable. Laboratory experiments showed gamma interferon to be more potent in combating cancer, and Biogen began testing it on the virus associated with acquired immunodeficiency syndrome (AIDS). Success in producing and marketing cancer and AIDS therapies could mean $2 billion to $5 billion a year in profits.

Success in these ventures, however, did not come soon enough for Gilbert. An accumulating deficit, rapidly declining stock values, and friction with other Biogen managers led to his resignation in 1984, reportedly under pressure. He remained on the company's board and scientific oversight committee but returned to Harvard.

The biggest of all problems about the genetic code remained to be solved: reading the entire human genome (all the human genetic information), a sequence of approximately 100,000 genes spelled out by three billion bases. Gilbert was convinced that systematic sequencing should begin as soon as possible, and other scientists agreed, because once the entire genetic code (also called the "Book of Man") is known, it will be easier and quicker to find cures for the thousands of inherited diseases. Yet the undertaking was daunting, and, in 1986, when the U.S. government first gathered leading geneticists and molecular biologists for a conference on the "Genome Project," scientists estimated that it would cost $3 billion and take at least fifteen years, requiring sophisticated new DNA-sequencing machines and the most advanced computers available.

After initial support, the government was slow to get the project started. Gilbert grew impatient. In 1987, he surprised the scientific community by quitting a National Academy of Sciences' advisory committee for the Genome Project and announcing that he would start his own company to undertake the massive project independently for profit. Gilbert sought private money for the venture, arguing that when his company unlocked all the genome's information, he could sell it piecemeal for use in genetic research and engineering. Little investment money was forthcoming, however, and Gilbert has had to scale down the project, hoping to cooperate with the government in the sequencing effort and to market information as it becomes available, even before the entire genome is read.

Gilbert's business enterprises have drawn criticism from fellow scientists, who are bothered by an attempt to profit from as fundamental an entity as the human genome and object to patenting genetic research results. Yet Gilbert has forged ahead, insisting that quickly bringing the fruits of research to technology will improve society. The U.S. government also moved ahead, establishing the Office for Genome Research in 1989, with Gilbert's old friend Jim Watson as its director.

Controversial or not, Gilbert's accomplishments have earned for him the highest respect among colleagues and scores of honors, including honorary doctorates from Columbia University, the University of Chicago, and the University of Rochester; memberships in the American Academy of Arts and Sciences and the National Academy of Sciences; a Guggenheim Fellowship; and many scientific awards.

Bibliography

Primary
CHEMISTRY: "Isolation of the *Lac* Repressor," 1966 (with Benno Müller-Hill); "The

Lac Operon Is DNA," 1967 (with Benno Müller-Hill); "The Nucleotide Sequence of the *Lac* Operon," 1973 (with Allan M. Maxam); "Contacts Between the *Lac* Repressor and DNA Revealed by Methylation," 1976 (with Allan M. Maxam and Andrei Mirzabekov); "A New Method for Sequencing DNA," 1977 (with Allan M. Maxam); "Why Genes in Pieces?" 1978; "The Evolution of Genes: The Chicken Preproinsulin Gene," 1980 (with F. Perler, A. Efstratiadis, P. Lomedico, R. Kolodner, and J. Dodgson); "Sequencing End-Labelled DNA with Base-Specific Chemical Cleavages," 1980 (with Allan M. Maxam); "Useful Proteins from Recombinant Bacteria," 1980 (with L. Villa-Komaroff); "Genomic Sequencing," 1984 (with G. M. Church); "Detection In-vivo of Protein-DNA Interactions Within the *Lac* Operon of *Escherichia-coli*," 1985 (with H. Nick); "Genes-in-Pieces Revisited," 1985; "The Genomic Sequencing Technique," 1985 (with G. M. Church); "The Antiquity of Introns," 1986 (with M. Marchionni and G. McKnight); "The RNA World," 1986; "Sequencing the Human Genome," 1987; "Formation of Parallel Four-Stranded Complexes by Guanine-Rich Motifs in DNA and Its Implications for Meiosis," 1988 (with D. Sen).

Secondary

Dulbecco, Renato. *The Design of Life*. New Haven, Conn.: Yale University Press, 1987. This medium-length book offers a detailed account of genetic mechanisms and can be read by nonscientists, who will profit from the many clear illustrations and graphs. It also covers ethical issues and theoretical questions, such as the fundamental nature of life in biological terms. Gilbert is not mentioned, but the work provides a solid background for understanding the innovations of his thought and business enterprises.

Hall, Stephen S. "Biologist in the Boardroom." *Science 85* 6 (January/February, 1985): 42-50. Hall recounts Gilbert's tenure as head of Biogen but includes a biographical sketch enlivened by Gilbert's own reminiscences. Businesslike in approach, the article portrays primarily Gilbert the businessman and his policies toward scientific research.

Jenkins, John B. *Genetics*. 2d ed. Boston: Houghton Mifflin, 1979. A history of genetic theories and research, this college-level text also explains the nature of chromosomes, genes, and the genetic code. Gilbert's "rolling-circle model" of DNA replication is described. The book is readable but technical.

Kanigel, Robert. "The Genome Project." *The New York Times Magazine* 13 (December, 1987): 44. A lucid and complete account of the background, politics, and development of the effort to unlock the secrets of the genome. The article focuses upon Gilbert and his maverick venture to perform the research and market its results through a publicly held company. The author captures the dynamism of Gilbert's personality.

Nossal, G. J. V. *Reshaping Life: Key Issues in Genetic Engineering*. Cambridge, England: Cambridge University Press, 1985. Nossal presents a readable explanation of cell biology for a popular audience and then broadens the discussion to social and philosophical issues affecting recombinant-DNA research. He briefly mentions Gilbert's role in the genetic engineering industry. An excellent book for those coming to genetics for the first time.

Stent, Gunther S., and Richard Calender. *Molecular Genetics: An Introductory Narrative*. San Francisco: W. H. Freeman, 1979. This is a lengthy, college-level textbook, introducing the field thoroughly, and requires some knowledge of chemistry and biology. It puts Gilbert's *E. coli* research and the Gilbert-Maxam method of sequencing in the context of molecular biology and genetics.

Roger Smith

1980

Chemistry
Paul Berg, United States
Walter Gilbert, United States
Frederick Sanger, Great Britain

Physics
James W. Cronin, United States
Val L. Fitch, United States

Physiology or Medicine
Baruj Benacerraf, United States
George D. Snell, United States
Jean Dausset, France

Economic Sciences
Lawrence R. Klein, United States

Literature
Czesław Miłosz, United States

Peace
Adolfo Pérez Esquivel, Argentina

FREDERICK SANGER
1980

Born: Rendcombe, Gloucestershire, England; August 13, 1918

Nationality: British
Area of concentration: Molecular biology

Sanger helped prove that a genetic code determines the construction of proteins in living organisms and pioneered methods for reading that code, which is contained in the deoxyribonucleic acid (DNA) molecules of cell nuclei. His work contributed significantly to the understanding of genetic mechanisms

The Award

Presentation

Frederick Sanger shared half the 1980 Nobel Prize in Chemistry with Walter Gilbert of Harvard University; the remaining half went to Paul Berg of Stanford University. It was Sanger's second Nobel Prize. Professor Bo G. Malmström of the Royal Swedish Academy of Sciences presented the award to the three men on December 10, 1980, emphasizing their contributions in analyzing one of the most complex entities known to science, the human body. Discoveries such as theirs, Malmström pointed out, are critically important to the advancement of medical science, a practical benefit of the intellectual curiosity that inspires biochemists to describe fundamental life processes in chemical, molecular terms.

Specifically, Malmström praised them for methodological innovations that elucidated the relationship between DNA's chemical structure and its biological function. Berg's work lay in building DNA molecules from genetic material of different species, for example from human genes and bacterial genes. Sanger and Gilbert independently devised procedures for identifying the exact sequence of nucleotides, the chemical building blocks of the DNA molecule.

Malmström stressed that their efforts have provided extremely valuable tools for the burgeoning technology of genetic engineering, enabling the manufacture of beneficial proteins, such as interferon and human hormones, by the manipulation of DNA. This "recombinant DNA" technology promises the development of new weapons against such medical problems as cancer and congenital diseases. Dismissing early concerns that genetic engineering might create monsters, Malmström concluded that Sanger, Gilbert, and Berg had advanced man's knowledge of how DNA governs the cell's chemical machinery.

Nobel lecture

Sanger delivered his Nobel lecture, entitled "Determination of Nucleotide Sequences in DNA," on December 8, 1980. In opening, he remarked upon the importance of learning the precise sequence of nucleotides in the DNA molecule and the difficulty in doing so because of the great length and complexity of even the smallest DNA strand. (The shortest, belonging to bacteria-eating viruses, contain about five thousand nucleotides.)

Sanger was particularly well qualified to undertake the monumental task of reading the sequence of nucleotides in DNA because of his earlier work in analyzing the sequence of amino acids in proteins. He embarked upon the "decoding" of DNA via the intermediate project of decoding the simpler ribonucleic acids (RNA), some of which have as few as seventy-five nucleotides. With George G. Brownlee and B. G. Barrell, colleagues at the Medical Research Council Laboratory of Molecular Biology in Cambridge, England, Sanger developed a rapid, small-scale method for breaking the nucleotide chain into small bits and finding the sequence of these bits individually.

Sanger next described his attempts to copy specific regions of DNA molecules, a prelude to the identification of nucleotide sequences. Through the use of cloning, he obtained single-stranded fragments of DNA that could be radioactively labeled, which enabled him to identify the sites of specific nucleotides, and by comparison, the complementary sites on the original DNA that had been the template of the clone. He was able to establish the sequence in the DNA of approximately two hundred nucleotides. By repeating the process along the length of the DNA molecule, he read increasingly longer sequences and then used computer programs to store, overlap, and arrange the data.

He first succeeded in using this copying procedure to sequence the 5,386-nucleotide, single-stranded DNA molecule of a virus. The process unexpectedly revealed the presence of "overlapping genes." Earlier research had led scientists to believe that genes are arrayed in strictly linear order, each gene encoded by a unique region of the DNA. The sequencing showed clearly, however, that some regions of viral DNA code for two genes. Sanger next recounted the sequencing of the small, double-stranded DNA of human and bovine mitochondria, small organelles in the cytoplasm of cells that convert nutrients into usable energy. Again, he discovered the unexpected. There was an apparent difference between mitochondrial genetic coding and that of other biological systems. The difference was surprising, because it was thought that the basic signals of the genetic code were universal.

Sanger concluded with a discussion of protein-coding genes in the special mammalian mitochondrial DNA. He isolated these by first searching the DNA for "reading frames," long stretches of DNA containing no termination markings and thus capable of coding for long polypeptide chains. With polypeptides whose amino acid sequences were known, he identified the genes that coded for them. He reasoned that mitochondria have a simpler, and perhaps more primitive, system of coding.

Critical reception

Sanger's second Nobel Prize in Chemistry was a well-earned tribute to a great scientist, according to newspaper and scientific journal accounts of the presentation.

The New York Times noted that the 1980 award placed Sanger in the company of some of the twentieth century's most illustrious scientists, including Linus Pauling, who won both the chemistry and peace prizes, and Marie Curie, who won in chemistry and physics. Only one person other than Sanger had won twice in the same field: John Bardeen in physics.

Fellow scientists agreed that Sanger's work in sequencing amino acids and DNA was central to the development of molecular biology. In an interview with Horace Freeland Judson in *The Eighth Day of Creation*, Jacques Monod credited Sanger with beginning the present-day understanding of molecular specificity in living processes, proving that a unique genetic code is responsible for the production of amino acids and proteins in the cell, rather than the sort of general chemical law that operates in inorganic processes. Sanger's former student, George Brownlee of the University of Oxford, was quoted by *New Scientist* as saying that Sanger's research always had a catalytic effect on research in other fields, which made it even more important. G. Nigel Godson, chairman of the biochemistry department at the New York University Medical Center, told *The New York Times* that "[Sanger] deserves two Nobel Prizes. He single-handedly engineered two revolutions in biology."

The first revolution came with Sanger's method for identifying the amino acid sequence in proteins, especially his work with insulin (for which he won the 1958 Nobel Prize in Chemistry), but most accounts of the 1980 prize focused on the revolution in genetic engineering that Sanger was instrumental in fostering. Pearse Wright of *The Times* of London saw Sanger's work as laying the foundation for the new microbiological technology, and other writers echoed his view. Because of such pioneering work, wrote Jeremy Cherfas in *New Scientist*, genetic engineering had advanced by "leaps and bounds."

Commentators frequently mentioned the determined but unassuming manner with which Sanger approached his work. Brownlee told *Science*'s Gina Bari Kolata that Sanger never gave himself airs and seemed more like the lab caretaker than its star researcher. Shunning notoriety, Sanger quietly pursued his lifelong work in sequencing, firmly believing that the genetic code could be read by very simple methods. Known to work seven days a week and long hours each day, Sanger was consistently rewarded for his determination. Colleagues praised his research as elegant and efficient because of his painstaking methods. He also received praise for the thorough deliberation of his publications. He typically said little about his work until he felt confident of his ideas, and only then did he publish. According to Godson, Sanger preferred to tackle problems that seemed unsolvable and then show the world how to solve them.

Biography

The younger son of a prosperous country doctor, also named Frederick Sanger, and Cicely Crewson Sanger, Frederick Sanger was born in the village of Rendcombe, Gloucestershire, England, on August 13, 1918. Influenced by both his father and his brother, Theodore, he developed an early interest in biology. By his own account, his performance at Bryanston School and St. John's College, University of Cambridge, was only above average, and he soon gave up plans to follow his father's example in studying medicine. Science, however, held a firm hold on him; instead of medicine, he thought a career in which he could concentrate on a single goal would suit him better. The newly opened biochemistry department at Cambridge offered him the opportunity, and he took it up with enthusiasm, hoping to understand living matter in a way that would give a more scientific basis to solving medical problems.

Sanger took his bachelor's degree in 1939 but remained at Cambridge for advanced work in biochemistry. In 1940, he married Margaret Joan Howe, and they were to have three children—a daughter and two sons. Exempted from military service as a conscientious objector, he spent World War II working on his Ph.D., which he earned in 1943 for his study of the metabolism of the amino acid lysine. Receiving a fellowship a year later, he stayed at Cambridge, investigating the molecular structure of proteins under the guidance of the influential chemist and new chairman of the biochemistry department, Albert C. Chibnall. In 1951, he became a staff member of the Medical Research Council and remained at his Cambridge laboratories in this capacity until he retired in 1983. He continued living in Cambridge with his wife after his retirement. Sanger has said that she contributed more to his work than anyone else, by providing a peaceful, happy home. He has spent his leisure time with his family and in such activities as gardening and sailing.

Scientific Career

Sanger's belief that a knowledge of molecular sequences would be the key to an understanding of living matter provided the theme for his career in scientific research, and for this reason he devoted himself to basic problems during his forty-year tenure in Cambridge laboratories. That his work confirmed his belief has had a profound effect on biology. Under the direction of Chibnall, Sanger began his postgraduate research probing the structure of proteins. They sought to test the hypothesis of Emil Fischer, who in 1902 proposed that proteins are chains of amino acids connected by peptide bonds. Since an amino acid can involve itself in only two such bonds, one at each end of the molecule, the shape of a protein would have to be linear to enable the formation of polypeptides. Most scientists had accepted Fischer's model, but proof was still lacking.

Sanger found the proof by attaching a chemical label (in this case, a colored dye) to one end of a peptide chain in 1945. He learned that the reagent dinitrophenol would combine with the nitrogen terminus amino acid in a stronger chemical bond than the peptide bond, and so a protein could be split at the termini, breaking the peptide bonds. Using chromatography, a process that gauges the absorption rates of different chemicals, Sanger could then identify the individual amino acids.

Sanger used insulin for his research because it could be obtained in pure form, thereby simplifying the experiments. He discovered that it was a polypeptide construction of two nitrogen-terminating amino acid chains of unequal lengths, and in 1949 he devised a way to separate the two chains in order to work on the sequencing of each chain individually. Working with Austrian chemist Hans Tuppy, he divided the longer chain into small sections with enzymes. Examining the various sections, they were able to reconstruct the chain's precise sequence. Repeating the method with the shorter chain took longer because it was more resistant to enzyme action, but Sanger finished in 1953, and by 1955 he had discovered the molecular location of the bond that linked the two chains. He had determined the structure of insulin completely, and it was the first protein to be so analyzed: It verified Fischer's hypothesis of half a century earlier.

The success earned for him the Nobel Prize in Chemistry in 1958, because it was a crucial step toward further development of molecular biology. He demolished the theory held by some chemists that proteins are simply mixtures of similar chemical compounds by showing conclusively that each protein has a unique structure of specific amino acids in a specific sequence. Using Sanger's method of chemically reducing the chains, other scientists were able to identify the structures of other proteins. His enzyme reaction technique became a basic research tool.

At Cambridge, Sanger made friends with Francis Crick, who had discovered the structure of the DNA molecule with James D. Watson, and Crick interested Sanger in genetics. Largely because of his friendship, Sanger turned his attention to the sequencing of the two nucleic acids, DNA and RNA. It was a seemingly impossible task because of their intricate structure. DNA is made up of two chains of complementary nucleotides twisted together along a vertical axis in a double helix formation. Each nucleotide comprises a sugar molecule combined with a phosphate molecule and one of four bases—thymine, cytosine, adenine, and guanine. The structure is often compared to that of a spiral staircase: The sugar and phosphate components provide the frame, and the bases of each nucleotide, paired by hydrogen bonds with the bases of the nucleotide on the parallel chain, form the steps. Adenine joins only with thymine and cytosine only with guanine, a specificity that allowed the sequence to be deduced. Sequences of from ten thousand to one hundred thousand base pairs compose the genes, which, linking together, make up the DNA molecule. Genes contain the codes that eventually create the proteins that the body requires.

RNA provides an intermediate "messenger" service between the genetic code in the cell nucleus' DNA and the cytoplasm, where the proteins are actually built. Free-floating nucleotides become attached to an exposed section of DNA to form the messenger RNA (mRNA) chain, which leaves and goes into structures in the cytoplasm called ribosomes. There, short segments called transfer RNA (tRNA), which carry specific amino acids to the complex, build on the mRNA, then detach and, after collecting further amino acids, return to the mRNA for formation of the protein, which is then freed to perform its metabolic job.

Little was understood of this process when Sanger undertook his investigation of nucleic acids. Robert W. Holley had analyzed the nucleotide sequence of a tRNA by

1965, but his method worked only on their relatively short sequences (fewer than one hundred nucleotides). Sanger wanted to find a more efficient technique that could also be used on mRNA. He developed a small-scale method for splitting ("fractionating") phosphate-labeled oligo-nucleotides. He broke down the large molecules with enzymes, separated the segments, and then determined their sequences, much as he had done with insulin. When he had thus analyzed a sufficient number of the segments, he was able to deduce the sequence of the entire molecule.

The method was too cumbersome, however, to be used with ease on sequences of more than fifty tRNA nucleotides. To improve the process, Sanger followed the lead of other researchers in using procedures to synthesize a complementary copy of the single-stranded RNA chain, and, because the nucleotides of the clone were radioactively labeled, he could read their sequences after they linked together, thus also reflecting the structure of the original RNA.

Sanger next used the cloning procedure on DNA itself. He copied a single-stranded DNA, using DNA polymerase and a single-stranded oligo-nucleotide primer that was complementary to the region of DNA being sequenced and could therefore be hybridized with it. In later experiments, he used the newly discovered restriction enzymes, which could generate fragments more readily. The procedure produced short segments of labeled DNA that could be partially digested. The difficulty lay in finding a way to break the DNA into small enough fragments. Sanger achieved this by incorporating ribonucleotides in place of the deoxy-ribonucleotides in DNA polymerase chains. The ribonucleotide bonds could be broken with alkali at specific points where deoxyribonucleotides would not break, so that residues of specific bases could be gathered and analyzed. The method proved to be laborious, necessitating many fractionations and analyses.

These experiments revealed another way to segment the DNA, this time on the basis of chain length. He separated DNA into single strands and then gathered the strands into four samples. He incubated each sample so that it would begin to reform the double chain of the DNA, and he then stopped the growth at different nucleotides for each sample by replacing the nucleotide in each sample with a related molecule that terminated the chain. In each sample, he obtained rebuilt chains of different lengths that always ended with the same nucleotide. Thus he was able to construct a map of the entire molecule. This ingenious "plus-minus" method was much faster and more accurate than previous methods, and in 1975 Sanger completely sequenced a viral DNA molecule of 5,386 nucleotides.

Sanger continued to search for more efficient sequencing techniques. In the dideoxy method, he treated single-stranded bits of DNA with DNA polymerase in four specifically defined chemical mixtures. In each mixture, he put the strands of DNA to be sequenced, a small DNA primer to initiate a complementary DNA chain, DNA polymerase, and the four triphosphates needed to build the DNA chain. Then, in each tube, he added different nucleotides lacking an essential element for growth and thus terminating the chain. After incubating and stopping the reactions in the four mixtures, he obtained "nested segments," bits of DNA whose terminating nucleotides he knew. These he analyzed with electrophoresis, a process that separates particle mixtures by their differential rates of passage through a liquid in an electric field. The segments were radioactive, so that he could photograph them, and since most of the fragments terminated at the same nucleotide, the photography looked like a picket fence with a line marking the position of each terminating nucleotide. After each sample was analyzed, he had a picture of the synthesized DNA that reflected the original DNA and accomplished the sequencing of the entire molecule.

Meanwhile, Walter Gilbert and Allan Maxam at Harvard University were developing yet another method for rapid sequencing. Whereas Sanger built up a strand of DNA with nested segments, Gilbert and Maxam produced segments by breaking the DNA at specific points with restriction enzymes. For sequencing short segments of DNA, only a few genes long, the Sanger method and the Gilbert-Maxam method work with about equal speed; for longer segments, however, Sanger's method is more efficient. Both have become crucial tools in genetic engineering and in the attempt to map the entire human genome.

Bibliography

Primary

CHEMISTRY: "The Free Amino Groups of Insulin." *Biochemical Journal*, vol. 39, 1945; "The Amino-Acid Sequence in the Glycyl Chain of Insulin: The Identification of Lower Peptides from Partial Hydrolysates," *Biochemical Journal*, vol. 53, 1953 (with E. O. P. Thompson); "Use of DNA Polymerase I Primed by a Synthetic Oligo-Nucleotide to Determine a Nucleotide Sequence in Phage f1 DNA," *Proceedings of the National Academy of Sciences, USA*, vol. 70, 1973 (with J. E. Donelson, A. R. Coulson, H. Kössel, and D. Fischer); "A Rapid Method for Determining Sequences in DNA by Primed Synthesis with DNA Polymerase," *Journal of Molecular Biology*, vol. 94, 1975 (with A. R. Coulson); "The Nucleotide and Amino-Acid Sequences of the N (5') Terminal Region of Gene G of Bacteriophage øX174," *Journal of Molecular Biology*, vol. 96, 1975 (with G. M. Air, E. H. Blackburn, and A. R. Coulson); "Gene F of Bacteriophage øX174. Correlation of Nucleotide Sequences from the DNA and Amino-Acid Sequences from the Gene Product," *Journal of Molecular Biology*, vol. 107, 1976 (with G. M. Air, E. H. Blackburn, A. R. Coulson, F. Galibert, J. W. Sedat, and E. B. Ziff); "Nucleotide and Amino-Acid Sequences of Gene G of øX174," *Journal of Molecular Biology*, vol. 108, 1976 (with G. M. Air and A. R. Coulson); "DNA Sequencing with Chain-Terminating Inhibitors," *Proceedings of the National Academy of Sciences, USA*, vol. 74, 1977 (with S. Nicklen and A. R. Coulson); "Different Patterns of Codon Recognition by Mammalian Mitochondrial tRNAs," *Proceedings of the National Academy of Sciences, USA*, vol. 77, 1980 (with B. G. Barrell, S. Anderson, A. T. Bankier, M. H. L. de Bruijn, E. Chen, A. R. Coulson, et al.); "Cloning in Single-Stranded Bacteriophages as an Aid to Rapid DNA Sequencing," *Journal of Molecular Biology*, vol. 143, 1980 (with A. R. Coulson, B. G. Barrell, A. J. H. Smith, and B. A. Roe); "Sequencing and Organization of the Human Genome," *Nature*, vol. 290, 1981 (with S. Anderson, A. T. Bankier, B. G. Barrell, M. H. L. de Buijn, A. R. Coulson, J. Drouin, I. C. Eperon, et al.); "Determination of Nucleotide Sequences in DNA," *Science*, vol. 214, 1981 (Nobel lecture); "Nucleotide Sequence of Bacteriophage Lambda DNA," *Journal of Molecular Biology*, vol. 162, 1982 (with A. R. Coulson, G. F. Hong, D. F. Hill, and G. B. Petersen).

Secondary

Dulbecco, Renato. *The Design of Life*. New Haven, Conn.: Yale University Press, 1987. Written for the educated general reader, this book explains genetics in detail, with a generous supply of illustrations and graphs to clarify the molecular mechanics. It also addresses ethical and theoretical questions such as the nature of life in biological terms. It is a solid introduction.

Feinberg, Gerald. *Solid Clues: Quantum Physics, Molecular Biology, and the Future of Science*. New York: Simon & Schuster, 1985. Presents a rather speculative account of advanced scientific theory for a popular audience, intending to identify probable developments in basic research and its applications. Fascinating and contentious, the book argues that all scientific disciplines are constellating around the core sciences of physics and biology. Sanger's innovative use of computer programs for the sequencing is discussed. The author provides a thought-provoking overview of molecular biology's role in elucidating basic natural processes.

Judson, Horace Freeland. *The Eighth Day of Creation: Makers of the Revolution in Biology*. New York: Simon & Schuster, 1979. Although now out of date, the book has the virtue of presenting the discovery of DNA's structure and functions in the words of many of the researchers who made the crucial steps. Judson interviewed the scientists for his book, which originally was serialized in *The New Yorker*, and a fair portion of the text is direct quotation. The book captures the excitement and awe that scientists felt during the formative period of molecular biology.

Nossal, G. J. V. *Reshaping Life: Key Issues in Genetic Engineering*. New York: Cambridge University Press, 1985. Nossal seeks to introduce the general reader to the background, potentiality, and problems of recombinant-DNA technology. Introductory chapters supply a useful explanation of DNA's structure and functions, while the remainder of the text discusses philosophical issues affecting DNA research. Sanger's work is mentioned in the context of molecular biology's historical development.

Re, Richard Noel. *Bioburst: The Impact of Modern Biology on the Affairs of Man*. Baton Rouge: Louisiana State University Press, 1986. With lucid explanations, Re unfolds the mysteries of the new biotechnology for the general reader and then expands upon its potential contributions to the eradication of diseases, public safety, aging, the understanding of evolution, and philosophy. A readable, amusing book. The explanation of Sanger's sequencing method is well done.

Schlief, Robert. *Genetics and Molecular Biology.* Reading, Mass.: Addison-Wesley, 1986. This college textbook provides a comprehensive, detailed explanation of the chemical and biological mechanisms of genetics. It is most useful for those readers with a basic grounding in chemistry. Sanger's sequencing method receives a clear, concise treatment and is compared with the Gilbert-Maxam method.

Steiner, Roger, John L. Ingraham, Mark L. Wheelis, and Page R. Painter. *The Microbial World.* 5th ed. Englewood Cliffs, N.J.: Prentice-Hall, 1986. This hefty textbook for college science majors assumes an understanding of biology and chemistry, and for those who have the background it elucidates the complex world of molecular biology with thoroughness. Sanger's method is covered, as well as the Gilbert-Maxam method, and the uses of sequencing are discussed.

Roger Smith

1981

Chemistry
Kenichi Fukui, Japan
Roald Hoffmann, United States

Physics
Nicolaas Bloembergen, United States
Arthur L. Schawlow, United States
Kai M. Siegbahn, Sweden

Physiology or Medicine
Roger W. Sperry, United States
Torsten N. Wiesel, Sweden
David H. Hubel, United States

Economic Sciences
James Tobin, United States

Literature
Elias Canetti, Great Britain

Peace
Office of the U. N. High Commissioner for Refugees

KENICHI FUKUI
1981

Born: Nara, Japan; October 4, 1918

Nationality: Japanese
Areas of concentration: Electronic structure and organic reactions

Fukui discovered that of the many electronic orbitals involved in molecular structure, only those of the highest energy dominate the reaction. Fukui found that these frontier orbitals could account for many organic reactions not otherwise understood

The Award

Presentation

Inga Fischer-Hjalmars, member of the Royal Swedish Academy of Sciences, presented the Nobel Prize in Chemistry to Kenichi Fukui and Roald Hoffmann on December 10, 1981. In her address, Fischer-Hjalmars emphasized that chemical reactions have a daily impact. Although one does not often focus upon this fact, many of the tasks involved in daily life and the process of life itself involve chemical reactions. These reactions involve the formation and deformation of chemical compounds. These processes can be utilized to design compounds, however, only if the methods to be used are reliable and predictable. The nature and laws of transformation for molecules need to be understood.

Fischer-Hjalmars explained how reactions occur at the molecular level. Molecules are made of atomic nuclei held together by electrons. The nuclei and electrons are in constant motion, with electron motion best described by paths called orbitals. These orbitals, when between atoms, are called the bonds between atoms. In chemical reactions, molecules impinge upon one another. The electrons in their orbitals are influenced by these new nuclei, and the orbitals, electron paths, may change. These changes result in the breaking and forming of chemical bonds that create new molecules. One factor that determines how this phenomenon occurs is energy. A release of energy may often take place, as reactants slide down the energy hill to form products. This intermediate point of collision is not well understood and will require explanation to determine how and why chemical reactions occur. Fischer-Hjalmars pointed out how the cowinners had aided the understanding of this process.

Fukui helped to simplify the understanding of the barriers and routes of chemical reactions. The pathways depend upon the transformation of electronic orbitals from those of the reactant to those of the product. He discovered that only a few orbitals, those of the highest energy, will dominate and determine the successful path of a reaction. These orbitals, influencing reactions at the interface of molecular interactions, were named frontier orbitals. Fukui used this frontier orbital theory to define the laws for many organic chemical reactions.

Fukui also showed that the frontier orbital theory enabled the discovery of solutions to some intricate problems in the three-dimensional aspects of product formation. Fischer-Hjalmars noted that his drastic simplification of the interactions in molecular collisions has revealed completely new aspects and "beautiful generalizations" concerning chemical reactions. His theoretical work has forged new tools for the design of chemical experiments.

Nobel lecture

On December 8, 1981, Fukui delivered his Nobel lecture, entitled "The Role of Frontier Orbitals in Chemical Reactions." This lecture began by tracing the history of predictivity in chemical reactions, explained some of the current theory, and concluded with his vision of the future and its direction. The lecture revealed his sense of order, purpose, and vision in using applied quantum chemical calculations in reaction dynamics. Fukui began his historical account with the nature of the electronic theory of chemical reactions. In this theory, considering all electrons and their distributions about a molecule is presumed necessary to understand their static and dynamic behaviors. Yet, this method is found to be less than satisfactory in predicting even the simplest of reactions. Fukui pointed out that it was for this reason that he began his investigation with the nature of individual orbitals in molecules, rather than with the overall electron density.

In Fukui's original work, he noted the possibility that, much like valence electrons in atoms, only those electrons in high energy states should be responsible for reactivity. What began with highly symmetric, simplistic cases grew to encompass many new and novel reaction mechanisms. In these studies, he discovered that two particular orbitals, for a wide range of chemical compounds, act as the essential part in determining a chemical reaction. These orbitals, at the edge between reacting species, are referred to as "frontier orbitals." The frontier orbitals responsible are called the highest-energy occupied molecular orbital (HOMO) and lowest-energy unoccupied molecular orbital (LUMO). (Molecular orbitals are the paths that electrons can take around molecules. Of the possible paths, some are higher in energy than others. Only some of these orbitals are used, or "occupied," in molecules. The HOMO is the highest energy path with electrons, while the LUMO is the lowest energy path without electrons. The LUMO is always higher in energy than the HOMO.)

Fukui showed that an understanding of the nature of these orbitals and their interactions means predictability in chemical reactions. His work determined that the electron delocalization between the HOMO on one reacting species and the LUMO on another was the principal factor determining the ease of a chemical reaction and its path. At this point in his lecture, Fukui acknowledged many of the other scientists who had added to or contributed to his ideas. In his usual self-effacing manner, he described the importance of these contributions while minimizing his own original ideas.

Fukui went on to describe the extent of further work in progress in reaction pathways and other subfields of chemistry that have been reopened as a result of the frontier orbital theory; his stated purpose was to stimulate younger chemists to enter these promising fields. He concluded with a challenge for quantum chemistry to focus upon its chemical usefulness. This chemical usefulness has two major themes: to contribute to the comprehension of empirical observation and to promote empirical investigation by suggesting direction. Kenichi Fukui utilized quantum mechanics in chemistry for both of these purposes—understanding and vision. His lecture demonstrated these characteristics of his work.

Critical reception

The Nobel Prize in Chemistry for Kenichi Fukui was hailed by his closest associates. Yet, his receipt of the award went unheralded by many chemists outside his subfield, because they were unfamiliar with his name. This confusion was a significant portion of the reaction by scientists to the selection of Fukui by the Nobel Committee. Many had heard of and utilized the frontier orbital approach but were unaware of its discoverer. The lack of name recognition did not, however, detract from the acceptance of this significant piece of work, nor from the idea that its author should be recognized. Fukui mentioned that many scientists had not heard of him but may know of some of his methods. *The New York Times* attributed his lack of name recognition to factors dependent upon the publications themselves. Many of Fukui's original works had never been translated into English but remained in Japanese—often in relatively obscure journals. In addition, the highly mathematical expressions of quantum mechanics, especially applied quantum mechanics, were beyond the comprehension of many chemists of the day. Fukui stated, however, that the antagonistic attitude of his colleagues in Japan was also to blame. The typically conservative Japanese reaction to any new theory resulted in his Japanese colleagues' either attacking or ignoring Fukui's work.

Kenichi Fukui was the first Japanese to win the Nobel Prize in Chemistry and one of only a few Japanese to win any of the science Nobel Prizes. *The New York Times* cited his achievement as running counter to the notion held in Japan and elsewhere that the Japanese are strong in practical application but weak in fundamental research. In fact, many chemists consider the frontier orbital theory to be one of the most important conceptual advances of the 1950's. Although few recognize its founder's name, most chemists know about the theory and recognize its effect of changing the whole approach to chemical reactions.

Biography

Kenichi Fukui was born on October 4, 1918, to Ryokichi and Chie Fukui in Nara, Japan. He was the eldest of three sons, and Ryokichi Fukui took a keen interest in his education. During his high school years, Fukui was not very interested in chemistry, yet he did have an interest in science and mathematics. His father's employment as foreign trade merchant and factory manager supplied him with numerous contacts in education and business. Ryokichi Fukui turned to an elder from his native province, Gen-itsu Kita, for advice concerning his son's undergraduate education. Kita, a professor of Kyoto Imperial University, suggested that young Fukui be sent to the Department of Industrial Chemistry at Kyoto, with which Kita was affiliated.

After he was graduated from Kyoto University in 1941, having completed his undergraduate and graduate studies, Fukui was employed by the army and was engaged in experimental research on synthetic fuel chemistry. His results earned for him a prize and a position at Kyoto Imperial University. He started as a lecturer in 1943, became an assistant professor in 1945, and subsequently professor in 1951. He met and married his wife, Tomoe Horie, in 1947. In the years that followed, they had a son, Tetsuya, and a daughter, Miyako.

Kenichi Fukui has been at Kyoto University since his early years as a student. In that time, his accomplishments and publication list have grown. He credits his achievements to his teachers, colleagues, and family. Yet, he credits Kita as the greatest influence. It was Kita who suggested his course of study and encouraged his theoretical ideas, even hinting, in 1952, at the possibility of the Nobel Prize.

Fukui is characterized by his colleagues as a low-key, modest, and pleasant individual. His quiet manner belies the intensity that he brings to his work. He enjoys fishing, golf, and walking, which afford him the opportunity to be alone to do some thinking.

Scientific Career

Kenichi Fukui's scientific career did not begin until he attended college. At the insistence of his father, he was enrolled in the Department of Industrial Chemistry at Kyoto University. His father's decision was based upon the advice of an elder from their home province, who was affiliated with that department at Kyoto. This man, Gen-itsu Kita, was to become Fukui's lifelong teacher, mentor, adviser, and friend.

At Kyoto, Fukui was trained as a chemical engineer; then, he discovered some very interesting theoretical problems in chemistry. This self-discovery sustained Fukui, and he continued at Kyoto for his undergraduate and graduate education. This wide range of interests and ability, from that of a practical, experimental engineer to that of the esoteric, theoretical quantum chemist, has been blended into much of Fukui's work. His papers demonstrate a command of both the subtleties of theory and the intricacies of experiment.

Upon receiving his graduate and undergraduate education from Kyoto in 1941, Fukui worked at the Army Fuel Laboratory in experimental research. The result of this work was a prize, awarded to him in 1941. At the same time, he began his tenure at Kyoto University in a teaching position. He began to assemble a research group, which included a subgroup of theoreticians.

In 1952, under Fukui's direction, this group found a correlation between the frontier electron density and the chemical reactivity in aromatic hydrocarbons. It was this seminal work of 1952 for which the Nobel Prize was awarded to him. In this first paper, Fukui outlined the basis for the use of frontiers, the HOMO and LUMO, in determining the outcome of chemical reactions. Since that time, Kenichi Fukui has continued to work on his frontier orbital theory. The early results of that work appeared mostly in Japanese journals, few of which were seen outside Japan. At the same time, he has continued his experimental organic-chemical research into reaction kinetics and catalytic engineering.

His theoretical group continued to expound upon the chemical reactivity theory, applying it to a wider range of compounds and reactions. At the same time, other work by Fukui included the theory of gelation, organic synthesis using inorganic salts, and polymerization kinetics and catalysis. His interest and ability in experimental organic synthesis and reaction characterization were complemented by his activities in theoretical mechanistic determination.

In 1970, Fukui began to receive some of the recognition due him for his work. In addition, he began a new breakthrough in the formulation of the path of chemical reactions. His first paper on the subject appeared in 1970. In this article, the role of frontier orbitals in chemical reactions was made more distinct through the visualization of the orbitals. This provided new information concerning the geometrical shape of reacting molecules. At the same time, he went to the United States as a National Science Foundation Senior Foreign Scientist at the Illinois Institute of Technology. He returned again to the United States in 1973 as part of the U.S.-Japan Eminent Scientist Exchange Program. He has continued his activity in the study of organic reactions and their mechanisms.

Fukui's diverse research interests can be characterized as a search for understanding organic reaction theory that has utilized a wide range of techniques. These have involved both theoretical and empirical aspects of quantum, physical, kinetic, and organic chemistry, with an eye to making all aspects work together for a more complete understanding. In recognition of his diverse interests and achievements, Kenichi Fukui was elected to the National Academy of Sciences as a Foreign Associate in 1981.

Fukui has addressed his ability in science to a wide range of topics, all with the goal of understanding chemical reactions more completely. In him is the pragmatism of an engineer, the inquisitiveness of an experimentalist, and the mathematical ability of a theoretician combined within an individual of enormous talent. This talent was spotted, inspired, and encouraged by Kita, and the chemical world has been changed by it.

Bibliography

Primary

CHEMISTRY: "A Molecular Orbital Theory of Reactivity in Aromatic Hydrocarbons," *Journal of Chemical Physics*, vol. 20, 1952 (with T. Yonezawa and H. Shingu); "Molecular Orbital Theory of Orientation in Aromatic, Heteroaromatic, and Other Conjugated Molecules," *Journal of Chemical Physics*, vol. 22,

1954 (with T. Yonezawa, C. Nagata, and H. Shinzu); "Recognition of Stereo-chemical Paths by Orbital Interaction," *Accounts of Chemical Research*, vol. 4, 1971; "Molecular Orbital Calculation of Chemically Interacting Systems: Interactions Between Radical and Closed-Shell Molecules," *Journal of the American Chemical Society*, vol. 94, 1972 (with H. Fujimoto, S. Yamabe, and T. Minato); "Molecular Orbital Calculation of the Electronic Structure of Borane Carbonyl," *Journal of the American Chemical Society*, vol. 96, 1974 (with S. Kato, H. Fujimoto, and S. Yamabe); "Chemical Pseudoexcitation and Paradoxical Orbital Interaction Effect," *Journal of the American Chemical Society*, vol. 97, 1975 (with S. Inagaki and H. Fujimoto); "The Role of Frontier Orbitals in Chemical Reactions," *Science*, vol. 218, 1982.

Secondary

Carey, Francis A., and Richard J. Sundberg. *Advanced Organic Chemistry, Part A.* New York: Plenum, 1977. This advanced textbook describes the experimental evidence and theoretical background of frontier orbital theory. An excellent bibliographic source for extensions to Fukui's theory.

Lowry, Thomas H., and Kathleen Richardson. *Mechanism and Theory in Organic Chemistry.* New York: Harper & Row, 1981. The focus of this text is the general theory of reaction mechanisms in organic chemistry. This includes a generalized approach to bonding theory and includes several chapters devoted to the consideration of frontier orbitals in the mechanisms of organic reactions.

Orchin, Milton, and H. H. Jaffe. *Symmetry, Orbitals, and Spectra.* New York: Wiley-Interscience, 1971. This book integrates the topics of symmetry, molecular orbital theory, and absorption spectroscopy. A good text for learning about molecular orbital theory and its applications beyond synthesis.

Pearson, Ralph G. *Symmetry Rules for Chemical Reactions.* New York: Wiley-Interscience, 1976. Intended for the sophisticated reader, this book serves as a guide for the prediction of reaction mechanisms for organic molecules. A highly specialized look at organic reactions based upon the premise of frontier orbital theory.

Scott A. Davis

1981

Chemistry
Kenichi Fukui, Japan
Roald Hoffmann, United States

Physics
Nicolaas Bloembergen, United States
Arthur L. Schawlow, United States
Kai M. Siegbahn, Sweden

Physiology or Medicine
Roger W. Sperry, United States
Torsten N. Wiesel, Sweden
David H. Hubel, United States

Economic Sciences
James Tobin, United States

Literature
Elias Canetti, Great Britain

Peace
Office of the U. N. High Commissioner for Refugees

ROALD HOFFMANN
1981

Born: Zloczow, Poland; July 18, 1937

Nationality: American
Area of concentration: Electronic structure of compounds

Hoffmann recognized the importance of both the energy and the symmetry of electronic orbitals in chemical reactions. His development of the theory of orbital symmetry has become an exceedingly practical instrument for a wide variety of chemical syntheses

The Award

Presentation

Inga Fischer-Hjalmars, a member of the Nobel Committee for Chemistry, presented the Nobel Prize in Chemistry to Kenichi Fukui and Roald Hoffmann on December 10, 1981. In her address, Fischer-Hjalmars pointed out the presence of chemical reactions common in daily life. She explained how everyday activities, from starting a car to the existence of life itself, involve chemical reactions. These chemical reactions create new compounds. In fact, the preparation of new compounds can be designed; Fischer-Hjalmars pointed out, however, that these designs are unreliable until the laws of transformation for molecules are understood.

Fischer-Hjalmars described the state of affairs at the molecular level. Molecules are composed of atoms held together by electrons. All these particles are in constant motion, with electron motion described by paths called orbitals. These orbitals, when occurring between atoms, determine the bonds between the atoms. In a chemical reaction, as molecules impinge upon one another, electrons are influenced by new atomic nuclei, and their orbitals change. These changes can result in some bonds being broken while others are created, resulting in new molecules. One governing factor that decides the sequence of events is energy. A release of energy often takes place, and reactants slide down the energy gradient (slope) to form products. Although much is known about the starting material and the final products, the intermediate point of collision has long been less well understood, and it has required an explanation of how and why chemical reactions occur. She pointed out that the cowinners had aided in the understanding of this process.

Hoffmann helped define the obstacles and preferred paths of chemical reactions. These barriers depend upon the transformation of electronic orbitals. Hoffmann discovered, in collaborating in the synthesis of vitamin B_{12}, that not only the energy but also the symmetry properties of an orbital will determine its reactivity. Hoffmann has continued to develop his theory, which enables the generalization from interactions in molecular collision to the predictions of reaction products. Fischer-Hjalmars noted that the simplification of the theory of orbital symmetry has enabled "beautiful generalizations" to be made about reaction dynamics and experimental conditions necessary for the achievement of desired products.

Nobel lecture

On December 8, 1981, Hoffmann delivered his Nobel lecture, entitled "Building Bridges Between Inorganic and Organic Chemistry." It projected the broad vision he possesses for chemical theory, while revealing his desire for aesthetic beauty in rigorous calculations. In his address, the overall concept of bond formation by orbital overlap for any chemical system was demonstrated with clarity of purpose; Hoffmann relied upon the inherent artistic features of the system and the calculations involved. He began his address by paying tribute and dedicating it to a fellow Nobel laureate, Robert Burns Woodward. It was Woodward, he said, who taught him the importance of experiments to theory, the craft of constructing an explanation, and the importance of aesthetics in science. The lecture concentrated on the characteristics of experimentation, explanation, and aesthetics in providing a conceptual understanding of electronic structure in both organic and inorganic molecules.

The orbitals that contain electrons—both electrons that remain with their parent nuclei and those that share with others—are the building blocks of molecular structures. The special orbitals that are involved in the sharing process are widely varied. These three-dimensional probability boundaries for electron population constitute the electronic structure of a molecule. Hoffmann's cowinner, Fukui, showed that, of all the overlap orbitals that form when a molecule is made, the frontier orbitals are the most important orbitals for predicting chemical reactions. Hoffmann demonstrated that a chemical compound could be considered to be the combination of different pieces, or fragments, of a molecule. These fragments would have available the frontier orbitals that are not involved in the bonding. In fact, any molecule may be considered as the addition of a number of fragments and their associated frontier orbitals.

A fragment, then, can be thought of as a collection of atoms possessing one or more orbitals capable of attaching to the other orbitals. These orbitals, or lobes, will differ by various characteristics: the number, symmetry, energy, and shape of the lobes. Those fragments that are similar in these characteristics are said to be isolobal. The isolobal model allows for the prediction and characterization of products from among myriad possibilities, based upon the properties of the frontier orbitals of the fragments.

This ability to predict products of a reaction enables a simplification in the understanding of the electronic structure of complex molecules. It also allows for the prediction of new structures that are possible based upon theoretical arguments, which the experimental literatures can attest, based upon the isolobal model. In these constructions (fragments and frontier models), little mention is made of the fragments used, be they organic or inorganic. It is the bridging of this apparent rift that this model accomplishes. At once it explains chemical structure and reactivity at the molecular level, independent of the specific nuclei involved and dependent instead upon the frontier orbitals to which electrons are confined. This theory of electronic structure allows for an understanding of a deeper unity amid the apparent diverse complexities that occur when chemistry is viewed as separate subfields.

Critical reception

The Nobel Prize in Chemistry to Roald Hoffmann was hailed by his colleagues, for he contributed to one of the most important conceptual advances in chemistry since the 1950's. Many of his closest associates expected that he would receive a Nobel, especially considering his association with Robert Burns Woodward, who won the chemistry prize in 1965. Hoffmann's theory bridged the gap between quantum theory and practical chemistry, enabling the prediction of possible products and reaction conditions by (as *The New York Times* described it) "jotting pictures on the back of an envelope." Although easily used in practice, the rules of orbital symmetry were arrived at by the observation, consideration, and condensation of a large body of chemical theory, under the tutelage of Nobel laureates Woodward and William N. Lipscomb. Hoffmann was able to accomplish this task because of his "tremendous knowledge of science," coupled with the "authentic genius" that many scientists saw in him from the beginning of his career.

Of the two cowinners, Hoffmann was the more recognizable name, because of several advantages. In addition to having a renowned thesis adviser in Lipscomb and colleague in Woodward, he had the advantage of publishing in major journals in English and the ability to communicate his theory in a form that was understandable to most chemists. Regardless of such considerations, however, his extension of Fukui's frontier orbital method (independently derived by Hoffmann) to include symmetry considerations was cited as changing the whole approach to chemistry and the way chemists think about reactions.

Biography

Roald Hoffmann was born Roald Safran on July 18, 1937, to Clara (née Rosen) and Hillel Safran in Zloczow, in what was then Poland, now part of the Soviet Union. His father was a civil engineer and his mother a schoolteacher. In 1939, World War II began, and the family lived in the part of Poland under Russian occupation. In 1941, Nazi Germany invaded Poland, and the Jewish family found itself in a labor camp after a short time in a ghetto. Young Roald and his mother were smuggled out of the camp in 1943 and hidden by a Ukrainian family until after the war. His father remained behind and was executed by the Nazis later that same year for organizing an escape attempt that was discovered. Most of his family suffered the same fate as his father. Those family members who did survive were freed by the Soviet Army in June, 1944. At the end of 1944, the remaining family moved to Krakow. In Krakow, Roald's mother remarried, to Paul Hoffmann; Roald Safran became Roald Hoffmann and finally began to attend school. From 1946 to 1949, the family moved throughout Europe, until they emigrated to the United States.

Roald Hoffmann attended public schools in Brooklyn, New York, and went on to Stuyvesant High School. At that time, Stuyvesant was one of New York's selective science schools (where classmates excelled in nonscience areas as well), providing a stimulating educational experience for him. To round out his education, in summer his parents sent him to Camp Juvenile in the Catskills.

In the spring of 1955, Hoffmann was a winner in the National Westinghouse Talent (Science) Search. He began college at Columbia College as a premedical student that fall. During the summers, he worked at the National Bureau of Standards in Washington, D.C., for two years and at Brookhaven National Laboratory for another. It was his summer experiences that opened his eyes and mind to the joys of research. While his summers prepared him for his career in chemistry, his scholastic activities prepared him for his love of the arts, and his eye for aesthetics (he almost switched his major to art history).

In 1958, he began graduate work at Harvard University in theoretical chemistry with M. P. Gouterman. The following summer was spent at a summer school in Stockholm, Sweden. It was in Sweden that Hoffmann met Eva Börjesson, a summer receptionist at the school, whom he married the following year. After another year at Harvard, Hoffmann and his wife participated in the United States-Soviet Union graduate student exchange program at Moscow University. Upon his return to Harvard, he changed advisers and became one of William N. Lipscomb's first graduate students at Harvard.

In 1962, having received his doctorate, he chose to accept a junior fellowship in the Society of Fellows at Harvard. The three years of the fellowship enabled him to switch from pure to applied theory and work with Woodward and E. J. Corey. Also during that time, he and Eva had two children. In 1965, Hoffmann went to Cornell University, where he would remain. He would receive numerous awards and prizes. In 1974 he became the John A. Newman Professor of Physical Science.

Scientific Career

Hoffmann began attending Columbia College in 1955 as a premedical student. During the summers of 1956 and 1957, he worked at the National Bureau of Standards in Washington, D.C. In the summer of 1958, he worked at Brookhaven National Laboratory. These experiences were crucial to Hoffmann's career choice. He had changed his mind regarding medical school and contemplated switching to a major in art history, but his experiences in the summers introduced him to the joys of research, which he chose to pursue in spite of his academic coursework. Having completed college by 1958, Hoffmann began graduate work at Harvard. His interest was in theoretical chemistry, and, after his first choice of advisers died, he worked with M. P. Gouterman. As a result of his interest in theoretical chemistry, he was awarded a scholarship to attend a summer school in quantum chemistry held in Sweden.

After a brief return to the United States, Hoffmann participated in the United States-Soviet Union graduate student exchange program, working on exciton theory with A. S. Davydov at Moscow University. All this extended training and experience was to serve him well upon his return to the United States in 1960. His return marked the beginning of his construction of the computational methods he would employ throughout his career.

In 1960, upon his return from the Soviet Union, Hoffmann began work with Lipscomb on the electronic structure of boron hydrides. With Lipscomb's encouragement and guidance, this work was accomplished by Hoffmann and L. L. Lehr in the form of computer programs that utilized what later became known as the "extended Hückel method." This technique enables an approximate calculation of a portion of a molecule's electronic structure. It can also predict approximate molecular conformations (shapes). Hoffmann has used this method throughout his career for the solution of the electronic structure of many different molecules. The programs were first applied to the boron hydrides and other polyhedral molecules. One day Hoffmann discovered that a problem involving the internal rotation of ethane could be solved using this method. This was the beginning of his work on organic molecules.

In 1962, having received his doctorate, Hoffmann had several academic positions and a continuation of his association with Harvard from which to choose. This was his second major career decision, his decision to work with Lipscomb (thereby developing the extended Hückel method computer programs) having been the first. He chose to remain at Harvard as a junior fellow in the Society of Fellows at Harvard. The three years of the fellowship (1962-1965) afforded Hoffmann the time to shift his interests from pure theory to applied theory, especially as it applied to organic chemistry. It was at Harvard during this time that E. J. Corey taught him, by example, about the challenges of organic chemistry. This led to his investigation of many organic transformations from the viewpoint of a theoretician. This applied theoretical approach to organic reactions was only beginning to be utilized as a way of understanding and codifying reactions for further use. In the spring of 1964, Hoffmann began his collaboration with Robert Burns Woodward. Woodward asked some questions regarding a class of reactions (later to be called pericyclic reactions) that occurred under a variety of conditions and yielded widely differing products.

These questions and their subsequent answers were the beginning of a long and fruitful collaboration between Woodward and Hoffmann, the beginning of Hoffmann's lifelong research pursuits, and the basis of Hoffmann's Nobel Prize in Chemistry. Hoffmann brought his extensive theoretical and artistic background, while Woodward brought his encyclopedic knowledge of experimental chemistry to the search for these reaction mechanisms. Their collaboration continued even after Hoffmann left Harvard in 1965 to teach at Cornell University. At Cornell, Hoffmann's research interests included the electronic structure of stable and unstable molecules, and of transition states in reactions. His first major contribution was the development of the extended Hückel method (allowing the calculation of the approximate sigma and pi electronic structure of molecules). His second major contribution was the application of simple but powerful arguments of symmetry and bonding to the analysis of concerted reactions. This was an outgrowth of the exploration of the electronic structure of transition states and intermediates in organic reactions. It has resulted in a theory of remarkable predictive value and has stimulated much experimental work. These analyses have been performed upon most types of reactive intermediates in organic chemistry, and this was the work that was honored by the Nobel Committee.

Hoffmann has continued to investigate chemical reactions, applying his combination of molecular orbital calculations and symmetry-based arguments to inorganic chemistry. He and his coworkers have explored the basic structural features of every kind of inorganic molecule. From this intensive study, a heretofore undiscovered unity in the structure and function of molecules has emerged. Hoffmann seeks to bridge the artificial gaps between subfields of chemistry by demonstrating the commonality of electronic structure. This has yielded predictions concerning the reactivity, stability, and structure of inorganic and organometallic compounds. These activities have also led to investigations of extended solid-state systems and the design of novel conducting systems.

In 1968, Hoffmann was promoted to professor at Cornell and in 1974 was named John A. Newman Professor of Physical Science. He is especially proud of two accomplishments in his career: his teaching and the recognition by others of his eclectic interests in chemistry. He has continued to teach the first-year course in chemistry, and occasionally the nonscientists' course, since he began teaching. His accomplishments in teaching are evident from the full classes he attracts. Another prized achievement, in addition to the Nobel Prize, has been the recognition of the far-reaching impact of his theory. He has been awarded the American Chemical Society's A. C. Cope Award in Organic Chemistry (with Woodward) and the Inorganic Chemistry Award, the first person to receive both these awards from different subfields of chemistry.

Bibliography

Primary
CHEMISTRY: "Stereochemistry of Electrocyclic Reactions," *Journal of the American Chemical Society*, vol. 87, 1965 (with R. B. Woodward); "Selection Rules for Concerted Cycloaddition Reactions," *Journal of the American Chemical Society*, vol. 87, 1965 (with R. B. Woodward); "Selection Rules for Sigmatropic Reactions," *Journal of the American Chemical Society*, vol. 87, 1965 (with R. B. Woodward); *Conservation of Orbital Symmetry*, 1969 (with R. B. Woodward); "Orbital Symmetry Control of Chemical Reactions," *Science*, vol. 167, 1970 (with R. B. Woodward); "Theoretical Organometallic Chemistry," *Science*, vol. 211, 1981.
POETRY: *The Metamict State*, 1987.

Secondary
Carey, Francis A., and Richard J. Sundberg. *Advanced Organic Chemistry, Part A.*

New York: Plenum, 1977. This advanced textbook describes the symmetry postulated by Hoffmann and the experimental evidence for it. The text is an excellent bibliographic source for extensions of Hoffmann's theory.

Cotton, F. Albert. *Chemical Applications of Group Theory*. New York: Wiley-Interscience, 1971. In this textbook, Cotton works through several simple examples to demonstrate how the symmetry rules of Hoffmann were derived. He goes on to generalize and summarize the results. A good elementary text on molecular orbital theory and symmetry.

Lehr, Roland E., and Alan P. Marchand. *Orbital Symmetry*. New York: Harper & Row, 1981. This book outlines the general background and theory behind Hoffmann's theory. The second half of the book is a collection of problems taken from the literature (and referenced) that may be worked out by the reader. An excellent text for teaching about these reactions.

Lowry, Thomas H., and Kathleen Richardson. *Mechanism and Theory in Organic Chemistry*. New York: Harper & Row, 1981. The focus of this text is the general theory of reaction mechanisms in organic chemistry. Includes a generalized approach to bonding theory and several chapters on the symmetry and reaction theory of Hoffmann. A good text for showing how Hoffmann's rules fit into the overall mechanistic scheme of organic chemistry.

Orchin, Milton, and H. H. Jaffe. *Symmetry, Orbitals, and Spectra*. New York: Wiley-Interscience, 1971. This book integrates the topics of symmetry, molecular orbital theory, and absorption spectroscopy. The authors devote a chapter to the application of Hoffmann's rules to the excited states of organic and inorganic molecules. A good text for learning about molecular orbital theory and its applications beyond synthesis.

Pearson, Ralph G. *Symmetry Rules for Chemical Reactions*. New York: Wiley-Interscience, 1976. Intended for the sophisticated reader, this book is intended to serve as a guide for the prediction of reaction mechanisms for organic molecules. A highly specialized look into reaction mechanisms explained by Hoffmann's rules.

Scott A. Davis

1982

Chemistry
Aaron Klug, South Africa and Great Britain

Physics
Kenneth G. Wilson, United States

Physiology or Medicine
Sune K. Bergström, Sweden
Bengt I. Samuelsson, Sweden
Sir John R. Vane, Great Britain

Economic Sciences
George Stigler, United States

Literature
Gabriel García Márquez, Colombia

Peace
Alva Myrdal, Sweden
Alfonso García Robels, Mexico

AARON KLUG
1982

Born: Zelvas, Lithuania; August 11, 1926

Nationality: South African; later British
Area of concentration: Structural molecular biology

Klug applied the techniques of X-ray diffraction to electron microscopy and was a pioneer in the field of structural molecular biology

The Award

Presentation

Bo G. Malmström, a biochemist and member of the Royal Swedish Academy of Sciences, presented the Nobel Prize in Chemistry to Aaron Klug on December 10, 1982. In his presentation speech, Malmström emphasized that the secret of life is not to be found as some mysterious life force but, instead, lies in the chemical properties of atoms and molecules which arise from their structural organization. He spoke about the important technique of X-ray diffraction, which, in the hands of crystallographers, had deciphered the patterns of periodic organization of atoms in simple crystals and even, in recent times, the molecular structure of key molecules in living systems, the proteins and nucleic acids.

Life can be thought of, Malmström noted, as depending on interactions between the genetic material of the cell, deoxyribonucleic acid (DNA), and proteins, which provide the machinery for operating the chemical processes of the cell. The genetic material of the cell, in the form of chromosomes, is found as an aggregate of DNA and literally thousands of protein units. Viruses, which are also aggregates of nucleic acid and proteins, are somewhat less complex than the genetic material of higher organisms and provide suitable model systems for study of the organization of nucleic acid-protein complexes.

Malmström cited Klug's achievements: To overcome difficulties inherent in utilizing traditional X-ray crystallographic techniques with large biological aggregates, Klug developed ingenious methods of applying principles of diffraction to electron microscopy, thereby increasing greatly the amount of structural information obtained. As a result of his work, the principles governing the structures of viruses and even the material of the chromosomes were better understood.

Nobel lecture

Klug's Nobel lecture, entitled "From Macromolecules to Biological Assemblies," was delivered on December 8, 1982. He began by pointing out that the inception of the field of molecular biology was marked by the 1962 Nobel Prize in Chemistry to Max Perutz and John Kendrew for protein structure and the 1962 Nobel Prize in Physiology or Medicine to Francis Crick, James Watson, and Maurice Wilkins for determining the structure of DNA. The techniques of X-ray crystallography were central to those discoveries; hence, it was highly appropriate for Klug to extend crystallography into electron microscopy in his attempts to understand the physical arrangements of giant assemblies composed of proteins and nucleic acids.

In describing the subject of his first major biological investigation, of tobacco mosaic virus (TMV), Klug paid tribute to the late Rosalind Franklin, who had introduced him to the study of viruses. After helping to develop from X-ray diffraction the knowledge of the overall structure of TMV, a rodlike or helical particle, Klug and coworkers began to study a class of spherical viruses. As a result of experience gained with these materials and because of obvious difficulties in doing X-ray crystallography with such systems, they turned to the more easily obtained images produced by electron microscopy.

Here, again, Klug came up against many limitations inherent in the physical technique as it was then utilized. He was able to overcome many of the problems by use of computer and optical procedures for processing and reconstructing the images from electron micrographs. Klug and his coworkers were able to employ optical techniques together with mathematical procedures and a computer to process the blurry, two-dimensional images in electron micrographs of molecular aggregates and to reconstruct with precision the three-dimensional arrangements that had produced the image originally.

Because of the power and versatility of the techniques that his group developed, they and others, Klug noted, had been able to determine the structural principles governing such diverse materials as viruses, cell walls and subcellular particles, flagella of bacteria, chromatin from the genetic material of the cell nucleus, and various proteins such as hemocyanin or enzymes such as catalase and cytochrome oxidase.

Klug concluded by noting that he had been able to make the interpretation of the seemingly confused and confusing images in the electron microscope into a quantitative discipline capable of yielding precise structural information. Having worked on many difficult biological problems, he had solved the structures of many important biological systems, and his work on the challenging problem of the structure of chromatin would continue.

Critical reception

The popular and scientific press were unanimous in their praise for Klug. *The Washington Post* (October 19), in reporting on the recipients of the Nobel award, stressed that Klug had "opened up a new branch in the study of molecular shapes," and *The New York Times* of the same date stated that Klug was "considered a pioneer of research in molecular biology, particularly in the study of structure and function of what are often called macromolecular assemblies."

Chemical and Engineering News, in an article in the October 25 issue reporting Klug's award, commented that in order to attack difficult structural problems, Klug did not hesitate "to invent or perfect new analytic methods, and a series of improvements of electron microscopy to provide three-dimensional images is especially noteworthy." The article went on to state: "Important though method development has been throughout Klug's career, it has never kept him from a pursuit of interesting biological questions."

The New York Times quoted a colleague of the "short, slim, graying, bespectacled" Klug as saying that "you'd never notice him in a crowd." Nevertheless, scientists had come from all over the world to work in the stimulating research environment that he had created in his laboratory. In an article in *Science* (November 12), former colleagues Donald Caspar and David DeRosier wrote that one of Klug's many talents lay in the ability to form "productive collaborations with people having complementary abilities."

Chemical and Engineering News again reported Klug to have credited the rather cramped quarters in his Medical Research Council Laboratory of Molecular Biology with fostering interactions between scientific colleagues, and to have paid tribute to the workshops there, where new apparatus and techniques could be tested. Klug compared the shop to one in a physics department, where, indeed, many of his colleagues had started, having learned biology later in their careers.

Dan Jacobson, a close friend of Klug and a fellow South African expatriate, was quoted by Ros Herman in *New Scientist* (October 21) as saying that Klug was one of a group that had left South Africa not for political reasons but "in search of wider horizons" and to escape what was called "a particular sense of isolation." Jacobson further wrote of the laureate's unassuming personality: "An intellectually aggresive man, he has made mincemeat of many a scientist who has chosen to disagree with him." Klug's main concern, when interviewed by *New Scientist* after the award was announced, however, was to express his thanks to the Medical Research Council for supporting his research over the many years it took to "bear fruit."

Peter Osnos, writing in *The Washington Post* (December 13), described the human scale of the Nobel ceremonies. Klug, when asked how he would spend the Nobel award, told attendants at a press conference that he had ridden the same bicycle for thirty years, and guessed he would be buying a new one.

Biography

Aaron Klug was born in 1926 to Lazar and Bella (née Silin) Klug in Zelvas, Lithuania. At the age of two, he emigrated with his parents to Durban, South Africa, where he went to public schools. A voracious reader, he was drawn to science, particularly microbiology, through reading Paul de Kruif's book *Microbe Hunters* (1926). In 1942, Klug entered the University of Witwatsrand in Johannesburg, where he undertook the premedical curriculum. Feeling the need for a basic understanding of science, however, he soon turned to chemistry and eventually to mathematics and physics, earning a B.S. in 1945.

Having decided to pursue the study of physics, Klug moved to the University of Cape Town and took an M.Sc. degree. At Cape Town, he came under the influence of R. W. James, formerly a member of the School of Crystallography at Manchester, founded by Sir William Henry Bragg and his son, Sir Lawrence Bragg (co-recipients in 1915 of the Nobel Prize in Physics).

Klug and Liebe Bobrow were married in 1948, and a year later they moved to the University of Cambridge. Wishing to undertake research on crystallography of proteins, Klug tried to join the groups of Perutz and Kendrew at the Medical Research Council unit. Finding no space available, he did a Ph.D. thesis on the structure of steel under D. R. Hartree. After further research at Cambridge and a period at Birkbeck College in London, he returned to Cambridge and joined the newly built Medical Research Council Laboratory of Molecular Biology in 1962, eventually becoming its director in 1986.

Scientific Career

Aaron Klug's career may be described as a search for understanding of the structure of complex biological aggregates. He was fortunate to begin his study of the basic method of molecular structural determination, X-ray crystallography, with a very stimulating teacher, R. W. James, who was known at the University of Cape Town as a person of widely varied interests. He had, among other things, served as physicist on the Shackleton Antarctic Expedition of 1907-1909. Klug has attributed his feeling for optics and knowledge of Fourier mathematics to James's teachings. (X-ray crystallography is a study of the periodic patterns produced when X rays are scattered from an ordered arrangement of particles, ions, atoms, or molecules. Fourier theory can be applied both to the mathematical analysis of such periodic patterns and to attempts to reconstruct the three-dimensional arrangements that cause the scattering.)

After taking his master of science in physics at Cape Town, Klug, determined to pursue his interest in structure and aided by a scholarship and research studentship, moved to Cambridge, England, to pursue a research program at the Cavendish Laboratory. Hoping to do what he termed "unorthodox" X-ray crystallography of biological materials, he applied to work in the groups of John Kendrew and Max Perutz in the Medical Research Council unit. (Kendrew and Perutz were to share the 1962 Nobel Prize in Chemistry for determination of structure of oxygen-carrying proteins in muscle and red blood cells.) When Klug found that there were no places available, he soon learned enough metallurgy to do a Ph.D. thesis on the changes that occur when molten steel solidifies. This work was done under D. R. Hartree, who had been a colleague of both James and Sir Lawrence Bragg at the School of Crystallography at Manchester.

After obtaining the Ph.D., Klug stayed in Cambridge for one more year in the Department of Colloid Science, investigating the problem of rates of transport and simultaneous chemical reaction when dissolved oxygen enters the red blood cell. Having thus rekindled his interest in biological matters, he received a fellowship to Birkbeck College, London, where he soon began a project that was to lead to his life's work: the study of virus structure.

Viruses, consisting of complexes of protein and nucleic acids, are one of the simplest forms of "living" matter. Klug credits Rosalind Franklin, with whom he began to work at Birkbeck, with setting him on his future path when she showed him her "beautiful" X-ray diffraction photographs of tobacco mosaic virus (TMV). Franklin, whose generally unrecognized contributions to the prizewinning double helical structure of DNA Klug had long championed, was a meticulous researcher and a very private person who, nevertheless, had an important influence on Klug's career in research. Working with Franklin and a student, Kenneth Holmes, Klug was able to develop the general description of the rodlike structure of TMV. Some twenty years of further study were to be required before the process of self-assembly of the TMV particle was to be fully understood. Klug and his colleagues showed that the protein subunits of the virus aggregate into a "disk," a two-layered cylindrical structure that combines with a specific site on the viral ribonucleic acid (RNA) component, dislocates into a sort of "lock washer" form, and begins to grow into the helical, rodlike virus particle. This disk is considered to be a necessary intermediate in virus assembly. It has the ability to recognize a specific viral RNA and initiate growth of the virus.

Following Franklin's untimely death in 1958, Klug became director of the virus group at Birkbeck College and shifted much of his attention to the types of plant viruses known as "spherical viruses." This category includes a large number of disease-causing species, such as turnip yellow mosaic virus and tomato bushy stunt virus. In 1962, when the newly built Medical Research Council (MRC) Molecular Biology Laboratory at Cambridge opened, Klug was invited to join by Francis Crick. Klug remained at that institution, becoming joint head of the Division of Structural Studies in 1978 and Laboratory Director in 1986. (The Medical Research Council is Great Britain's version of the United States' National Institutes of Health, located in Bethesda, Maryland.)

Klug encountered a variety of difficulties in his attempts to understand the structure of the spherical viruses. They were known to consist of a number of identical protein subunits packed around a nucleic acid core. Only 60 subunits, however, could fit into a perfectly regular spherical shell, and a virus such as tomato bushy stunt virus has 180 subunits. Klug and coworker Donald Caspar theorized that the protein subunits were arranged, instead, in a slightly irregular fashion, so that they were almost equivalent (termed "quasi-equivalent"), in a structure geometrically similar to the geodesic domes invented by R. Buckminster Fuller. The structures proposed by Klug and Caspar were disputed by a number of researchers, but subsequent investigations confirmed their validity for the spherical viruses.

In the early 1970's, Klug used X-ray diffraction to determine the structure of transfer RNA (tRNA), the molecule within the cell that "reads" the message of the genetic code and carries the appropriate amino acid to the site of protein assembly. Almost simultaneously, a team at the Massachusetts Institute of Technology headed by Alexander Rich published their own X-ray structure of tRNA. Results from the two groups confirmed that the molecule resembled a kind of "bent hair pin" in shape, with structural features expected to be common to all tRNA molecules and regions specific for binding a particular amino acid and for attaching to messenger RNA (mRNA), the template that carries the genetic code from the DNA.

Having begun to study spherical viruses by X-ray methods, Klug soon turned to electron microscopy because of its speed and relative ease of producing a "direct" image. Again, many problems had to be overcome, including scattering of the observing electron beam out of the field of view by electrons in the sample molecules and the inherently great depth of field of the technique, which resulted in an overlaying of images. Such difficulties resulted in photographs of low resolution: Details were fuzzy and difficult to relate to the real object.

Over a period of a decade or more, Klug and his associates, using as a basis techniques originating in X-ray diffraction, developed optical and computer methods for processing the two-dimensional images produced in the electron microscope, so that it became possible for them to reconstruct the three-dimensional images of biological samples. The methods became known as crystallographic electron microscopy. As a result of these and other innovations, Klug's group was able to detail the methods of self-assembly of the TMV and to determine structures of a number of other viruses, subcellular functional units, and enzymes, the protein catalysts of the cell.

Beginning in the 1970's, Klug's group undertook a long-range study of the genetic material of the cell, the complex of DNA and protein that forms the chromosome. The DNA in only one chromosome is believed to consist of a single molecule that would stretch at least several centimeters if it were straightened out. The protein part is a set of small proteins called histones. When extracted from the cell, chromosomal material is called chromatin. Roger Kornberg and Klug studied chromatin by X-ray diffraction, and Kornberg was eventually able to combine the X-ray results with those from chemical studies to show that chromatin is made up of a succession of subunits, termed nucleosomes.

Klug continues to work on chromatin and related problems, problems that represent, certainly, the toughest challenge he has set for himself. Although knowledge about chromatin structure is incomplete, Klug has made significant contributions already. He has shown, for example, that the DNA part of the nucleosome is in a double helical arrangement that is further coiled in what may be called a "superhelix" around a spool-like core consisting of eight histone units. By means of high-resolution X-ray crystallography, Klug has found that this superhelical DNA has sharp bends that permit interactions with the histone units contained within the superhelix. The picture that has emerged for chromatin is that of a variant on a highly convoluted string of beads, the DNA being the "string" that is wound around the clumps of histone "beads."

In an interesting corollary to the work on chromatin, Klug's group has studied the structure of a so-called regulatory protein that binds to a portion of the chromosome and activates the process of transcribing the DNA code into RNA. They have isolated such a protein from frog ovaries and have found in the protein a remarkable repeating structure consisting of small loops of amino acid sequences folded around zinc ions. Klug terms these loops "DNA-binding fingers." Further experiments have indicated that each of these fingers binds to and, thus, recognizes the sequence on approximately a half-turn of the DNA double helix in the nucleosome. Klug's prediction that such structures may be common to many other regulatory proteins has been confirmed.

Klug has stated that the philosophy guiding his work is to attempt to understand how complex biological systems function in terms of their structures in three dimensions and the interactions between the molecules that form them. In this difficult endeavor, he has had striking success. He often has expressed his gratitude to the Medical Research Council for continuing to support his work (rather than insisting on quick or short-term answers) throughout the many years it took to produce significant results.

In the January, 1983, issue of *Physics Today*, one of Klug's former coworkers, Donald Caspar, remarked on the man and scientist, pointing to "the dazzling range of [Klug's] accomplishments, which bears the unmistakable imprint of his talent and insight in mathematics, physics, chemistry, and biology. Conceptual barriers between different disciplines do not exist for him."

Bibliography

Primary

CHEMISTRY: "Physical Principles in the Construction of Regular Viruses," *Cold Spring Harbor Symposia on Quantitative Biology*, vol. 27, 1962 (with Donald Caspar); "The Nucleosome," *Scientific American*, February, 1981 (with Roger Kornberg); "Structure of the Nucleosome Core Particle at 7 Angstrom Resolution," *Nature*, vol. 311, 1984 (with T. J. Richmond, J. T. Finch, B. Rushton, and D. Rhodes); "Molecules on a Grand Scale," *New Scientist*, May 21, 1987.

PHYSICS: "The Nature of the Helical Groove on the Tobacco Mosaic Virus Particle," *Biochimica et Biophysica Acta*, vol. 19, 1956 (with Rosalind Franklin); "Joint Probability Distributions of Structure Factors and the Phase Problem," *Acta Crystallographica*, vol. 11, 1958; "Diffraction by Helical Structures," *Acta Crystallographica*, vol. 11, 1958 (with F. H. C. Crick and H. W. Wycoff).

Secondary

Alberts, Bruce, Dennis Bray, Julian Lewis, Martin Raff, Keith Roberts, and James Watson. *Molecular Biology of the Cell*. New York: Garland, 1989. This massive text is intended to cover the subject of cellular molecular biology. It is encyclopedic in scope but with a biological emphasis. Included is a section on microscopy with a brief discussion of X-ray diffraction and image reconstruction. Also contains a helpful section on the spherical viruses.

Chedd, Graham. *The New Biology*. New York: Basic Books, 1972. A general narrative version of the high points in the development of molecular biology. The book contains a useful chapter on the three-dimensional structure of proteins and a clear explanation of Klug's early ideas about TMV and of what the author calls the Caspar-Klug quasi-equivalance theory of the structure of the spherical viruses.

Darnell, James, Harvey Lodish, and David Baltimore. *Molecular Cell Biology.* New York: Scientific American Books, 1986. This text presents modern molecular biology in a clear fashion, providing excellent diagrams of cellular processes. There is ample introductory material on the structures of simple biomolecules and on basic biochemistry. The perspective is well balanced between biology and chemistry. The assembly of TMV and the proposed structure of chromatin are well presented.

Doolittle, Russell. "Proteins." *Scientific American*, October, 1985: 88-99. This article describes the structures of certain typical proteins and of the common amino acids from which proteins are made. The figures and diagrams are particularly helpful. There is a lengthy section on protein evolution based upon comparisons of amino acid sequences determined for the same type of protein molecules isolated from different organisms. The implications of evolution for ideas about molecular genetics are emphasized.

_____. "Structures of DNA." *Cold Spring Harbor Symposia on Quantitative Biology* 47, pts. 1/2 (1982). A general symposium on DNA structure, this volume is intended to update the ideas current among experts in the field at the time of its publication. This monograph is of interest to the lay reader because it amply demonstrates the degree of complexity that has increasingly characterized the subject of DNA since the "beautiful, simple, unifying" concept of the double helix was first proposed in 1953. The symposium volume is notable for the helpful summary of the proceedings, written by Klug, which appears at the end of part 2.

G. R. Barker
Laylin K. James

1983

Chemistry
Henry Taube, United States

Physics
Subrahmanyan Chandrasekhar, United States
William A. Fowler, United States

Physiology or Medicine
Barbara McClintock, United States

Economic Sciences
Gerard Debreu, United States

Literature
William Golding, Great Britain

Peace
Lech Wałesa, Poland

HENRY TAUBE
1983

Born: Neudorf, Saskatchewan, Canada; November 30, 1915

Nationality: American
Areas of concentration: Reaction kinetics and inorganic synthesis

Taube elucidated the accepted mechanism for inner-sphere electron transfer processes. This information has fostered important understanding concerning the function of enzymes, as well as a broader understanding of the principles underlying inorganic chemistry

The Award

Presentation

On December 10, 1983, the Nobel Prize in Chemistry was presented to Henry Taube of Stanford University. Ingvar Lindqvist, a member of the Royal Swedish Academy of Sciences, made the presentation. Lindqvist began his remarks by pointing out that most past research is forgotten, as the outlook of chemistry is constantly changing. Exceptions are contributions that have a profound impact on ideas of basic chemical relationships. These are contributions awarded in "the spirit of Alfred Nobel," and they are, in general, important to applied chemistry.

Lindqvist used concepts developed by previous Nobel winners Svante Arrhenius and Alfred Werner to show the fundamental importance of Taube's contributions. Arrhenius proposed that ionic compounds, such as table salt, exist in water as separated positive and negative ions rather than as discrete neutral molecular units. Using this definition, in solution a cobalt ion with a charge of positive three will oxidize, or remove an electron from, a chromium ion with a charge of positive two. The net effect is an increase in the charge of chromium and a decrease in that of cobalt as a result of electron transfer.

Werner refined this conceptually simple idea by proposing that metal ions in solution are surrounded by certain numbers of neutral molecules or ions, collectively called ligands, in specific geometric orientations. He would thus have explained electron transfer as involving both a change in charge of the metal ions and transfer of a ligand from one metal ion to another. This explanation offers no pathway; it describes only the initial and final states of the system.

Taube's contribution Lindqvist noted, is that he explained the mechanism, or pathway, of this process. The key item is the existence of an intermediate state in the reaction in which a ligand is bound simultaneously to both metal ions, forming a bridge between them that allows electron transfer. By extensive investigation, Taube has refined this idea, making it an important part of the paradigms of chemistry.

Nobel lecture

Henry Taube's Nobel lecture, "Electron Transfer Between Metal Complexes—

Retrospective," was presented on December 8, 1983. He began by stating that he wished to discuss in historical perspective early developments in electron transfer chemistry. His background placed him in a unique position to do so. In order to understand electron transfer, oxidation-reduction, or redox, processes and substitution processes must be understood. Redox involves coupled loss and gain of electrons between two reactants. Ligands are molecules or atoms chemically bonded to a central metal atom. This conglomerate is generally termed a complex. Substitution is a replacement of a ligand by another type of ligand, and substitution processes usually accompany a redox step. Substitution may dictate how fast the overall change proceeds.

Discovery of artificial radioactivity facilitated tracer studies of transfer reactions between like atoms with different charges. Evidence at the early stages of research indicated that substitution was involved in the mechanism. Taube cited several reasons for interest in these reactions, in which there is no apparent chemical change, then summarized significant advances in the field after World War II and outlined his own early work in electron transfer kinetics. He pointed out that he had personally performed most early experiments; his students thought that this area was less exciting than other projects. A course he taught stimulated Taube's interest in substitution in complexes. An intensive literature search enabled Taube to develop a correlation between the electronic structure of complexes and their substitution rates. He also did research to determine how many water molecules would become bonded as ligands to certain metal ions when the metal ion was placed in water. He justified this work by pointing out that in order to understand the pathway of a reaction, one must understand the initial and final states of the reaction. These early studies set the stage for crucial experiments leading to elucidation of a specific mechanism for electron transfer.

Beginning with simple test tube experiments, Taube outlined how chloride ions are transferred from one complex to another during a reaction. This occurrence was explained by his proposal that the reaction passed through a state in which the chloride formed a bridge between the metal centers. Electron transfer was coupled with this bridge formation. This interpenetration of the ligand groups on each metal was termed the inner-sphere mechanism. Taube noted that these findings were greeted with great interest when presented.

Taube then moved on to a discussion of subsequent progress in the study of inner-sphere mechanisms, such as the use of rapid mixing and measuring techniques, theoretical developments, and correlation of electron configuration with the mechanism of electron transfer. The electron configuration is the specific arrangement of electrons in a chemical substance. He also described some significant advances in descriptive chemistry, including evidence that the bridging atom in an inner-sphere process is not necessarily transferred. Other findings included processes involving transfer of two electrons.

Continuing the discussion of his own research, Taube treated investigations of different bridging groups, focusing on organic molecules with extended double bonds. This type of system theoretically provides a "conduit" for electron transfer and led to the proposal of a "hopping" model for electron transfer, in which the electron moves first from a metal center to the ligand and subsequently from the ligand to the second metal center. Further work used a system in which this hopping pathway was blocked, but transfer occurred nevertheless. Taube then mentioned how this process led to synthesis of binuclear complexes, which contain two metal centers; to the study of intramolecular electron transfer; and to the isolation of mixed valence compounds, compounds in which two identical metal atoms in the same molecule have different charges. In these complexes, absorption of light may cause movement of the electron from one center to another, and this movement may lend the substances extra stability. Taube concluded this discussion by pointing out his interest in the energetics associated with intramolecular electron transfer. In closing, he stated that knowledge of electron transfer mechanisms remained incomplete, then acknowledged his coworkers and funding agencies.

Critical reception

News of Taube's Nobel Prize was greeted with unanimous personal praise as well as praise for his many significant contributions to the science of chemistry. A certain amount of national pride surfaced in contemporary American publications as Taube's award completed what was termed a "clean sweep" of the awards by American scientists, the first time for such an occurrence since 1976. This award to Taube also continued four decades of United States domination in chemistry, according to *Time* magazine.

Taube himself was very jovial about the award, as evident in a press conference held on the campus of Stanford University, details of which were reported in *New Scientist*. He expressed his belief that there were many people equally deserving of the award. When asked by a reporter if he could explain his work in layman's terms, he replied, "Nope." Taube maintains excellent relationships with his graduate students and is very cordial with those whom he meets at seminars and meetings. Fittingly, he celebrated his award at a burger and beer party with his research group.

Much significance was attached to Taube's receipt of the award in both the popular and, to a much greater extent, the scientific press. *The New York Times* noted that the award to Taube marked a shift in the Nobel Committee's emphasis away from biochemistry, which had dominated the recent chemistry awards. Much enthusiasm for the award was expressed by fellow chemists, many of whom believed that the award was long overdue. Taube's fundamental work in developing a theory for the mode of electron transfer was widely credited within the scientific community with fostering the maturation of inorganic chemistry as a discipline. Prior to his work, it was a somewhat nebulous area in chemistry, with few well-defined predictive laws or theories. According to *New Scientist*, prior to Taube's award the field was in the "academic doldrums." Taube's elegant and sound experimentation on fundamental systems was greatly admired within the scientific community. It was his care in research that caused widespread acceptance of his results and conclusions. The startling nature of his work is well expressed in *Science*, which stated that Taube "revolutionized" understanding of oxidation-reduction processes. According to *Nature*, Taube "singlehandedly made inorganic chemistry a predictive as well as descriptive science." Taube's receipt of the Nobel Prize continued a tradition of academic excellence at Stanford; he was the fourth Nobel winner from the department of chemistry at Stanford as well as the tenth living laureate at Stanford, noted *New Scientist*.

Taube's modesty made him a "rare figure among internationally acclaimed scientists," according to *Science*. There was a general feeling that while Taube had been well honored within his profession by his peers, his work, which *New Scientist* noted was "not terribly easy to read but is experimentally solid and dependable," was not generally publicized or understood by the general public. While statements by colleagues conveyed to the public the respect that the scientific community held for Taube, many publications presented brief surveys of his career, stressing primarily those developments that had easily been seen as benefits for the public. In particular, his synthesis of technetium compounds useful in medicinal chemistry was widely cited. There remains no doubt that Taube ranks as one of the premier figures in inorganic chemistry.

Biography

Henry Taube was born on November 30, 1915, in Neudorf, Saskatchewan, to Albertina (née Tiledetzki) and Samuel Taube. He was educated in local schools and obtained his bachelor of science degree from the University of Saskatchewan in 1935. He received his master of science degree there in 1937. Taube then completed his doctorate with William C. Bray at the University of California, Berkeley, in 1940. He remained at Berkeley as an instructor for one year, then accepted a position at Cornell University.

Taube became a naturalized citizen of the United States in 1941. He remained at Cornell as an assistant professor until 1946, when he moved to the University of Chicago. He rose through the academic ranks there, reaching the rank of full professor before he left in 1961. From 1956 to 1959, he had served as the chairman of the Department of Chemistry. In 1962, Taube moved to Stanford University in California, where he has periodically served as department chairperson. While at Stanford, his primary focus has been on his research program and teaching graduate-level courses.

Taube was married to Mary Alice Weche in 1952; the couple would have four children. In addition to his Nobel Prize, Taube has received many other prestigious academic honors in recognition of his outstanding research and teaching accomplishments. Perhaps the best-known of his hobbies is his extensive collection of 78 rpm records, numbering more than eight thousand.

Scientific Career

Henry Taube's career as a researcher has focused to a great extent on fundamental studies of basic chemical processes. He has accomplished much in developing theories to explain the mechanisms of inorganic chemical reactions, as well as in synthesizing many new and interesting chemical compounds. A review of his scientific publications gives some indication of the development of his program; his work indicates a steady refinement of his ideas.

The most common thread in the tapestry of his career has been the utilization of transition metal complexes. Transition metals are elements in the central portion of the periodic table, characterized by having several stable charges, or oxidation states, as well as unusual magnetic properties. While Taube's research at first glimpse may seem uncomplicated, he routinely made use of sophisticated experimental methods and analytical techniques to provide reasonable explanations for processes not previously understood.

Taube has had a consistent interest in the field of reaction kinetics, the study of reaction rates and laws governing these. A chemical reaction often can be postulated to proceed by a sequence of simple chemical steps called a mechanism. Vigorous experimentation may support or disprove proposed mechanisms for a particular reaction. Much of Taube's research has been concerned with the proposal and defense of reaction mechanisms as well as with a study of the energy barriers in these mechanisms.

Taube's early work dealt with mechanistic studies in water of reactions of ozone with substances such as hydrogen peroxide, formic acid, or bromide. In related work, he studied the reactions of halogens, such as chlorine and iodine, with organic acids. In these studies, he uncovered evidence for chemical chain reaction mechanisms. In a chain reaction, the change is initiated by some process, such as irradiation of a compound by ultraviolet light, that results in the formation of a highly unstable reactive material such as a free radical. A free radical has a single unshared electron and typically undergoes a reaction rather rapidly. In the chain reaction mechanism, this initiation is followed by one or more propagation steps, in which the desired product and additional short-lived intermediates are produced. These intermediates are consumed in subsequent steps of the mechanism. The entire process may be ended by several possible chain termination steps. Taube studied the effect of ratios of various amounts of reactants on the rate of these reactions. Most of the systems studied during this phase of Taube's research program were found to proceed by free-radical chain reaction mechanisms. These mechanisms were determined by studying the reaction rate at various conditions to determine a mathematical expression relating the initial amount of reactants to the rate of the reaction. This expression is called the experimental rate law and includes a proportionality constant known as the rate constant. In the course of these studies, Taube found that certain substances, such as manganese ions, behaved as catalysts in the halide-acid reactions. (A catalyst speeds a reaction but is chemically unchanged in the process.) Determination of rate laws and mechanisms would continue to be a fundamental part of Taube's research.

In the late 1940's, Taube began to express interest in the chemistry of coordination compounds, which are also commonly known as complexes. In a complex, a transition metal atom is bonded chemically to several different substances, collectively known as ligands, each of which donates a pair of electrons to form the bond. Ligands may be neutral molecules or electrically charged ions. The ligands are arranged in some orderly geometric fashion about the central atom. For example, in complexes with six ligands, the ligands are arranged at the vertices of a regular octahedron centered in the metal atom. These ligands bonded directly to the central metal constitute what is known as the first coordination sphere. Other groups may be loosely arranged about the complex outside this sphere.

One aspect of complexes is that they undergo ligand substitution reactions at various rates. Some substances exchange ligands extremely rapidly, while others exchange so slowly that the exchange is virtually undetectable. One of Taube's more significant achievements was to correlate observations of exchange rates of various metal ions with the electronic structure of the complexes. Substances that undergo rapid ligand exchange are said to be labile, while those that exchange slowly are termed inert. Electrons in complexes can exist only in certain allowed energy levels, called orbitals. There are several different types of orbitals, each with its own symmetry and orientation. Taube found, qualitatively, that the lability of a complex can be related to the number of electrons present in certain orbital sets. Some complexes exist in which electrons occupy a type of high-energy orbital called an antibonding orbital. This destabilizes the metal-ligand bond and as a result increases the lability of the complex.

At the other extreme are complexes with fewer electrons to be placed in orbitals, so that energetically favorable, but empty, orbitals exist, possessing a symmetry such that a ligand electron pair can approach this orbital, and thus the complex, easily. This ease of approach leads to increased lability. Between the two extremes are complexes with an intermediate number of electrons, in which the arrangement is less amenable to ligand exchange and the complexes are inert. Taube's empirical rules were of much use to him and other inorganic chemists as knowledge of the relative lability of complexes facilitated the design of experiments dealing with oxidation-reduction chemistry.

Another area that Taube explored dealt with what seems on the surface a simple matter, the determination of hydration numbers in water of certain ions. The hydration number is simply the number of water molecules bound as ligands to a metal center. This quantity is experimentally difficult to determine, and much effort has been expended in this area. The approach of Taube and his coworkers, John Hunt, Aaron Rutenberg, Robert Plane, and Harold Feder, utilized oxygen isotopes. (Isotopes are atoms of the same element but with differing numbers of neutrons in the nucleus and different atomic weights.) Water molecules bonded as ligands should be distinguishable from unbonded water molecules in the solution when a metal ion is dissolved in water. In order to differentiate them, the metal ion was dissolved in water with a high concentration of water containing an easily detectable isotope of oxygen. The water was thus enriched with this isotope. Over time, some of this water is incorporated into the complex through ligand exchange. The resulting change in the amount of unbonded water containing the detectable isotope facilitates determination of how many water molecules are incorporated into the complex. The technique developed by Taube and his colleagues is most easily applicable to relatively inert ions, as mixing and sampling can be done rapidly relative to the rate of exchange. In general it was found that the hydration numbers corresponded to what would be expected based on the physical properties of the substances involved.

It was determination of hydration numbers that led to the groundbreaking experiments in the elucidation of the inner-sphere electron mechanism. Taube's familiarity with lability in complexes aided in the design of experiments to determine the inner-sphere mechanism. In the prototypical experiment, two complexes were utilized as reactants, chosen for their relative labilities. The first of these was a chromium complex in which the chromium had a charge of positive two. Six water molecules were bound as ligands to this metal center. In the other complex, five ammonia molecules and a negatively charged chloride ion were bound to a cobalt atom with a charge of positive three. This cobalt complex is inert to substitution, while the chromium complex is labile. When the two compounds react, some important observations may be made. The chloride ion ends up being transferred to the chromium atom, the charge of the cobalt atom is reduced by one, and the charge of the chromium atom is increased by one. Results also indicate that the chloride ion transfer is quantitative, or complete. Furthermore, when the reaction is carried out in a solution in which isotopically enriched free chloride ions are available and could potentially be incorporated, no incorporation of chloride from the solution into the final products is observed. This indicates that the chloride ion must transfer directly from one complex to the other in a single step. This information, coupled with information about the relative labilities of the reactants and products, led the researchers to the conclusion that electron transfer from the chromium atom to the cobalt atom and chloride transfer occurred in some related process. Taube's general explanation of the pathway followed in the reaction may be summarized as follows.

First, the two reactant complexes form a "precursor" complex in which a suitable ligand is bonded simultaneously to both metal centers. The labile starting complex loses one of its ligands and attaches to a ligand on the inert complex to facilitate this formation. An electron is transferred from one metal center to another, leaving a successor complex in which the bridge between the metal centers still exists. Subsequently, this complex breaks up to yield the two product complexes. Since this initial work, Taube has continued to study the inner-sphere mechanism, exploring the effect of various bridging ligands on the mechanism as well as conducting experiments to determine the actual mode of electron transfer in the mechanism. It has subsequently been found that the bridging group may be a polynuclear material and not necessarily a single atom. Taube worked with organic ligands containing a sequence of alternating double and single bonds. This alternating sequence of bonds is called a conjugated system, and electrons can move freely through this sequence of bonds. This type of bridge provides a long pathway through which an electron can move. This discovery led to the idea of a hopping mechanism, in which the electron moves first from one metal center to the bridging ligand, then from the ligand to the second metal center.

Taube also synthesized many new inorganic compounds for the purpose of studying electron transfer. The most useful of these are complexes containing two metal centers connected by some bridging group. Unlike the intermediate state in the inner-sphere mechanism, which breaks apart rapidly after the transfer of the electron, these binuclear compounds have greater stability and thus are more easily studied. A wide variety of these complexes have been produced, with interesting bridging groups such as di-nitrogen. Binuclear complexes provide a means to study intramolecular transfer, electron transfer within a molecule. A related type of complex is one in which the metal centers are the same element, but the charges differ. These are known as mixed-valence compounds and offer the opportunity to study in greater detail the electron transfer process. It often happens that absorption of light causes the electron to transfer from one atom to another, causing intense color in the complex. Thus these mixed-valence complexes have interesting spectral properties as well.

With Carol Creutz, Taube produced a di-ruthenium complex in which a pyrazine ring bridges the two metals, which is commonly known as the Creutz-Taube ion. In mixed-valence complexes, the charge of the metals may be localized or delocalized. In other words, if electron transfer is slow, then the two metal atoms should have distinct charges, making the structure of the complex immediately about the two metal centers slightly different. These differences can be detected by various analytical methods. On the other hand, the electron may move very rapidly back and forth between the two metal centers, a situation known as resonance delocalization. If this is the case, distinct charges on the two metal centers will not be detectable and the structure about the two centers will be identical, so that the complex will be symmetrical. Applying methods of measurement that operate on differing time scales makes it possible to determine the time scale of electron transfer. These compounds are also useful in studies to determine the energy barriers to electron transfer. Taube's career-long interest in electron transfer chemistry has benefited many researchers in the scientific community.

One of the more exotic compounds synthesized by Taube and coworker Richard Armstrong was a technetium compound with ammonia ligands. Technetium presents special synthetic problems, as it is a synthetic element and must be produced by some sort of nuclear reaction, either by bombardment or as a fission product. This compound and other technetium compounds have been very useful in the field of nuclear medicine, specifically for noninvasive internal organ examinations, as the complexes are gamma emitters. Another significant finding, of Taube and Daniel Geselowitz, was stereoselective behavior in an outer-sphere process. Stereoselectivity is the preferential formation of only one product out of several possible product structures.

This brief overview only partially represents the breadth and importance of the research career of Henry Taube. His work stands on its own merit, and further proof of its importance is the impressive list of honors that he has accumulated over the years. Among his awards are the Priestley Medal of the American Chemical Society in 1984 and the Award in Chemical Sciences of the National Academy of Sciences, as well as numerous honorary degrees. Perhaps the most telling proof of the importance of his research to the field of inorganic chemistry is the universal incorporation of his inner-sphere mechanism and lability rules into inorganic chemistry textbooks.

Bibliography

Primary
CHEMISTRY: "The Production of Atomic Iodine in the Reaction of Peroxides with Iodide Ion," *Journal of the American Chemical Society*, 1942; "Rates and Mechanisms of Substitution in Inorganic Complexes in Solution," *Chemical Reviews*, 1952; "Use of Oxygen Isotope Effects in the Study of Hydration of Ions," *Journal of Physical Chemistry*, 1954; "Evidence for a Bridged Activated Complex for Electron Transfer Reactions," *Journal of the American Chemical Society*, 1954 (with Howard Myers); "The Role of Kinetics in Teaching Inorganic Chemistry," *Journal of Chemical Education*, 1959; "Formation of $Ru(NH_3)_5N_2^{2+}$ in Aqueous Solution by Direct Action of Molecular Nitrogen," *Journal of the American Chemical Society*, 1967 (with David Ellsworth Harrison); "Direct Approach to Measuring the Franck-Condon Barrier to Electron Transfer Between Metal Ions," *Journal of the American Chemical Society*, 1969 (with Carol Creutz); "Organic Molecules as Bridging Groups in Electron Transfer Reactions," *Accounts of Chemical Research*, 1969 (with Edwin Gould); "Rates of Intramolecular Electron Transfer," *Journal of the American Chemical Society*, 1973 (with Stephen Isied); "Mixed Valence Compounds of Ruthenium Ammines with 4, 4 ' Bipyridine as Bridging Ligand," *Journal of the American Chemical Society*, 1974 (with Glenn Tom and Carol Creutz); "Chemistry of Trans-aquonitrosyltetraammine-technetium(I) and Related Studies," *Inorganic Chemistry*, 1976 (with Richard Armstrong); "Stereoselectivity in Electron Transfer Reactions," *Journal of the American Chemical Society*, 1980 (with Daniel Geselowitz); "Redox-Promoted Linkage Isomerizations of Aldehydes and Ketones on Pentaammineosmium," *Journal of the American Chemical Society*, 1988 (with Dean Harman and Mikiya Sekine).

Secondary
Cotton, F. A., and G. Wilkinson. *Advanced Inorganic Chemistry*. 5th ed. New York: John Wiley & Sons, 1988. One of the more comprehensive texts, it contains an immense body of material and provides detailed discussion of many areas of Taube's research. Included is a section on technetium as well as detailed discussion of inorganic reaction mechanisms. The book is extremely well referenced.

Creutz, Carol. "Mixed Valence Complexes of d^5-d^6 Metal Centers." In *Progress in Inorganic Chemistry.* Vol. 30. New York: John Wiley & Sons, 1983. A lengthy technical article by the codiscoverer of the Creutz-Taube ion, this well-referenced work deals in depth with stabilities, classification, and energetics of mixed-valence dinuclear compounds.

Haim, Albert. "Mechanisms of Electron Transfer Reactions: The Bridged Activated Complex." In *Progress in Inorganic Chemistry.* Vol. 30. New York: John Wiley & Sons, 1983. An excellent detailed work on history, experimental work, and specific chemical behavior and mechanisms peculiar to electron transfer reactions. It is a more detailed work than Taube's Nobel lecture, and work of many researchers is presented in this extensive, well-referenced review.

Jolly, William. *Modern Inorganic Chemistry.* New York: McGraw-Hill, 1984. This intermediate-level text is written with an excellent narrative style and affords the reader with some chemistry background an excellent explanation of much of Taube's work. Within the text are discussions of electron transfer, mixed-valence compounds, and other aspects of coordination chemistry.

Craig B. Lagrone

1984

Chemistry
Robert Bruce Merrifield, United States

Physics
Carlo Rubbia, Italy
Simon van der Meer, The Netherlands

Physiology or Medicine
Niels K. Jerne, Denmark
Georges J. F. Köhler, West Germany
César Milstein, Great Britain

Economic Sciences
Sir Richard Stone, Great Britain

Literature
Jaroslav Seifert, Czechoslovakia

Peace
Desmond Tutu, South Africa

ROBERT BRUCE MERRIFIELD
1984

Born: Fort Worth, Texas; July 15, 1921

Nationality: American
Area of concentration: Protein and peptide synthesis

Merrifield's methods of synthesizing proteins and peptides catapulted biochemistry into a new era. Biomolecules that previously would have been almost impossible to make could be produced within a few weeks, contributing to advances in immunology, genetics, and biotechnology

The Award

Presentation

Bengt Lindberg delivered the presentation address for the awarding of the 1984 Nobel Prize in Chemistry to Robert Bruce Merrifield. Expressing the sentiments of the Royal Swedish Academy of Sciences, Lindberg, a chemist at the University of Stockholm, recognized Merrifield as a scientist whose work was a watershed in protein and peptide synthesis. Lindberg cited historical developments in chemistry that significantly influenced events leading to Merrifield's work. Among those mentioned was Emil Fischer, Nobel laureate of 1902. Although Fischer won his Nobel Prize for research on sugars and purines, he had proposed a peptide synthetic method that was widely used during the sixty intervening years leading to the Merrifield method. He also first suggested the concept of protecting various reactive portions of amino acids, the materials necessary to make proteins. Unfortunately, the Fischer concept was simpler in design than in reality. The ensuing chemical tangles caused much grief to designers of protein molecules.

Other laureates named included Vincent du Vigneaud (1955), for his synthesis of a hormone, oxytocin, which is a small peptide that can prompt uterine contractions; Fredrick Sanger (1958), for work in determining the full amino acid sequence in the hormone insulin, which regulates the amount of blood sugar; and the research team of Stanford Moore and William H. Stein (1972), for determining the sequence, or order, of amino acids in a biologically active enzyme, ribonuclease. Ribonuclease is a protein that functions as an enzyme, or biological catalyst, which works upon the genetically important ribonucleic acid (RNA). Merrifield made this molecule in 1971, using his solid phase peptide synthesis. The molecule made in the laboratory showed the same type of chemical activity as the molecule isolated from nature.

In his closing comments, Lindberg praised Merrifield for the concept and development of "a completely new approach to organic synthesis [which] has created new possibilities" for advances in medical research in pharmacology, biochemistry, molecular biology, and genetic engineering. To the thousands of research biochemists who use this method, the statement is irrefutable.

Nobel lecture

Robert Bruce Merrifield delivered his Nobel lecture, "Solid Phase Synthesis," on December 8, 1984, to an audience of faculty, students, and noted scientists. Merrifield opened his presentation with a historical account of the conceptualization, development, and applications of his solid phase peptide synthesis (SPPS). In his introductory statement, Emil Fischer was recognized as the originator of the concept of laboratory synthesis of proteins. Merrifield reflected upon the successes of researchers such as Vincent du Vigneaud, who synthesized an important biological hormone using the approach of Emil Fischer. Vigneaud's accomplishment was noteworthy and valiant.

The obstacles to synthesizing large, biologically important proteins captured the imagination of the young biochemist. Revealing the problems associated with the Fischer design—namely, product yield and purity, the lengthy time and human effort required, and the awkwardness of repeatedly having to shuffle small molecules through a complex series of chemical reactions—Merrifield explained what had motivated him to pursue advances in protein and peptide research. Specifically, his goal was to develop a methodology that simultaneously would be simple, expedient, and productive, resulting in both high purity and high yield of the desired protein.

Merrifield further described how the solid phase concept was a creative, refreshing new approach that eliminated many of the haunting problems encountered in traditional liquid phase chemistry. Amino acids could be sequentially added to build large protein structures if the starting amino acid were securely anchored to a solid support, or resin. The molecule could be custom designed as needed within one reaction vessel.

Merrifield continued with details pertaining to the physical and chemical qualities necessary in a suitable solid support. In a chronological manner, he traced much of his research. Original work in the automated design of an SPPS instrument was described, as was the ultimate success in synthesizing a biologically active enzyme, ribonuclease. At last, a completely automated laboratory system successfully produced a biologically sound, and active, molecule from what had once been jars of chemicals housed among laboratory shelves.

Merrifield's closing statements affirmed the powerful impact of SPPS methodology on biochemistry. The use of the SPPS synthetic routes can be found in cases of drugs developed to treat diabetes insipidus, hyponatremia, and Paget's disease; of potential vaccine developments; of potential synthetic hormones that could regulate growth or prevent dwarfism; or of the use of human leucocyte interferon in combating cancer. Merrifield noted that there were other scientists utilizing this technique with encouraging results and stated that he was optimistic about future developments.

Critical reception

The name Robert Bruce Merrifield was already synonymous with protein and peptide chemistry by the time of the 1984 Nobel announcement. Undergraduate students had learned of the Merrifield synthesis of proteins and peptides in biochemistry textbooks, such as the popular text written by Albert Lehninger. Graduate students had applied solid phase synthetic techniques to their own research. In many laboratories, Ph.D. scholars fed from the success of Merrifield's SPPS concept as it pertained to disciplines of organic chemistry, biochemistry, pharmacology, immunology, and genetics. Many researchers, therefore, felt that Merrifield's receipt of the Nobel award was more than deserved, if not overdue; he had, after all, published his original work on SPPS in the *Journal of the American Chemical Society* in 1963. An article printed in *Nature* reports that "the number of synthetic peptides prepared with its [SPPS's] aid must now be counted in the thousands. . . . [Clearly] the impact of Merrifield's work is without question."

Perhaps only one person, the chemist himself, was surprised at the October 17 announcement. The laureate was conducting research at Rockefeller University, where he had been since 1949, at the time of the prestigious recognition. According to E. T. (Tom) Kaiser, who wrote an article for *Science*, Merrifield learned of his world acclaim, not from a member of the Royal Swedish Academy, but rather from a laboratory assistant. The author of the article, entitled "The 1984 Nobel Prize in Chemistry," who was also a professor of bioorganic chemistry and biochemistry at Rockefeller University, described the event as "entirely consistent with the modest and self-effacing manner" of Bruce Merrifield.

In the German journal *Deutsche medicinische Wochenschrift*, G. F. Domagk of Göttingen commented on the high productivity of Nobel-winning research conducted at Rockefeller University, the academic home to nineteen recipients. To the author of the article, "Chemie-Nobelpreis 1984," this fact seemed rather phenomenal, especially so given, from a European time scale, the relative youth of that university.

Biography

On July 15, 1921, in Forth Worth, Texas, Robert Bruce Merrifield, the first and only child of George and Lorene Lucas Merrifield, was born. In 1922, his father left his job as a salesman with Manning's department store and moved the family to California. His father repeatedly moved the small family along the California coast in an attempt to find a good sales market; young Bruce attended roughly a dozen schools during his primary and middle-school years. Eventually his family settled in Montebello, California, where they lived for five years. There, Merrifield attended Montebello High School. He joined the Astronomy Club (which his chemistry teacher had organized and advised) and later recalled a project in which each of the club members built a telescope. Merrifield fondly remembered building the tube and frame necessary to hold the mirrors and lenses, which he ground and polished by hand; he also remembered that it worked. Merrifield later speculated that even as a youngster he wanted to be a chemist.

In 1939, Merrifield was graduated from Montebello High School and set forth to pursue studies in chemistry. Pasadena City College, a junior college, gave him a good educational start. While there, Merrifield volunteered to be an assistant in the teaching laboratories. His chemistry professor allowed him to gain experience in the analytical chemistry laboratories, where he assisted students and took care of chemical reagents.

After completing his first two years of college study, he transferred to the University of California at Los Angeles (UCLA). As a college senior, Merrifield joined Max Dunn, a professor of biochemistry, as a part-time laboratory assistant. Dunn was operating a nonprofit laboratory that synthesized amino acids exclusively for the scientific research community. There Merrifield learned how to synthesize a substance called DOPA (dihydroxyphenylalanine); dopamine would later prove medically important in the treatment of Parkinson's disease. In 1943, he was graduated with a bachelor's degree in chemistry.

Merrifield's position was with the Philip R. Park Research Foundation, a company that produced vitamin supplements to be added to animal feeds. His duties included determining the amount of vitamin D that animals absorbed from their diets, as well as cleaning cages. Since most of his work was nonchemical, he found himself wondering if he wanted this kind of job for a lifetime. One year later, the young chemist went back to UCLA to begin graduate studies in chemistry.

While in graduate school, Merrifield once again worked with Dunn, but this time he served as a teaching assistant in the biochemistry laboratories. He also received a fellowship sponsored by Anheuser-Busch, which provided him with the funds required to do his doctoral work. Later, he was a research assistant at the UCLA medical school. Under Dunn's guidance, Merrifield worked on his doctoral dissertation, through which he developed microbiological methods to quantify the presence of purines and pyrimidines. He received his Ph.D. in 1949 from UCLA.

Merrifield became a Ph.D. chemist on a Sunday; on Monday he married his girlfriend, Elizabeth Furlong, a zoology student whom he had met during his first week of graduate school; and on Tuesday the newlyweds departed from California to pursue their dreams in New York City. An assistantship awaited Merrifield at the Rockefeller Institute for Medical Research, as the Rockefeller University was then known. He began his chemical research there in 1949 and has remained there for all of his career. He became an assistant professor in 1957, was promoted to associate professor in 1958, and became full professor in 1966.

Over the years, Merrifield became recognized by his peers as a chemist of excellence. He received numerous awards, medals, and recognitions. Some of the more familiar ones are the Lasker Award for Basic Medical Research (1969), the American Chemical Society Award (1972), the Nichols Medal (1973), and the Alan E. Pierce Award (1979). After becoming a Nobel laureate, he continued to receive honors and recognitions. Particularly noteworthy was his induction into the Chicago Museum of Science and Industry's Nobel Hall of Science in 1985.

Merrifield's proliferation of scientific publications, lectures, and positions on the editorial boards of *The International Journal of Peptide and Protein Research* and several other journals, keep him in the forefront of chemical research. Merrifield has a family of six children, five daughters and one son. The family resides in Cresskill, New Jersey.

Scientific Career

Robert Bruce Merrifield was a born inventor. As a boy he enjoyed building models and motors, and he secretly believed that it would be his destiny to invent something great, although he could not then have guessed what. Within one week of receiving his Ph.D., his career as a professional chemist began when he moved to work under the supervision of D. W. Woolley of Rockefeller University in 1949. Woolley greatly inspired his junior investigator, who plunged into synthesizing protein molecules according to the classical methods.

In his early years at Rockefeller, Merrifield mastered the ability to determine the sequence, or order, of amino acid units that made compounds known as protein growth factors. The protein growth factors are actually hormones that have a special biological function in regulating various stages of growth and maturation. Determining the sequence is the first step in understanding how these molecules function in a living system. This activity, along with his synthetic work, kept Merrifield busy in the laboratory.

After a ten-year period of classical methodology, Merrifield had grown weary of having to take so many steps to produce new chemical bonds. In order to make even the simplest dipeptide, which has only two amino acid units linked chemically to each other, his procedure had been as follows: For the first amino acid, he would have to block, or protect, reactive parts that he did not want altered; the same protective steps were followed for the second amino acid; after that, he would combine the first amino acid to the second one. The two amino acids would then form a new chemical bond, which is called a peptide bond. Once the dipeptide was prepared, it had to be isolated, or recovered, from the reaction mixture. This process required a lengthy crystallization step.

It does not require a trained chemist to recognize that this process is laborious and tedious. Also, if a nine-member peptide were needed for a research problem, the entire process would have to be repeated nine times. The synthesis of large molecules made of several hundred amino acids, which are called proteins, would require years to make, and the amount of final protein product would be very small.

On May 26, 1959, Bruce Merrifield scrawled in his research notebook an idea that he called a "New Approach to the Continous, Stepwise Synthesis of Peptides." Within his entry, he described the basic principles of what would become known as solid phase peptide synthesis. He outlined a synthetic pathway that would use a solid material to which he would attach one amino acid. After the first connection, other amino acids would be added in the sequence necessary to design a particular peptide. Once the chemists had all the units in place, the completed chain could then be chemically plucked off the solid support. A completed peptide or protein can be used as nature designed it to function, or for testing what can go wrong.

The envisioned advantage of this newly proposed design was that it would circumvent the need to crystallize between each step, since all the peptide would be anchored onto a solid support. Washings could be done between each step without fear of losing the growing peptide. Perhaps most appealing of all was the fact that one could dream of automating the process. This dream led to the construction of a peptide-making machine.

An article printed in *Chemical and Engineering News* (August 2, 1971) describes Woolley's first response to his junior associate's idea. As Merrifield remembered, "He didn't say much when I suggested the idea to him. [He] just got off the elevator and that was that. [The] next day he came into my office and said, 'Do you know about that idea you were talking about yesterday? Maybe you ought to try it.'"

With his mentor's approval, Merrifield launched a research campaign. He would use a solid material, cellulose, for his solid support. It was then that the challenges began to appear. Every step in the problem, which he thought would be simple to solve, became a chemical ordeal. A project that he thought could be completed in three months required three years. An account of this time in his life appeared in *Research Profiles*, which quoted Merrifield as saying, "During all that time, I produced no publications and it didn't appear I was making progress. In some other places, I think there would have been raised eyebrows."

Finally, in 1962, Merrifield presented his research to a group of fellow scientists at a Federation of American Societies for Experimental Biology (FASEB) meeting. The lecture was delivered before a skeptical and critical audience, but their comments and questions drove Merrifield onward in his effort to produce a scientifically credible document. The resulting publication appeared in the *Journal of the American Chemical Society* the following year. "Solid Phase Peptide Synthesis. I. The Synthesis of a Tetrapeptide" (July 20, 1963) is a thorough, precise, and beautiful piece of chemistry. It was clearly a major accomplishment in organic and biochemical syntheses.

Bruce Merrifield has claimed that his success is a result of his self-prescribed attribute of being "a plodder." Perhaps his career best demonstrates the principle that "good things come to those who wait." After going public with his SPPS methods, Merrifield set his goals on producing biologically important protein and peptide molecules and on developing an automated peptide-making machine. Several of his publications describe how SPPS methods were used to make a variety of compounds.

In particular, bradykinin, a nonapeptide known to lower blood pressure, to cause the sensation of pain, and to prompt smooth muscle contractions, was produced in his laboratory. Merrifield demonstrated that the synthesized peptide had the same biochemical activity as the naturally occurring peptide. In addition, the nonapeptide had been completely made in one week. Surprisingly, another Rockefeller chemist working with Woolley, John Stewart, had also been working on a bradykinin synthesis, by conventional methods. It took him approximately one year to produce his first three analogues. Stewart then adopted the new solid phase technique and was able to produce some fifty complete preparations within the same time period.

With this news, Merrifield and Stewart decided to join their efforts to build a prototype automatic peptide synthesizer using SPPS techniques. The two chemists worked evenings, weekends, and countless hours building the model in the basement of Merrifield's home. With Stewart acting as the electrician and Merrifield as the plumber, a third party was recruited—Nils Jernberg, who developed the switching valves. The major components included a reservoir for dispensing reactants and solvents, a rotary valve system that directed the chemicals from the reservoirs to the reaction vessel, and a rotating metal drum that controlled the time and rate of chemical delivery. The resulting prototype looks a bit antiquated today, but in 1965 it was a mechanical marvel. Since then, the original machine has been modified to include microprocessors and computers to control the time and rate of chemical delivery.

The chemical flair of the mechanized machine was eloquently demonstrated when Bernd Gutte and Bruce Merrifield synthesized an important enzyme, ribonuclease, which is involved in the degradation of nucleic acid. In a press conference held on January 16, 1968, Merrifield explained that the production of this enzyme required 369 chemical reactions, had involved 11,931 steps in the machine's drum program, and required only a few weeks of laboratory work to produce. Moreover, the synthesized enzyme showed identical chemical composition and 80 percent of the chemical activity of the native (naturally occurring) enzyme. If any scientists were still skeptical about Merrifield's work, their numbers were rapidly decreasing.

Since the ribonuclease production, Merrifield and his graduate students have synthesized such peptide hormones as glucagon, which aids in the regulation of blood sugar, and thymosin, which activates the production of T-cells in the immunological system. The group has also synthesized neuropeptides, which control brain functions, and peptide growth factors, such as epidermal growth factor, which prompts skin growth and may give clues as to what causes skin cancer. Additional work on producing toxins, which would permit the investigation of their role in damaging living systems, as well as synthesizing antibacterial proteins, has been done.

Devoted to peptide and protein research, Robert Bruce Merrifield has never tired of his work, continuing to publish numerous major scientific works, appearing in films showcasing his research, and lecturing on the progress and importance of protein and peptide research.

Bibliography

Primary

CHEMISTRY: "Solid Phase Peptide Synthesis. I. The Synthesis of a Tetrapeptide," *Journal of the American Chemical Society,* vol. 85, 1963; "Automated Synthesis of Proteins," *Science,* vol. 150, 1965; "Solid Phase Synthesis of the Cyclododecadepsipeptide Valinomycin," *Journal of the American Chemical Society,* vol. 91, 1969; "Regeneration of Activity by Mixture of Ribonuclease Enzymatically

Degraded from the COOH Terminus and a Synthetic COOH-terminal Tetradeca-peptide," *Journal of Biological Chemistry*, vol. 245, 1970; "Reactivation of Des (119-, 120-, or 121-124) Ribonuclease A by Mixture with Synthetic COOH-terminal Peptides of Varying Lengths," *Journal of Biological Chemistry*, vol. 247, 1972; "Quantitative Monitoring of Solid-Phase Peptide Synthesis by the Nin-hydrin Reaction," *Analytical Biochemistry*, vol. 117, 1981; "Synthesis of the Anti-bacterial Peptide Cecropin A (1-33)," *Biochemistry*, vol. 21, 1982; "A New Base-Catalyzed Reaction for the Preparation of Protected Peptides," *Tetrahedron*, vol. 40, 1984; "A General Approach to the Quantitation of Synthetic Efficiency in Solid-Phase Synthesis as a Function of Chain Length," *Journal of the American Chemical Society*, vol. 106, 1984; "Solid Phase Synthesis," *Science*, vol. 232, 1986.

Secondary

"The Chemical Innovators 15: R. Bruce Merrifield, Designer of Protein-Making Machine." *Chemical and Engineering News*, August 2, 1971: 22-26. An excellent article that describes Bruce Merrifield as a researcher as well as a person. It is well written, and the majority of the contents will make sense even to the novice.

Creighton, Thomas E. *Proteins: Structures and Molecular Properties*. New York: W. H. Freeman, 1984. This well-written text is for those persons who have some scientific background in chemistry, biology, or biochemistry. It gives a full treat-ment to the topic and discusses the role of proteins in living systems, their biosynthesis, structural aspects, and physical and chemical properties. The cor-relation between structure and function is investigated.

Dickerson, Richard E., and Irving Geis. *The Structure and Action of Proteins*. New York: Harper & Row, 1969. Although this book is dated as a science document, it is an excellent introduction to protein chemistry. With only five chapters, it sweeps through the many roles that proteins perform in biological systems and reveals structural details of these essential molecules.

Kaiser, E. T. "The 1984 Nobel Prize in Chemistry." *Science* 226 (1984): 1151-1153. This article is written by a former colleague of Bruce Merrifield; it reveals some personal insights. Portions are rather technical, but Kaiser is careful to avoid losing the reader. A chronological history of protein chemistry is given in brief.

Lehninger, Albert. *Biochemistry*. 4th ed. New York: Worth, 1975. This is an aca-demic approach to biochemistry. Some chapters specifically address the subject of proteins, or proteins serving specialized roles. This book will challenge those persons who have little chemistry background, but segments will be easily understood.

1986 Yearbook of Science and the Future. Chicago: Encyclopædia Britannica, 1986. This is a synopsis of Bruce Merrifield's work and the importance of his research. It is a brief piece, but is an excellent start for those less familiar with biochem-istry.

"The Road to Stockholm." *The Rockefeller University Research Profiles*, Spring,

1985: 1-6. This publication is available through the public information office at the university. It is a delightfully personal look at Bruce Merrifield and an excellently written overview of Merrifield's work. Can be appreciated by beginners as well as scholars.

Stewart, John M., and Janis D. Young. *Solid Phase Peptide Synthesis*. San Francisco: W. H. Freeman, 1969. This book gives a full and detailed description of the materials and equipment needed for SPPS. The chemistry of the solid support and resin is presented along with very specific synthetic procedures. It is a priceless book that documented SPPS when interest in this technique was at its peak. Contains a foreword by Merrifield.

"The Turn of the Peptide." *New Scientist*, October 25, 1984: 11-12. This brief article gives a clear explanation of the chemical beauty of the SPPS technique. While it is easy to read, it is equally informative.

Mary C. Fields

1985

Chemistry
Herbert A. Hauptman, United States
Jerome Karle, United States

Physics
Klaus von Klitzing, West Germany

Physiology or Medicine
Michael S. Brown, United States
Joseph L. Goldstein, United States

Economic Sciences
Franco Modigliani, United States

Literature
Claude Simon, France

Peace
International Physicians for the Prevention of Nuclear War

By-VARDEN

HERBERT A. HAUPTMAN
1985

Born: New York, New York; February 14, 1917

Nationality: American
Area of concentration: X-ray crystallography

Using X rays diffracted off the inner atomic planes of molecular crystals, Hauptman devised a mathematical method for determining molecular structure that solved the problem of phase differences between scattered X rays. As a result of his work, numerous complex chemical structures have been elucidated

The Award
Presentation

The award speech for Herbert A. Hauptman's 1985 Nobel Prize in Chemistry was given on December 10, 1985, by Professor Ingvar Lindqvist, of the Royal Swedish Academy of Sciences. He began by indicating the difference between the open acceptance of the idea of atoms and molecules today with the skepticism of the past, a marked disbelief removed in the late nineteenth century through the works of Jacobus van't Hoff, August Kekulé, and Alfred Werner. He pointed out that it was the twentieth century when methods finally became available to determine the structure of molecules, including geometrical arrangements and bonding distances between atoms.

The method of choice became X-ray crystallography, first investigated by Max von Laue and William and Lawrence Bragg, all of whom received Nobel Prizes in Physics for their work. Problems arose, because phase differences between different scattered X rays were not known or solvable. From 1950 to 1956, work by Hauptman and cowinner Jerome Karle allowed the possibility of determining structures from experimental data to be considered. Based on two assumptions—electron density and the applicability of statistical methods—their method became extremely efficient, using computers to produce quite complex structures. This has enabled molecules of desired structures to be produced and has also allowed previously unknown reaction mechanisms to be delineated.

Nobel lecture

Herbert A. Hauptman's Nobel lecture, given on December 9, 1985, was entitled "Direct Methods and Anomalous Dispersion." Pointing out that, prior to the 1950's, the view held was that crystal structures could not be determined by diffraction data, Hauptman presented the mathematical view of the phase problem associated with the method that he and Karle developed (the traditional direct method) of affixing structure. He explained how the electron density functions in a molecule to determine the diffraction pattern when crystals are considered to be composed of discrete atoms, each a discrete, nonvibrating point body under an electron density. The problem then can be solved in principle, the observed diffraction intensities overdetermining the crystal structure.

Hauptman showed that the "phases" can be considered as linear combinations of X-ray phases, called structure invariants, whose values were fixed by the structure of the unit cell for the crystal, and of seminvariants, for crystals with elements of symmetry. The theory of such seminvariants led to an understanding of origin and enantiomorph (that is, right- or left-handedness) specification. These structure seminvariants served to link the magnitudes with the desired phases, the fundamental principle of direct methods, leading to probability distributions for the electrons and atoms in the crystal and defining the neighborhood for each atom. Hauptman illustrated the procedure for the two-phase structure seminvariant in the space group P1 (where no element of symmetry is present). Probabilistic techniques were used to eliminate position uncertainties, allowing relations between the unknown phases to have probabilistic validity and affixing the atoms and their neighbors in space.

Hauptman then showed how the direct method, based on complex valued functions of (sin θ/λ), coupled with the neighborhood concept, can be used when anomalous scatterers are present, specifically the conditional probability distribution of the three-phase structure invariant. Hauptman mentioned the works of M. G. Rossmann, W. A. Hendrickson, and M. M. Teeter to illustrate how the presence of such scatterers actually facilitates the determination of crystal structures. He detailed the fusion of the two techniques and showed how it can be applied, using, for example, cytochrome c(550) of molecular weight 14,500. Hauptman concluded that combining the two methods gave models of unprecedented accuracy even for macromolecular crystal structures. Such usage has already given the solution of the unknown macromolecular structure Cd, Zn-Metallothionein.

Critical reception

The 1985 Nobel Prize in Chemistry was met with a round of international agreement as to the justification of the announcement. Hauptman and Jerome Karle, who had collaborated on the original work, using phase differences of diffracted X rays to locate the detailed structure of complex molecules, were considered deserving of the honor for their ability to solve a problem that had held back structural determination from taking its place as a meaningful realm of chemical knowledge. X-ray crystallography as a mature science had been pretty well ignored by the Nobel Committee for years, but that oversight was remedied with the 1985 award, given to Hauptman and Karle for their achievement in the development of direct methods for the determinations of crystal structures. As reported by *Physics Today* (December, 1985), many chemists, physicists, and biologists, ones whose works relied heavily on the crystallographic methods made possible by the two crystallographers, felt the prize long overdue.

Roughly three decades after the development of the mathematical method for affixing the three-dimensional structure of molecules by using the information supplied by diffracting X rays, it had been recognized that no chemist working with structures could survive without this Nobel Prize-winning work. As *Time* and *Newsweek* (October 28, 1985) put it, the honor was not entirely unexpected. As Karle remarked, "You get the clue that there are people around the world who are recommending you for something important. Still, when it happens, one is shocked." The remainder of the scientific community that routinely dealt with determination of chemical structures found the award endearing and rightly given, as was noted in *Science* (January 24, 1986). Colleagues of Dr. Hauptman at the private Medical Foundation of Buffalo were even more excited, both for him and for their little-known institution. Dr. Jane Griffin remarked, "There's no one could be jealous of this man; he's extremely popular." Dr. Hauptman's reaction was more expansive. "There was a lot of reaction to it [his technique], mostly because it wasn't understood. It was highly mathematical, and crystallographers didn't have the training to understand it. It was not generally accepted until the middle 1960's or so, when more and more people began to use it." He was extremely proud to have been awarded the prize, believing that it reflected well on his peers.

Biography

Herbert A. Hauptman was born on February 14, 1917, in New York City, the oldest child of three boys born to Israel Hauptman and Leah (née Rosenfeld). His interests in science and mathematics began very early, and they were evident through elementary school into high school. Deciding to excel in mathematics, he obtained his bachelor of science degree in mathematics from the City College of New York in 1937 and a master of arts degree in mathematics from Columbia University in 1939. He married Edith Citrynell on November 10, 1940, and they had two daughters, Barbara and Carol.

After serving in World War II, he decided to obtain an advanced degree. While working at the Naval Research Laboratory in Washington, D.C. (1947), Hauptman enrolled in the doctoral program at the University of Maryland, receiving his Ph.D. in 1954; his thesis was entitled "An N-Dimensional Euclidean Algorithm." While at the Naval Research Laboratory, he met and teamed with Jerome Karle, and together they laid the foundation of the direct method in X-ray crystallography.

In 1970, he became a professor of biophysics at the State University of New York at Buffalo. That year, he also joined the crystallographic group of the Medical Foundation of Buffalo, a private laboratory. He became research director there in 1972, then vice president. His work on the phase problem continued after he won the Nobel Prize, extending the groundwork he had laid in the 1970's for the probabilistic theories of the higher-order structure invariants and seminvariants formulated in his neighborhood principle and extension concept.

In more recent years, Hauptman has been attempting to combine the traditional techniques of direct methods with isomorphous replacement and anomalous dispersion in the solution of the problem of macromolecular crystal structures. A working professional, Hauptman also loves classical music, spends an hour daily swimming, and, in his spare time, designs stained glass in exquisite geometrical patterns. He enjoys long walks with his wife, during which he often thinks through the mathematical problems of his research.

Scientific Career

In 1947, Hauptman commenced working at the Naval Research Laboratory in Washington, D.C., collaborating with Jerome Karle in attempting to solve the phase problem of X-ray crystallography. Before this work, now considered to be pioneering, scientists working on molecular structures in three dimensions of even moderately large molecules had to proceed by some form of indirect sleight-of-hand. Crystals and minerals without a center of symmetry were ignored, while some molecules of importance, but without heavy atoms, took months or years to solve. Even then, the solutions were inadequate.

X rays, developed as a tool by Max von Laue and William and Lawrence Bragg (father and son), served as the most convincing demonstration of crystals being formed with regular arrangements of atoms. Each of the discrete atomic planes within the crystalline structure tends to reflect incoming X rays in such a manner as to form a unique X-ray diffraction pattern, with each pattern identifying a particular crystal structure repeated by the unit cell. In the intensities and phases of the diffraction pattern, Hauptman reasoned, there was also information about the molecules making up the crystal. The original rule to build such three-dimensional structures said that each diffraction pattern spot was a term in a Fourier transform of the molecular structure. This turned out to be a tremendous stumbling block, since few chemists had the extensive mathematical backgrounds needed to deal with Fourier transforms. Furthermore, photographic film adequately recorded intensity but not phases of X rays. Crystallographers had to invent various tricks to get around the phase problem, the primary idea being to substitute heavy atoms at selected positions in the molecule; the heavy atoms act as markers. Information was obtained by comparing patterns from modified and unmodified molecules. The technique was not very accurate, however, being based more on inspired guesswork than "good" science.

In the 1950's, Hauptman and Karle began to work on the idea that a mathematical solution could be derived for the phase problem, one that might lead to a direct determination of molecular structure. Their 1953 monograph, *Solution of the Phase Problem, I. The Centrosymmetric Crystal*, laid the foundation of the direct method in X-ray crystallography. The monograph contained their main ideas, the most important of which was the introduction of probabilistic methods—in particular, the joint probability distribution of several structure factors, the essential tool for phase determination. They introduced the concepts of the structure invariants and seminvariants, special linear combinations of the phases, and used them to devise solutions for structures found in centrosymmetric space groups.

Hauptman's reasoning was based on a straightforward counting argument. Originally, an X-ray beam was aimed at the crystal. As the beam traveled through the crystal body, the atoms present diffracted, or scattered, the X rays, producing fuzzy spots of varying intensity on the photographic film. The pattern that was produced somewhat resembled a string of beads. To overcome the tedious practice of scrutinizing the film, Hauptman contrived a complex statistical formula that used the position and brightness of the separate spots and reconstructed them into a three-dimensional picture of the crystal. Hauptman and Karle reasoned that, although the electron density distribution in the crystal seemed to be complicated, with mathematical analysis it could be broken down to a superposition of the electron densities of the component atoms, a feature already known. The information to do this was contained in the intensities of the diffraction spots. Noting that electron density can never be negative, Hauptman reasoned that this fact implied an infinite set of inequalities among the phases and magnitudes of the scattered X rays. Using statistical probabilities, he could make relationships between the phases, essentially forcing relations between various phases of the rays. Hauptman and Karle demonstrated the practicality of their technique by solving the structure of the mineral colemanite in collaboration with scientists of the U.S. Geological Survey. Despite negative comments from working crystallographers, who thought the procedure too difficult, the work continued, with great success, particularly when the sophisticated computers and programs were developed that speeded work greatly. The computer work was done by Michael Woolfson of York University, originally a major critic of the new technique.

In 1970, Hauptman joined the crystallographic group of the Medical Foundation of Buffalo. During the early years there, he formulated the neighborhood principle and extension concept, dealing with atoms located adjacent to the considered atom. The extension concept was independently proposed by C. Giacovazzo, under the name "representation theory." Both ideas have formed the foundation for new probabilistic theories of the higher-order structure invariants and seminvariants, which give an even clearer picture of complex molecular structures. In more recent years, Hauptman has been working to combine his direct method technique with isomorphous replacement (putting in calculations for atoms replacing others within a structure) and anomalous dispersion (the spreading of X rays from particles to give points not found in regular crystal structures) in order to solve structural problems of very large systems.

At first, many other scientists insisted the method would not work, it being too hard to understand. Almost thirty years were necessary to convey the ideas adequately. Commonly known simply as the "direct method," the Karle-Hauptman system is used in chemistry, biology, geology, and medicine. More than forty-five thousand molecules have been analyzed, including basic hormones and vitamins, and the system has been used for designing new antibiotics and vaccines. Hauptman's work, in collaboration with Karle, has extensive potential chemical and medical applications. As Ingvar Lindqvist of the Nobel Committee said, "It is not possible to name fields in chemistry where the method is not used." With the spread of high-speed computers, the power of the Karle-Hauptman method has become abundantly clear: Once it took years to analyze a small crystal; now it is done routinely in a day or so.

Hauptman's work over the years has garnered many awards and honors. Among those he prizes most are the Belden Prize in Mathematics (1936), Scientific Research Society of America Pure Science Award (1959), Patterson Award of the American Crystallographic Association (1984), and his election as president of the Philosophical Society of Washington (1969-1970).

Throughout his career, Hauptman has never been daunted by the apparent magnitude of the mathematical problems being faced, nor by the skepticism of his colleagues in anyone's ability to solve seemingly intractable problems. His greatest discoveries, in association with Jerome Karle, have had, and will continue to have, marked effects on numerous disciplines, including physics, chemistry, geology, mineralogy, crystallography, biology, and medicine. His phenomenal mathematical ability helped transform each of those fields, pushing back the frontier and creating a deeper understanding of how nature operates on the atomic and molecular levels.

Bibliography

Primary
CHEMISTRY: *Solution of the Phase Problem, I: The Centrosymmetric Crystal*, 1953 (with Jerome Karle); *Crystal Structure Determination: The Role of the Cosine Seminvariants*, 1972.

Secondary
Bertin, E. *Principles and Practice of X-Ray Spectrometric Analysis.* New York: Plenum, 1970. This reference covers the generation and use of X rays in a wide variety of applications, including structural analysis. Starting with equipment and X-ray generation, it delineates examples of analysis, showing how structures can be determined in crystals from diffraction data. Some extensive mathematics, but readable.

Holden, A. *Crystals and Crystal Growing.* Garden City, N.Y.: Doubleday, 1960. This is a layman's reader on the materials of crystallography. Starting with discussions of the states of matter and how crystals are grown, the work provides recipes for growing various types of crystals, illustrating the basic lattices. Shapes of crystals and arrangements of atoms in the crystals are detailed, as are experiments that can be performed by the reader. Well written, with excellent pictures and illustrations.

Luis, J., and M. Luis. *Molecular Crystals: Their Transforms and Diffuse Scattering.* New York: John Wiley & Sons, 1968. This work deals with X-ray scattering as the most accurate determinative means of crystal structure. From an analysis of basic scattering, using Fourier transforms, the author proceeds to actual X-ray scattering as observed in molecular crystals and to applications of the technique. Includes extensive references and is very mathematical, giving an excellent overview of the mathematics used by Hauptman.

Phillips, F. *An Introduction to Crystallography*. New York: John Wiley & Sons, 1971. Using a historical approach, this work details the basic principles of crystallography, including a detailed study of the analysis of internal structures by X rays. The classes of crystal symmetry are built up and the fourteen types of space lattices are derived from first principles. Very detailed, completely covering basics, with no assumption of prior mathematical or scientific knowledge. Well illustrated.

Whiston, C. *X-Ray Methods*. New York: John Wiley & Sons, 1987. This book provides a detailed working knowledge of different analytical applications of X-ray diffraction and X-ray fluorescence. Besides covering instrumentation, it discusses properties of X rays, how to perform diffraction by crystalline powders, and analysis of results from phase studies. Very well written in a question-and-learn style, with numerous problems worked with and by the reader.

Willard, H. *Instrumental Methods of Analysis*. New York: Van Nostrand, 1974. An extensive work on methods usable in chemistry. The chapter on X-ray methods provides good insight into production of X rays and instrumental considerations, with worked examples. Diffraction is explained in terms of lattice concepts, with diffraction patterns related to quantitative analysis and structural applications. Well written, with a minimum of mathematics.

Zachariasen, W. *Theory of X-Ray Diffraction in Crystals*. New York: John Wiley & Sons, 1945. An older book, this work provides the theory of space lattices and symmetry properties as determined by X-ray diffraction. After presenting the theory, the author illustrates X-ray interference in real crystals, with discussions of effects of temperature, crystal disorders, and differences between real and ideal crystals. Quite mathematical, written for very advanced laymen.

Arthur L. Alt

1985

Chemistry
Herbert A. Hauptman, United States
Jerome Karle, United States

Physics
Klaus von Klitzing, West Germany

Physiology or Medicine
Michael S. Brown, United States
Joseph L. Goldstein, United States

Economic Sciences
Franco Modigliani, United States

Literature
Claude Simon, France

Peace
International Physicians for the Prevention of Nuclear War

JEROME KARLE
1985

Born: New York, New York; June 18, 1918

Nationality: American
Area of concentration: X-ray crystallography

Karle, working with Herbert Hauptman, developed the "direct method" in X-ray crystallography to determine the structures of molecules. By applying probability theory to the diffraction patterns created by the molecules through which the radiation passed, they were able to solve the problem of the phase differences in the results of the X-ray scattering

The Award

Presentation

Ingvar Lindqvist, a member of the Royal Swedish Academy of Sciences, presented Jerome Karle for the Nobel Prize in Chemistry on December 10, 1985. In his presentation speech, Lindqvist reviewed the attempts of scientific thinkers to explain the structure and properties of molecules. By the end of the nineteenth century, these efforts had culminated in three unusual scientific ideas. Jacobus Henricus van't Hoff proposed his theory of the tetrahedral carbon atom, Friedrich August Kekulé launched his revolutionary concept of the ring structure of benzene, and Alfred Werner explained many metal complexes as "having octahedral, tetrahedral or planar square structures." It was only in the twentieth century, however, that researchers were able to devise methods for the complete determination of molecular structures, revealing not only the geometrical configurations of the atoms, but also the bonding distances between them. X-ray crystallography, in which X rays are passed through a crystal, and the rays are thus scattered in certain directions, is one of these methods. The intensity of the light is determined for each X-ray diffraction. In 1913, Max von Laue, who was the first to carry out this procedure, received the Nobel Prize in Physics in recognition of his achievement. Sir William Henry Bragg and Sir William Lawrence Bragg, his son, were the first to determine the structure of simple chemical compounds; in 1915, they too won the Nobel Prize in Physics.

When the physicist Jerome Karle and the mathematician Herbert A. Hauptman, in a series of papers published between 1950 and 1956, reported that they had solved the "phase problem" that had long plagued X-ray crystallography, by devising a method for determining the structure directly from the experimental data, without any assumptions or guesses, their claim aroused great interest, but also much opposition. They based their method on two established facts: that it is never possible for the electron density in a molecule to be negative and that the body of experimental data is large enough to allow the use of statistical methods. Subsequent developments proved them right, and modern computers have lent speed and efficiency to their methods. Yet it has also become increasingly important to know the exact structure of the molecules involved in significant chemical and biochemical reactions. The molecular mechanisms for more and more reactions have become known, Lindqvist concluded, and it is also possible to design molecules with structures and properties as desired.

Nobel lecture

Karle delivered his Nobel lecture, entitled "Recovering Phase Information from Intensity Data," on December 9, 1985. He began by explaining the scientific concepts and the methods of calculation and measurement that he and Hauptman used in developing their method (the "direct" method) for determining molecular structure. A crystal is considered to be a solid body, with its atomic or molecular units in an array, or series, having a recurring three-dimensional pattern. This repetition makes it possible to express the atomic composition by using a type of mathematical formula known as a Fourier series. In structural analysis of a crystal, the type of Fourier series used describes the electron density distribution in the crystal. This is essentially the same as showing the crystal structure, because the locations of the atoms are shown by the regions of highest density in the electron distributions.

The structure of crystals is analyzed by an experimental technique known as diffraction. In this technique, rays are directed in such a way that they strike a crystal, and, under the proper geometric conditions, "the rays are scattered as if they were bouncing off large numbers of different planes imagined to be cutting through the crystal. The collected intensities of scattering (often 5,000-10,000 in number)" are known as the diffraction pattern, and it includes the experimental data that form the basis on which the crystal structure is interpreted. The rays that are usually used are X rays, but other rays, such as those consisting of neutrons or electrons, may be employed as well.

Karle drew an analogy between the nature of the diffraction phenomenon and the patterns created by balls being bounced off a large object. Suppose, Karle suggested, one were to attempt to determine the shape of a large object, shielded from sight, by projecting balls at the object at precise angles. Suppose further that the effects of gravity could be minimized. If a large area were to be scanned at right angles to the angles at which the balls were being projected (and if the bouncing pattern was essentially parallel), one could conclude that the object had a flat surface that was perpendicular to the direction of the projected balls. By changing the position of the object and studying the patterns of the bounced balls (or their equivalent, the X-ray scattering pattern), the shape of the object could be determined with a large degree of detail.

From the submicroscopic point of view, however, the situation is a bit different. X rays can easily permeate crystals, and the interactions between the X rays and the atomic structure of the crystal are somewhat different from those of a ball bouncing off a surface. Particular geometric conditions must be met before it is evident that the rays have indeed been reflected. The manner in which the X rays interact with electron density distributions within the crystal produces a scattering pattern unique to each crystalline substance.

Karle pointed to the phase problem as having been one of the chief difficulties in proceeding with direct determination of crystal structure. The difficulty disappeared, however, once it was recognized that "the required phase information was contained in the experimental density information." What Karle and Hauptman had accomplished was to bring together the mathematics (that showed the relationships between phases and magnitudes) with the refined experimental data to develop "practical procedures for structural determination."

Critical reception

When the Royal Swedish Academy of Sciences announced in October, 1985, that it had decided to award the Nobel Prize in Chemistry to Herbert A. Hauptman and Jerome Karle, the news reached Karle while he was on an airplane flying back from West Germany to Washington, D.C. The captain had been notified by radio; he announced the news to his astonished passengers and ordered champagne served to all aboard, so that they might toast the honored scientist in their midst. A dramatic way, indeed, for Karle to learn that the value and importance of his work had finally been recognized. As the presentation for the Nobel Prize points out, the series of articles in which Hauptman and Karle explained their scientific discoveries appeared during the years from 1950 to 1956, and while their work was met with great interest, there was also opposition and skepticism.

By the time the award of the Nobel Prize to Karle was announced, however, scientists had come to appreciate and rely on Karle's theories and methods. Their methods were expanding the capacities of large areas of chemical, pharmaceutical, and biochemical investigation and were raising the prospect of new—even specially designed—chemical compounds, drugs, anesthetics, and hormones. As Wayne A. Hendrickson noted in *Science*, crystallography "remains indispensable for details of stereochemistry, but now a crystal structure is often also the approach of choice for simple chemical characterization of natural products or intermediates in a chemical synthesis."

The announcement of the award to Karle and Hauptman encouraged crystallographers all over the world. While X-ray diffraction results in chemistry had been involved in work that led to Nobel Prizes awarded since World War II, "not since the early prizes to von Laue in 1914 and to the Braggs in 1915 had contributions to diffraction analysis been directly recognized," an article in *Nature* stated. Although Karle was trained as a physicist and Hauptman as a mathematician, the announcement of the 1985 Nobel Prize aroused pride and delight among crystallographers. The two men had been "such fixtures at meetings of the American Crystallographic Association that possibly none has been held without one or both in attendance." As an article in *New Scientist* of October 24, 1985, observed, the pioneering efforts of Karle and his colleague "could one day change the face of molecular biology."

Karle had done his research at the Naval Research Laboratory in Washington; he thus became the first scientist to win the Nobel Prize while working for the United States Navy. One science journal asked rhetorically "whether he was the first scientist to make the highest echelons of science while coping with the standard pay and conditions laid down for the scientific civil service in the U.S." Whatever the answer to this question, Karle's share of the $225,000 prize in chemistry must have been a welcome form of recognition. Some articles in the press, such as one in *The New York Times*, cited the limits of the achievement, saying that the direct methods could not be used for the structural analysis of larger molecules, such as proteins. The report in *Nature*, however, stated flatly that Karle "was trying to do exactly that." The reception of the new technique perhaps was reported most fairly in *Time*: "At first, scientists insisted it could not possibly work. Then they said it was too hard to understand." Three decades later, however, "no chemist can live without it."

On May 30, 1986, at the commencement exercises of The City College, City University of New York, three members of the class of 1937, all of them Nobel Laureates—a remarkable achievement in any single college class—were each awarded an honorary doctor of science degree. One of them was Hauptman; another was Karle. A brief quotation from the citation for Karle's degree may serve as an appropriate summary of the accomplishments that earned for him the Nobel Prize:

> Your discoveries have made possible the development of new drugs to treat cancer. The same techniques have been used to study antibiotic drugs, and thousands of three-dimensional structures of small biological molecules have been worked out through the methods you developed with Dr. Hauptman. Your work has made possible a wealth of valuable new information for understanding the most detailed chemistry of life.

Biography

Jerome Karle was born in New York City on June 18, 1918, into a family whose members were interested in art and music. His uncle taught for many years at the Art Students' League in New York, and his mother was a talented pianist and organist who hoped that her son would develop into a professional pianist. In spite of modest success in music competitions, he found that he had no liking for public performance. In contrast, at an early age he felt a strong attraction to the life of a scientist. He received his early education in the public schools of New York City, where he found that "the standards of education, character building and discipline were very high" and of great benefit to him. The more advanced students were allowed to go ahead at their own pace. He studied at Abraham Lincoln High School in Brooklyn, where the chemistry and physics courses were taught by the same teacher. This man recognized his young student's interests and strongly encouraged him. Karle enjoyed sports and swimming in the ocean nearby, and he lost no opportunity to engage in outdoor games.

In 1933, Karle entered The City College of New York, where, at first, he found his situation rather difficult. The academic standards were very high, and there was a concentration of the best students in New York. Moreover, it took him three hours a day to travel on the subway system from the college to his home and back. There were no tuition fees at The City College, the only charge being one dollar a year for a library card. The broad course requirements for all students included mathematics, the physical sciences, the social sciences, literature, and even compulsory public speaking courses for two years. Karle took additional mathematics, some physics, and much chemistry and biology beyond the requirements.

Upon graduating from The City College, he studied biology at Harvard University, receiving his master's degree in 1938. A short time later, he went to work for the New York State Department of Health in Albany. At that time, a beginning was being made in the fluoridation of drinking water. Karle developed a technique for determining the amount of fluorine in water supplies that became a standard procedure, and he later felt that this was his first modest contribution to science. He worked at the Department of Health until he had saved enough money to go back to graduate school, and in 1940 he entered the chemistry department of the University of Michigan. It was here, on the first day of his class in physical chemistry, that he met Isabella Helen Lugoski, who occupied a neighboring laboratory desk. They were married in 1942. Both were interested in physical chemistry, and both earned their doctoral degrees with Lawrence O. Brockway, who specialized in the study of gas-phase molecular structure by means of electron diffraction.

Karle received his Ph.D. in 1944, but he had completed all the work for it in the summer of 1943, when he left to work on the Manhattan Project at the University of Chicago, where his wife joined him a few months later. They returned to the University of Michigan in 1944, where he worked on a project for the Naval Research Laboratory and she was an instructor in the chemistry department. In 1946, the young couple left for Washington, D.C., where they were to work permanently for the Naval Research Laboratory.

In spite of all her research activities, Isabella Karle became the mother of three children: Louise, in 1946, who is a theoretical chemist; Jean, in 1950, who is an organic chemist; and Madeleine, in 1955, who received her training in geology and is a museum specialist. Karle himself has expressed his appreciation of the strong support, both technical and spiritual, given to him by his wife throughout their married life, as well as of the supportive atmosphere created by the Naval Research Laboratory. This was particularly meaningful to him in the early 1950's, when so many fellow scientists were skeptical about his work.

Scientific Career

In spite of Karle's love for the piano, the consuming interest of his life has been science. From the time he majored in both chemistry and biology at The City College, throughout the years of his professional career, he has devoted himself tirelessly to the pursuit of scientific knowledge and research. (Had it not been wartime, he has admitted, he might also have taken a degree in mathematics.) Inspired by a stimulating course in physical chemistry with Brockway at Michigan, Karle and his wife Isabella decided to study electron diffraction with gaseous molecules.

By the standards of the 1940's, their apparatus was excellent, but it had home-made electronic circuits and vacuum systems that were difficult to maintain. The electron beam was passed through the gas, and images of the diffracted, concentric rings were recorded on a photographic plate. By mathematical analysis of the measurements of the positions and the intensities of the rings, it was possible to calculate the interatomic distances and angles of the gas molecules. These calculations were tedious; trigonometric functions on strips of paper strategically placed along the edge were aligned to aid the computations. The arithmetic was done on a calculator cranked by hand.

After working on the Manhattan Project in Chicago, Karle returned to the University of Michigan, where he worked on a project for the Naval Research Laboratory; his wife was an instructor in the chemistry department. When World War II ended, however, his work for the Naval Research Laboratory was over, and her position at the university offered no future. Although they both liked academic life, policies directed against nepotism made it impossible for them to find permanent positions where they could be together. In 1946, they were fortunate enough to have the Naval Research Laboratory in Washington offer them an opportunity to continue their research on the quantitative aspects of analysis of gas electron diffraction. This appointment was a permanent one, and it was of critical importance to the subsequent development of their scientific careers and to the remarkable research that eventually led to the Nobel Prize for Karle and Hauptman. Through the foresight of the administration of the Naval Research Laboratory, the laboratory became a center of investigation of molecular structure analysis, producing work of great distinction. The Naval Research Laboratory had an excellent machine shop, and two duplicate state-of-the-art diffraction instruments were constructed, to ensure that at least one of them would be leakproof. Tandem electromagnetic lenses that enhanced the quality of the electron beam were an important feature of the system. Carbon dioxide was one of the first molecules analyzed: For the first time, vibrational parameters were determined in carbon dioxide by electron diffraction. The solution of a critical problem in such analyses was significant both for crystal structure analysis and for other areas of structure determination.

In 1947, Herbert Hauptman also decided to come to the Naval Research Laboratory, and he soon joined the Karles in pursuing crystal structure analysis. Hauptman had been trained as a mathematician, and the combination of his mathematical skills with Karle's physics background formed an ideal combination. The work done by Hauptman and the Karles eventually resulted in direct methods of crystal structure analysis; most of the mathematical foundations and procedural insights were established in the early 1950's. Karle himself has explained that solving problems in X-ray diffraction requires a considerable amount of bridging, that is, "the mutual process in which theory is adapted to the limitations of experimental data and experimental data are adapted to the limitations in theory." At this time, most crystallographers believed that no direct mathematical solution to the phase problem existed and therefore believed that there could be no direct determination of molecular structures.

The names Karle and Hauptman appeared on some thirty articles during the 1950's and early 1960's, nearly all of them in the pages of the journal *Acta Crystallographica*. At the very beginning, in 1950, their significant insight was that the electron density can never be negative. This nonnegativity principle suggested an infinite set of inequalities among the phases and magnitudes of the scattered X rays, so the next step was to develop the proper theory of probability. In 1953, the two researchers published their monograph *Solution of the Phase Problem, I: The Centrosymmetric Crystal*, in which they used probability theory to solve the crystallographic phase problem. (A centrosymmetric crystal is symmetrical with respect to a center point.) The first practical applications of their technique of structure determination for centrosymmetric crystals (involving probability measures and formulas derived from the joint probability distribution) were carried out in the middle 1950's, in collaboration with colleagues at the U.S. Geological Survey, on the mineral colemanite. In the second half of the 1950's, Isabella Karle succeeded in establishing an experimental X-ray diffraction facility in their laboratory. During the 1960's, there was an intensive effort in the laboratory to devise a method of crystal structure determination that would include noncentrosymmetric as well as centrosymmetric crystals. Such a method was devised, largely through the efforts of Isabella Karle. It was called the symbolic addition procedure, and the first application of this procedure was published in 1963. A number of exciting applications followed, and in the late 1960's many laboratories began to take an interest in the potential of the direct method of structure determination.

During the 1950's and 1960's, Karle also maintained an interest in gas electron diffraction and made some experimental and theoretical studies of effects inherent in this process. Karle has taught mathematics and physics, from time to time, at the University of Maryland. In 1968, the Naval Research Laboratory established a chair of science for him as Chief Scientist of the Laboratory for the Structure of Matter, and in this capacity he was able to build up a strong research group of about a dozen scientists. He occasionally collaborates with them on various projects, from organic crystal structures to amorphous scattering to the crystallography of proteins. Mainly, however, he has encouraged the independent careers of this highly respected group. He himself has received many honors and over the years has played an active part in the affairs of crystallography. He has, for example, served as president of the International Union of Crystallography (1981-1984), and he was elected to the National Academy of Sciences in 1976. In 1984, he and Hauptman shared the A. Lindo Patterson Award of the American Crystallographic Association for their major contributions to the theory of direct methods of determining crystal structure.

It should not be assumed that Karle's development of the direct methods of determining the molecular structure of crystals has solved all crystal problems or that there will now be little need for crystallographers. Although Karle has been working on it, there is the problem of the large molecule with many atoms. In the physical sciences, thinkers often build on the work of their predecessors, which they are glad to acknowledge. Less than a hundred years ago, van't Hoff, Kekulé, and Werner revealed their discoveries of the structure of crystals, but it was at least seventy-five years before the physicist Karle, working with the mathematician Hauptman, enabled the relatively new science of crystallography to make a quantum leap to the direct methods of crystal structure determination. The older, more cumbersome methods were slower, less accurate, and much more limited regarding the size of the molecule to which they could be applied. Through use of the theory of probability, the phase problem was solved; the computer, which was just becoming a powerful scientific tool at the time Karle and Hauptman made their breakthrough, made possible an enormous reduction in the time it took to analyze crystal structures. Michael Woolfson, who had once been a critic of the new analytic technique, designed a special computer program for it, which hastened its acceptance.

Whereas only small molecular structures could be analyzed before the direct methods came into use, since their application organic molecules have been usually considered routine if they have up to fifty nonhydrogen atoms. Those with fifty to one hundred atoms generally create little difficulty, and molecular structures have been analyzed with more than two hundred atoms in noncentrosymmetric crystals. All of this has led to important improvements in chemistry, pharmacy, and medicine. Isabella Karle, for example, has used the direct methods to study the effect of radiation on human cells; irradiated thymine, she has found, is related to the production of antibodies. She has studied the cyclic polypeptide molecule valinomycin, which transports potassium ions across membranes and is also an antibiotic for a type of tuberculosis. In addition, she has analyzed the structure of enkephalin, a natural analgesic occurring in the brain. Thus has the fundamental discovery by Karle led to important changes and advances in related fields and to benefits for the welfare of humankind.

Bibliography

Primary

CHEMISTRY: *Solution of the Phase Problem, I: The Centrosymmetric Crystal*, 1953 with Herbert Hauptman); "The Relative Scaling of Multiple-Wavelength Anomalous Dispersion Data," *Acta Crystallographica*, sec. A, vol. 40, 1984; "Rules for Estimating the Values of Triplet Phase Invariants in Multiwavelength Anomolous Dispersion Experiments," *Acta Crystallographica*, sec. A, vol. 40, 1984; "Crystallographic Statistics and the Development of Direct Methods," *Acta Crystallographica*, sec. A, vol. 40, 1984; "Triplet Phase Invariants from Single Isomorphous Replacement of One-Wavelength Anomalous Dispersion Data,"

Acta Crystallographica, sec. A, vol. 42, 1986; "Recovering Phase Information from Intensity Data," *Science* 232, 1986.

Secondary

Clarke, Maxine. "New Routes to X-ray Phases." *Nature* 317 (October 24, 1985): 663. This British article is a concise, well-written account of the work done by Karle and Hauptman that won for them the Nobel Prize. It is perceptive and historical, and includes all the main points without being too technical.

Hendrickson, Wayne A. "The 1985 Nobel Prize in Chemistry." *Science* 231 (January 24, 1986): 362-364. This long and accurate article is the best of those that have appeared in periodicals. Written by one of the former young colleagues in the research group Karle organized in the Naval Research Laboratory, this is an expert historical and scientific account of the achievements of both Karle and Hauptman. It is detailed and contains some formulas and mathematical equations, as well biographical information, but it is well written and highly readable.

Julian, Maureen M., and Roger R. Festa, eds. "Isabella L. Karle and a New Mathematical Breakthrough in Crystallography." *Journal of Chemical Education* 63 (January, 1986): 66-67. While this article is mainly about Isabella, it also has considerable biographical information about both her and her husband. The writer interviewed the Karles, who also read her article before publication. Since Isabella was an important contributor to the development of the direct methods and their subsequent practical applications, this is an authoritative and significant article.

MacKenzie, Debora, and Lionel Milgrom. "Nobels: How Maths Won the Chemistry Prize." *New Scientist* 108 (October 24, 1985): 22-23. This account consists of two parts. The first is a lively, but somewhat superficial, section, and the second is a thoughtful and analytical discussion of the history and development of the determination of crystal structure, with a good explanation of the phase problem.

Schechter, Bruce. "Nobel Prize in Chemistry to Hauptman and Karle." *Physics Today* 38 (December, 1985): 20-21. Offers a clear explanation of how Karle, his wife Isabella, and Hauptman solved the scientific problems they faced in developing the direct methods of crystal structure determination. Objective and forthright, it gives credit to the contributions of others, without diminishing the accomplishments of the chief participants.

Seymour L. Flaxman

1986

Chemistry
Dudley R. Herschbach, United States
Yuan T. Lee, China and United States
John C. Polanyi, Canada

Physics
Ernst Ruska, West Germany
Gerd Binnig, West Germany
Heinrich Rohrer, Switzerland

Physiology or Medicine
Stanley Cohen, United States
Rita Levi-Montalcini, United States

Economic Sciences
James M. Buchanan, Jr., United States

Literature
Wole Soyinka, Nigeria

Peace
Elie Wiesel, United States

DUDLEY R. HERSCHBACH
1986

Born: San Jose, California; June 18, 1932

Nationality: American
Area of concentration: Molecular reaction dynamics

Herschbach was one of a group of physical chemists who were the prime movers in the development of molecular beam machines. In part through his efforts, the molecular beam technique moved from early experiments using limited types of atoms to a modern technique capable of using any molecule. He was also instrumental in the development of the theoretical models to describe reactions

The Award
Presentation

Sture Forsén, professor of physical chemistry at the University of Lund, Sweden, and member of the Nobel Committee for Chemistry, presented Dudley Herschbach, John Polanyi, and Yuan Lee for the Nobel Prize in Chemistry on December 10, 1986. In his presentation speech, Forsén emphasized the complicated nature of even the simplest chemical processes when viewed on the microscopic to atomic scale. To understand them totally, one must understand the molecular processes that occur in them, but these molecular processes occur in the time scale of a millionth of a millionth of a second, so that it is difficult—but not impossible—to follow the course of a reaction. He lauded the 1986 laureates for devoting themselves to the development of experimental methods and the theoretical explanation of such elementary processes: for making the difficult possible.

The development of techniques to study the motion of molecules during collisions is a study in patience, trial and error, and great machining skills. When it is necessary to look at the results of a single collision, the experimentalist is immediately faced by the prospect of separating the results of the single collision from those of the same molecule immediately following the collision. The results of individual collisions can be separated only if the experimenter looks very quickly or if the collisions do not occur very often. The molecular beam technique allows for the detection of the scattered products under high vacuum conditions, where collisions do not occur very often. Herschbach was among those who developed and refined the molecular beam technique to the point where it could be used for a wide variety of reactions.

Nobel lecture

On Monday evening, December 8, 1986, Dudley Herschbach delivered his Nobel address, entitled "Molecular Reaction Dynamics of Elementary Chemical Reactions." Molecular reaction dynamics is a subfield of chemistry that examines the motions of atoms during a reaction. His lecture provided a clear, concise summary of many of the early efforts in molecular beam chemistry from the standpoint of one of the developers of the field. His lecture also celebrated both the joys and frustrations of doing scientific research at the frontiers of existing knowledge.

Herschbach began his lecture by mentioning the early twentieth century, when chemical kinetics was fast developing as an important subfield within the burgeoning field of physical chemistry. With the passing of time, as chemists became ever more interested in the exact details of reaction events, the separate subfield of molecular reaction dynamics was created, and reaction dynamicists became recognized as specialists. Herschbach's facility as a speaker made evident his enjoyment of his science and of the history of scientific evolution in his field, his pleasure in the study of the precise nature of the events that happen when two molecules collide, and the wondrous detail in which these can be observed in relatively simple experiments using simple detectors. From relatively simple arguments about the types of reactions, and from a chemical understanding of the reactants in an experiment, the consequences of choosing a particular pair of reagents can be readily seen in the distribution of molecular products at different angles in the molecular beams apparatus.

The development of simple theories to explain the observed product molecular distributions was the special forte of Herschbach and his group. They were able to take a set of very simple reactions, those involving alkali metals and halides, and discern the mechanism by which the reactions proceed. These elegant experiments provided some of the first direct experimental evidence for the mechanisms of chemical reactions and a starting ground for most types of reaction mechanisms known.

Critical reception

The awarding of the 1986 Nobel Prize to Dudley Herschbach and his colaureates was "greeted with enthusiasm among physical chemists," said Richard Zare, Stanford University professor and former graduate student under Herschbach. He also said that not only had the laureate's work been "seminal in the field of reaction dynamics, but the field of reaction dynamics has in turn come to pervade chemistry as a whole." The field has developed to the point where people talk about reaction pathways, meaning the details of the molecular interactions for any reacting system.

Richard Bernstein, professor of chemistry at the University of California at Los Angeles and author of a standard textbook in the field, stated that "Herschbach deserves credit not just for his work on molecular beams" but also for his contributions to the theory of chemical reactions, because of his great physical insight. He has the ability to devise simple models that account for the main features of the reaction in a way that is easy to understand.

Herschbach himself was characteristically understated about the first experiments leading to the award, stating that "those early experiments were delightfully crude. Later we learned that if we improved the vacuum enough, the absorbed gases and such would come boiling off the platinum wire, and pretty soon it would also start responding to both species. So I like to tell people that the experiment never would have worked if we'd had a really clean vacuum system!" Herschbach also pointed out that when the relevant electronic structures are examined, the similarities between reactions become quite obvious. "It's the closest thing we have to universals in chemistry." *Scientific American* stated that Herschbach "pioneered the method of crossed molecular beams, in which two beams of molecules are accelerated to known energies and made to collide at a known angle. By measuring the energies and angular distribution of reaction products one can infer how pairs of molecules in the beams have interacted."

Biography

Dudley Robert Herschbach was born in San Jose, California, on June 18, 1932, the first of six children of Robert and Dorothy Herschbach. His father was a building contractor and later a rabbit breeder where the family lived, a few miles outside San Jose. Herschbach's education through high school occurred there; he also participated in the usual farming activities of rural California and was involved in many outdoor sports. Herschbach attributes his early interest in science to a combination of reading popular literature and good teaching. Herschbach went to Stanford University on an academic scholarship, taking many mathematics and chemistry courses, giving up his athletic pursuits to leave time for science. He received his bachelor's degree in mathematics in 1954 and a master's in chemistry in 1955, with a thesis on the pre-exponential factor in bimolecular reactions, written under Professor Harold Johnston.

Herschbach continued his graduate career at Harvard University, where he completed his Ph.D. thesis (under E. Bright Wilson) on the hindered rotation of methyl groups and the observation of that effect using microwave spectroscopy in 1958. While at Harvard, he began the initial planning for a molecular beam machine to study elementary chemical reactions. Herschbach returned briefly to California, as an assistant professor of chemistry at the University of California, Berkeley, in 1959, and he was promoted to associate professor in 1961. In 1963, he returned to Harvard as professor of chemistry and chairman of the chemical physics program. There he met graduate student Georgene Botyos, and they were married in 1964.

In 1967, Yuan Lee joined Herschbach's research group and constructed the first universal molecular beam machine, revolutionizing the field by using a mass spectrometer rather than the tungsten filament as the product detector. Herschbach has more recently become involved in the construction of machines that can measure many product molecule properties simultaneously. He continues work on the development of new theoretical methods for determining the structure of liquids.

Scientific Career

Dudley Herschbach's lifelong interest in chemical kinetics and the fundamental processes of chemical reactions began when he was a graduate student under

Harold S. Johnston at Stanford University. His master's work analyzed bimolecular reactions, and his Ph.D. research under E. Bright Wilson at Harvard University concerned the microwave spectrum caused by rotation about bonds in methanol. The microwave spectra of molecules, which arise because of rotation of the entire molecule, are studied to obtain the precise molecular geometries, bond lengths, and bond angles. Thus, microwave spectra are extraordinarily sensitive to low-energy rotations about bonds in the molecule because of the distorted shape of the molecule that results. This is the case for the rotation of the methyl group with respect to the hydroxyl group in methanol (CH_3-OH). As the angle between the groups changes, the rotational energies of the molecule as a whole change slightly. It is these slight energy changes that the microwave spectrum can detect and that allow for the interpretation of energy changes in terms of the angles between the spikes changing cyclically with rotation about the carbon-oxygen bond.

While at Harvard, roughly the time of completing his Ph.D. thesis, Herschbach learned of experiments by Sheldon Datz and coworkers at Oak Ridge that described events occurring when a beam of gaseous molecules collided with other gaseous molecules. Herschbach immediately began designing a molecular beam apparatus for use in his new faculty appointment at Berkeley. He was especially glad to have received an appointment at Berkeley, since he could follow Bruce Mahan, who was already working on ion scattering experiments, and could continue discussions with Harold Johnston, who had moved to Berkeley from Stanford. At Berkeley, the first of several molecular beam apparatuses (soon to be appropriately dubbed Big Bertha) was constructed, and Herschbach began gathering experimental data on alkali metal and alkali halide reactions. As is typical of these apparatuses, Bertha had two beams of atoms or molecules, which crossed at 90 degrees. Detection of molecules following reaction (product molecules) was accomplished by measuring the current passing through a tungsten or platinum filament on which the product molecules land. These first crude experiments confirmed predictions made years earlier by Michael Polanyi that these reactions proceed with every collision of the reaction partners.

These experiments conducted by the Herschbach group and others were some of the early successes of the molecular beam technique. These groups concentrated their efforts on experiments which looked at the angular distributions of the products of collisions yielding alkali halide molecules because those were the only molecules to which the detector was sensitive. The key to these experiments is understanding that the angle at which a product is scattered is indicative of the mechanism of reaction. For example, if a reaction proceeds through a long-lived complex (defined as one in which the molecules remain bound for several rotational periods), then the product molecules are evenly distributed in angle. If the reaction proceeds with the molecules just whizzing past each other, however, called a direct reaction, the products are scattered into angles close to the incoming beam directions. A second effect seen here is that the probability of a reaction tends to be much lower for a reaction proceeding through a long-lived complex than for a direct reaction. Herschbach studied many different types of reactions during this period using alkali metal and alkali halide beams. Reactions included those of potassium atoms or potassium dimer, K_2, molecules reacting with halogen molecules, alkali halides, or halogenated molecules such as carbon tetrachloride. One of the great limitations of molecular beam chemistry through about 1967 was the complete inability of the apparatus to detect molecules other than alkali metals and halides. The biggest desire was for a "universal" machine capable of detecting any molecule as a product or reactant.

In 1967, Yuan Lee arrived from Bruce Mahan's group to begin a postdoctoral appointment in Herschbach's research group. He devised an apparatus with a rotatable mass spectrometer as detector for scattered molecules, using an elaborate design to reduce the number of stray molecules hitting the detector. The advantage to this apparatus was its sensitivity to all masses, and thus all molecules, because of the mass spectrometer detector. With this major advance in instrumentation, suddenly any reaction could be studied. Herschbach began by looking at the reactions of two halogen molecules.

Since 1967, experimentalists have worked on a far wider spectrum of molecular reactions, using a variety of schemes, from the now-conventional mass spectrometer to detection by chemiluminescence and by laser absorption. Chemiluminescence arises from light that is emitted from product molecules when they are in electronically excited states under high energy conditions. This light can be observed and measured. An example of a naturally occurring chemiluminescent reaction is the light given off by fireflies; this process, however, is much more complicated than the chemiluminescence given off by elementary processes such as the collisions of two molecules.

Other improvements to the molecular beams apparatus have been made by Herschbach and others. Perhaps most important is the use of a supersonic molecular beam, in which a high, single-velocity beam of molecules is created by the expansion of a gas at several atmospheres of pressure into a vacuum through a small orifice. Following the development of the supersonic beam source, the conditions under which collisions occurred became much more specified than previously, when each beam had a range of particle velocities within it. The development of the supersonic nozzle enhanced the utility of the molecular beams apparatus to reactions involving gases. The "seeded" supersonic-expansion molecular beam, involving the mixing of the vapors above liquids and solids with a gas, followed by expansion of the gas mixture out of a small orifice, made the molecular beam method applicable to essentially all reactants. The seeded molecular beam provides a method of creating single-velocity beams of virtually all molecules.

Herschbach expanded his research in the late 1970's to include the measurement of the properties of molecules formed in the ultracold environment of the -269 degree Celsius supersonic beam. These molecules are referred to as clusters, because they arise from the weak bonding together, or clustering, of molecules under these conditions. Clusters form when two or more molecules do not have sufficient thermal energy to break the bonds formed by weak intermolecular forces. The force required to break these bonds is of the order of the thermal energy near -200 degrees Celsius, so the clusters must be very cold in order to form. Herschbach has studied processes such as the attachment of an electron to clusters of carbon dioxide molecules, observing the resulting distribution of scattered carbon dioxide molecules. Herschbach is interested, too, in examining the properties of the cluster as the size of the cluster increases, since the properties of the isolated gas molecules must change into the properties of the liquid as the number of molecules in the cluster increases. Herschbach hopes to identify, one day, the number of molecules necessary for the properties of liquid to be reached. Another area in which Herschbach has become interested is the spectroscopy of surfaces, particularly the enhancement of Raman (light) scattering at the interface between the solid and the liquid.

Bibliography

Primary

CHEMISTRY: "Reactive Scattering," *Advances in Chemical Physics*, vol. 10, 1966; "Molecular Beam Reactive Scattering Apparatus with Electron Bombardment Detector," *Review of Scientific Instruments*, vol. 40, 1969 (with J. D. McDonald, P. R. LeBreton, and Y. T. Lee); "Molecular Beam Chemistry: Unimolecular Decomposition of Chemically Activated Chlorobromalkyl Radicals," *Journal of the American Chemical Society*, vol. 95, 1973 (with J. T. Cheung and J. D. McDonald); "Rotational Polarization of Reaction Products: Analysis of Electric Deflection Profiles," *Molecular Physics*, vol. 29, 1975 (with D. S. Y. Hsu and N. D. Weinstein); "Hydrogen Atom Scattering: Energy Dependence of the Total Collision Cross Section for Mercury," *Journal of Chemical Physics*, vol. 62, 1975 (with W. C. Stwalley and A. Niehaus); "Information Theory Analysis of Angular Momentum Disposal in Chemical Reactions," *Journal of Chemical Physics*, vol. 69, 1978 (with D. A. Case); "Vibrational and Rotational Relaxation of Iodine in Seeded Supersonic Beams," *Journal of Physical Chemistry*, vol. 83, 1979 (with B. M. McClelland, K. L. Saenger, and J. J. Valentini); "Surface Enhanced Raman Scattering from Molecules Adsorbed on Mercury," *Journal of Physical Chemistry*, vol. 84, 1980 (with R. Naaman, S. J. Buelow, and O. Cheshnovsky); "Vibrational Frequency Shifts Induced by Molecular Compression of Pyridine in Solution," *Journal of Chemical Physics*, vol. 85, 1986 (with M. R. Zakin); "Dynamical Aspects of Stereochemistry," *Journal of Physical Chemistry*, vol. 91, 1987 (with R. B. Bernstein and R. D. Levine); "Pseudomolecular Atoms: Geometry of Two-Electron Intrashell Excited States," *Zeitschrift für Physik D: Atomic, Molecular, and Clusters*, vol. 10, 1988 (with J. D. Loeser and D. K. Watson); "Electron Attachment to Carbon Dioxide Clusters by Collisional Charge Transfer," *Journal of Physical Chemistry*, vol. 93, 1989 (with E. L. Quitevis).

Secondary

Bernstein, Richard B. *Chemical Dynamics via Molecular Beam and Laser Techniques*. New York: Oxford University Press, 1982. The use of molecular beams in the study of reactions is examined in this book. It particularly views the technique as coupled with laser technology; the techniques are complementary and can provide a wealth of information.

Herschbach, Dudley R. "Molecular Dynamics of Elementary Chemical Reactions." *Chemica Scripta* 27 (1987); *Angewandte Chemie* 99 (1987); *Les Prix Nobel, 1986*. These references all reprint the text of Herschbach's Nobel award lecture, which is extremely readable to the layman and contains much of the early history of molecular beam chemistry as seen by the award winner himself.

Levine, Raphael D., and Richard B. Bernstein. *Molecular Reaction Dynamics*. New York: Oxford University Press, 1974. This book is of interest primarily because it was the first to survey the field of reaction dynamics; it summarizes the beginnings of the field.

_____. *Molecular Reaction Dynamics and Chemical Reactivity*. New York: Oxford University Press, 1987. This book, written at the advanced undergraduate level, reviews the field of collisional dynamics to 1986. Explains the theoretical and experimental chemistry involved in getting results and explaining collisions.

Zewail, Ahmed H., and Richard B. Bernstein. "Real Time Laser Femtochemistry." *Chemical and Engineering News*, November 7, 1988. This article contains many examples of work being done in molecular dynamics at the time it was written. It looks at the experimental techniques that allow intermediate species in a reaction to be examined.

Richard W. Schwenz

1986

Chemistry
Dudley R. Herschbach, United States
Yuan T. Lee, China and United States
John C. Polanyi, Canada

Physics
Ernst Ruska, West Germany
Gerd Binnig, West Germany
Heinrich Rohrer, Switzerland

Physiology or Medicine
Stanley Cohen, United States
Rita Levi-Montalcini, United States

Economic Sciences
James M. Buchanan, Jr., United States

Literature
Wole Soyinka, Nigeria

Peace
Elie Wiesel, United States

YUAN T. LEE
1986

Born: Hsinchu, Taiwan; November 19, 1936

Nationality: Chinese; after 1974, American
Areas of concentration: Molecular reaction dynamics and photochemistry

Lee helped revolutionize the field of molecular reaction dynamics through his construction of the first crossed molecular beams apparatus capable of detecting all molecules rather than select types. He conducted many experiments using these types of instruments and developed insight into the detailed mechanisms of bond formation and breaking in chemical reactions

The Award

Presentation

Sture Forsén, professor of physical chemistry at the University of Lund, Sweden, and member of the Nobel Committee for Chemistry, presented Yuan T. Lee for the Nobel Prize in Chemistry on December 10, 1986. In his address, Forsén surveyed the reasons for studying chemical reactions. He described the complexity of even simple processes such as the burning of a flame and discussed the problems faced by those who seek to unravel these very complex processes. He stressed the difficulty of experiments that examine the details of molecular collisions occurring in a millionth of a millionth of a second, on the "picosecond" time scale. Simplification of complex reaction situations (such as a burning flame) in order to examine molecular collisions can only occur if the reaction conditions are exactly controlled so that one can examine the results of single collisions of the molecules involved. Even so, the experimentalist can examine the results of groups of molecular collisions only if he knows exactly where each reactant started and of what it is composed, and then tries to infer what happened during an individual reactive collision or event. Yuan Lee's crossed molecular beams apparatus made this possible.

Forsén described Lee's contribution to chemistry (molecular dynamics) as consisting of experiments that have "enlarged our knowledge of the detailed events in chemical reactions." In particular, Forsén pointed to Lee's depictions of collisions between atoms, molecules, and photons, which now form the basis of our understanding of these events. Lee and his coworkers developed these depictions based on the precise, detailed experiments made possible by the crossed molecular beams technique. The technique is also a source of fundamental data for those who study chemical reactions in atmospheric and combustion chemistry.

Nobel lecture

On Monday, December 8, 1986, Professor Lee delivered his Nobel lecture, entitled "Molecular Beam Studies of Elementary Chemical Processes." He began by explaining the relevance of chemical reaction rates, and thus his underlying motivation for examining the elementary chemical processes occurring in reaction. Historically, chemists' understanding of the relationship between the energetics of a reaction and the rate or speed of a reaction extends back to Svante Arrhenius, the winner of the 1907 Nobel Prize in Chemistry. It is only since the advent of quantum mechanics in the late 1920's, however, that chemists and physicists have tried to describe in detail the rearrangement of atoms within molecules that occurs in a chemical reaction. In the past few decades, many methods have been developed with the intention of examining the detailed dynamics (motions of the atoms in a molecule) during a chemical reaction event. One of the methods that is capable of examining the detailed dynamics is the crossed molecular beams method, which, Lee said, has been extensively revised and extended by himself and others.

In his Nobel lecture, Lee gave several examples of recent work in which he was able to identify the mechanism of a reaction using this technique by measuring the velocity and angular distributions of products from a chemical reaction at a given initial collisional energy. These measurements provided a means of looking at the motions of the atoms in simple chemical reactions. The first of his examples is one of the simplest chemical reactions: that of fluorine atoms with hydrogen (deuterium) molecules to form hydrogen (deuterium) fluoride and hydrogen (deuterium) atoms. This reaction is simple enough that one can calculate the motions of the reacting atoms starting from laws of motion and thus obtain a microscopic comparison of theoretical calculations and the experiments performed by Lee and his coworkers. Such comparisons give chemists the opportunity to test theories of chemical reactions.

Other reaction examples presented by Lee included cases where the predictions of the mechanism were incorrect when they were based on experiments performed with multiple collisions for each atom. Lee's experiments conclusively demonstrated that an alternative mechanism must be considered in these examples: the reaction of oxygen atoms with ethylene and the production of electronically excited iodine monofluoride molecules.

Shortly before the Nobel award, Lee said, his research group had begun studying the effects of atomic and molecular orientation, with respect to their collision partners, on the probability of a reaction occurring. These experiments demonstrated how pointing the side of an atom either at the collision partner or perpendicular to the collision partner will change the reaction probability. Among the collision partners chosen were sodium atoms with their valence electron in the 4d orbital and a variety of other molecules.

Critical reception

Yuan Lee received his Nobel Prize in Chemistry after a period of time in which the crossed molecular beams method was recognized as an important technique for the elucidation of the mechanics of chemical reactions. The extent to which his research was regarded by scientists around the world as fundamental has been illustrated by the awards he has received, which include the Ernest O. Lawrence Memorial Award from the United States Energy Research and Development Agency (1981), the Peter Debye Award in Physical Chemistry of the American Chemical Society (1986), and the National Medal of Science of the National Science Foundation (1986).

The molecular dynamics community applauded the awarding of the Nobel Prize to three respected members of the community (Dudley Herschbach and John Polanyi, in addition to Lee). Richard Zare, a Stanford University professor and reaction dynamicist, writing in *Science*, called the award "a very gratifying moment. Not only has the work of the three laureates been seminal in the study of reaction dynamics, but the field of reaction dynamics has in turn come to pervade chemistry as a whole." Richard Bernstein, who is the coauthor of some of the standard textbooks on the field, stated, "Lee is the one who really implemented molecular beam chemistry. His universal machine took the technique from being an exotic curiosity and transformed it into a laboratory workhorse." Bernstein, in *Science*, also credited Lee with having developed the best molecular beam instrumentation in the world.

Articles that appeared in *Chemical and Engineering News* (a publication of the American Chemical Society), *Scientific American, Physics Today* (a publication of the American Physical Society), and *Time* basically explained the research that led to the Nobel Prize, without comment from outside observers. This Nobel Prize award was relatively noncontroversial. The laureates were recognized by the members of the chemical community as the leaders in their field, so the only controversy would have been among different fields in chemistry competing for the honor. Yuan Lee himself is apparently not a controversial figure, as there has been little mention of him in the news outside chemistry.

Biography

Yuan Tseh Lee was born November 19, 1936, in Hsinchu, Taiwan, to Tso Fan Lee, an accomplished artist, and Pei Tsai, an elementary school teacher. His early education was disturbed by World War II, when his family relocated to the mountains to avoid Allied bombing raids. After the war, however, it continued normally through high school graduation in 1955. He was active in sports from an early age, playing baseball and Ping-Pong while growing up, and he remained a strong challenge at Ping-Pong as an adult.

Lee entered the National Taiwan University in 1955. He found there an exciting atmosphere, dedicated instructors, and warm student friendships. By the end of his freshman year, he had decided on a chemistry major. His undergraduate thesis concerned the separation of strontium and barium using paper electrophoresis; he worked under the direction of Professor Hua-sheng Cheng. He was awarded a bachelor of science degree in 1959. Lee immediately began work on a master's degree at the National Tsinghua University, which he received in 1961. His master's thesis was on natural radioisotopes in hukutolite, a mineral contained in hot spring sediments, under H. Hamaguchi. Following graduation, he remained at the University to determine the X-ray structure of tricyclopentadienyl samarium under C. H. Wong.

In 1962, Lee arrived at the University of California at Berkeley to continue his graduate career. Shortly thereafter he married Bernice Wu, whom he had first met in elementary school. He pursued research under Bruce Mahan on chemi-ionization processes involving electronically excited alkali atoms. After receiving his Ph.D. in 1965, he continued in a postdoctoral position doing ion-molecule reactive scattering experiments. He joined Dudley Herschbach at Harvard University in 1967, where he spent part of his time developing the first universal crossed molecular beams apparatus. He accepted a position as assistant professor at the University of Chicago in 1968, where he and his students continued to develop further the design and methodology of crossed beam molecular dynamics. He was promoted to associate professor in October, 1971, and to full professor in January, 1973. In 1974, Lee moved back to Berkeley when he accepted a position as professor of chemistry and principal investigator at the Lawrence Berkeley Laboratory. He was there when he was awarded the Nobel Prize in Chemistry.

Scientific Career

Lee's scientific reputation as "one of the best experimental chemical physicists" has grown primarily in the field of molecular reaction dynamics, which is a subfield of chemical kinetics: the study of the rates or velocities of chemical reactions. For many years, only the rate of a chemical reaction could be studied. When many types of reactions are studied, the rate is found as the product of a rate coefficient and the concentrations of the reactants to various powers. Svante Arrhenius found that the rate coefficient is a function of the temperature. Arrhenius explained these results in terms of an energy barrier to reaction that must be overcome. Around 1930, a number of people began investigating the dependence of the rate coefficient on the initial relative speed of the reactant molecules. It was found that the rate coefficient could be expressed as the product of the relative speed of the two colliding molecules and the cross section for the process, where the cross section measures the size of the two molecules.

More recently, the crossed molecular beams method was developed to measure the angles at which the product molecules leave the collision. These experiments are done in very high vacuum conditions, comparable to the vacuum in outer space, in order to reduce the number of collisions between background gas molecules in the vacuum chamber and the desired scattered product molecules. The angles at which the product molecules are scattered are indicative of the ways that the reactant molecules come together and hit, much as the final resting place of vehicles involved in an automobile accident can be used to understand what happened during the accident.

There are several considerations in conducting experiments of this type. First, the molecules must be brought together under conditions such that they always have the same relative speeds and angles of approach. This is done by creating beams of molecules passing through the vacuum chamber at constant speed and by intersecting the two beams at an angle of 90 degrees. The second experimental consideration concerns the detection of product molecules. Here Lee revolutionized the field by replacing a detector for only alkali metals with the universal detector, the mass spectrometer. This replacement allowed for the detection of product molecules of many types involving many different reactions.

Lee's research efforts after his arrival at the University of Chicago concentrated on the use of the crossed molecular beams technique to examine more and more complicated and sophisticated experimental systems. Initially, he studied the collisions in simple atomic systems, for example, the collisions between two rare gas atoms. His later efforts clarified the mechanism for the attack of a fluorine atom on the double bond in the ethylene molecule. This last experimental measurement can be used to illustrate the type of information that can be gathered about the detailed arrangement of all the atoms in the reaction while they are bound together. Since the seven atoms in the ethylene-fluorine system (for example) are rotating while bound together, it is possible to tell if they are bound together for greater or less than one rotation by looking at the angular distribution of the product molecules. Such measurements are required in order to compare the results with theoretical predictions.

While at Chicago, Lee began a series of experiments on the reactions of fluorine atoms with hydrogen molecules and the isotopic variants of hydrogen. This particular reaction is important because it is perhaps the simplest reaction that can be studied using experimental as well as calculational techniques. The collaboration between the experimentalists and the theoreticians has allowed the theoreticians to improve dramatically their theories of chemical reactions. The basic theoretical understanding of a simple chemical reaction is that a reaction proceeds with the arrangement of atoms proceeding along a potential energy surface describing the reaction, which describes the relationship of kinetic (motional) and potential (positional) energies, a surface that looks somewhat like interconnected mountain valleys. This surface is in general written down as a complicated mathematical function, on which rocks, arrangements of atoms, are rolled. Counting the number of rocks (reaction atom pairs) that make it over the pass, and determining how and why they do, allows a better understanding of the mechanism of reaction. Lee continued to experiment on this reaction, obtaining more exacting results each time, first in the early 1970's, then in the early 1980's, and again in the later 1980's, as better theoretical predictions were made about details not sought in earlier experiments.

After his move to Berkeley in 1974, Lee's experiments became more and more innovative. In particular, he became interested in experiments that replaced one of the crossing molecular beams with a beam of photons. Lee's experiments with photons concentrated on two different types of experiments in which photons, light, interacted with molecules. The first experiments involved infrared light breaking apart molecules after the absorption of several photons. The second involved single photons of visible or ultraviolet light breaking bonds in molecules. Both experiments measured the speeds and angular distributions of the product molecules following bond breaking.

In these experiments, the molecule of interest, for example, sulfur hexafluoride, is mixed with helium in a gas cylinder, and a beam of molecules is created by forcing a high-pressure mixture of these gases through a small hole (several thousandths of an inch) into a vacuum chamber. The expansion of the gases into the vacuum causes the gases to cool to about -260 degrees Celsius. The resulting cooled molecular beam is crossed at a 90-degree angle with the light pulse from a pulsed laser, typically either a carbon-dioxide laser operating in the infrared or a fixed-wavelength excimer laser in the ultraviolet. Either of these pulsed-light sources delivers a powerful burst of photons in a very short period of time. The cooled molecules absorb the photons, gaining enough energy to fall apart. The particular manner in which the molecules fall apart is indicative both of the type of photon absorbed and of the particulars of the mechanism by which the molecule falls apart. Detection of the remnants of the dissociated (broken apart) molecules then provides an indication of how the molecule fell apart—whether by one bond breaking at a time or by many bonds breaking simultaneously. Typically, Lee has described the molecular fragments as a function of the mass of the fragment, the angle at which they appear, and the velocity at which the fragment appears.

Two different experiments have been conducted. In the first, multiple infrared (heat) photons are absorbed by a single molecule. In these experiments, it is found that a molecule's bonds break sequentially rather than simultaneously. This implies that multiphoton dissociation, the breaking of chemical bonds resulting from the absorption of many photons, occurs by the energy of the absorbed photons becoming concentrated in one bond at a time within the molecule and then randomly getting enough energy into a bond for it to break. This kind of sequential bond breaking is revealed in molecular-beam experiments by the angular symmetry of the fragments after bond breaking as well as by the fragments' velocities. These experiments are important to the chemical community because of its desire to succeed in breaking only a single bond within a molecule, rather than many.

The experiments with ultraviolet light yield a different kind of information about chemical bonding, because only a single chemical bond is typically broken—however, by a much higher-energy photon than in the previous experiments. The initial molecules are formed in a cooled molecular beam and then fragmented by a pulse of laser light of an appropriate wavelength. The fragments' velocities and angles are detected by a sensitive mass spectrometer. Information about the fragment's mass and velocity, and about the amounts of fragment at a given angle, is received at a specific energy given by the energy (alternatively, the wavelength) of the laser light. This type of photodissociation (light-induced breaking apart of the molecule) is often referred to as a half reaction, because the molecule is only flying apart rather than first coming together and then flying apart, as in a complete reactive collision. This is a simpler case for the chemists trying to understand the motions of atoms in molecules. The type of information proved by these experiments includes the symmetry of the electrons in the excited state, the exact energies of the bond that is broken (in most cases a difficult determination by other means), and an ability to determine exactly where the excess energy above bond breaking is deposited following excitation. Such experiments have helped resolve controversies regarding some of these properties for several molecules—for example, the difference in energy between two chemically different states of methylene (CH_2), a quantity that can be determined both experimentally and theoretically.

Lee has continued his experiments on reactive scattering of molecules and on his interpretation of molecular reactive scattering experiments on a variety of atoms, including oxygen, which now has given him the ability to study reactions that are important in the simple burning of a candle cited by Forsén in his award presentation. These reactions include those of the oxygen atom with the "aromatic" molecules benzene and toluene, which are so important in the combustion of flames.

Bibliography

Primary
CHEMISTRY: "Molecular Beam Reactive Scattering Apparatus with Electron Bombardment Detector," *Review of Scientific Instruments*, vol. 40, 1969 (with J. D. McDonald, P. R. LeBreton, and D. R. Herschbach); "Chemical Dynamics," *Annual Review of Physical Chemistry*, vol. 25, 1974 (with J. M. Farrar); "Multiphoton Dissociation of Polyatomic Molecule Studies with a Molecular Beam," *Springer Series on Optical Science*, vol. 7, 1977 (with E. R. Grant, P. A. Schulz, A. S. Sudbo, M. J. Coggiola, and Y. R. Shen); "Crossed Beam Studies Related to Gas Kinetics," *Journal of Physical Chemistry*, vol. 83, 1979 (with R. J. Buss); "Studies with Crossed Laser and Molecular Beams," *Physics Today*, vol. 33, 1980 (with Y. R. Shen); "A Crossed Molecular Beams Investigation of the Reaction Atomic Oxygen (^3P) + Benzene, Benzene, d_6," *Journal of Chemical Physics*, vol. 72, 1980 (with S. J. Sibener, R. J. Buss, P. Casavecchia, and T. Hirooka); "Reactive Scattering of Atomic Oxygen (^1D) + Diatomic Hydrogen," *Chemical Physics Letters*, vol. 82, 1981 (with R. J. Buss, P. Casavecchia, T. Hirooka, and S. J. Sibener); "Methylene Singlet-Triplet Energy Splitting by Molecular Beam Photodissociation of Ketene," *Journal of Chemical Physics*, 1982 (with C. C. Hayden, D. M. Neumark, K. Shobatake, and R. K. Sparks); "Molecular Beam Studies of Primary Photochemical Processes," *Laser Chemistry*, vol. 2, 1983; "Molecular Beam Studies of the Atomic Fluorine + Molecular Deuterium and Atomic Fluorine + Hydrogen-Deuterium (HD) Reactions," *Journal of Chemical Physics*, vol. 82, 1985 (with D. M. Neumark, A. M. Wodtke, G. N. Robinson, C. C. Hayden, K. Shobatake, R. K. Sparks, and T. P. Schafer); "Molecular Beam Studies of Laser-Induced Multiphoton Dissociation," *Topics in Current Physics*, vol. 35, 1986 (with A. S. Sudboe, P. A. Schulz, and Y. R. Shen); "Reactive

Scattering of Sodium ($3^2P_{3/2}$) + Hydrogen Chloride," *Journal of Chemical Physics*, vol. 84, 1986 (with M. F. Vernon, H. Schmidt, P. S. Weiss, and M. H. Covinsky).

Secondary

Bernstein, Richard B. *Chemical Dynamics via Molecular Beam and Laser Techniques*. New York: Oxford University Press, 1982. This book reviews the use of molecular beams to study chemical reactions, particularly as coupled with laser technology. The complementary techniques of studying velocity and angular distributions and of studying the internal state distribution with the laser provide abundant information about chemical reactions.

Levine, Raphael D., and Richard B. Bernstein. *Molecular Reaction Dynamics*. New York: Oxford University Press, 1974. This book was the first to review the new field of reaction dynamics, and is thus of interest. Some of the sections are of primarily historical interest, while the book as a whole summarizes the beginnings of this important field.

——————. *Molecular Reaction Dynamics and Chemical Reactivity*. New York: Oxford University Press, 1987. This book provides a review of the field of collisional dynamics up to the period of the 1986 Nobel award. While the book is fairly advanced (at the advanced undergraduate level) it does a good job of explaining all the experimental and theoretical chemistry necessary in getting results and explaining collisions.

Zewail, Ahmed H., and Richard B. Bernstein. "Real Time Laser Femtochemistry." *Chemical and Engineering News*, November 7, 1988. This article reveals the excitement in the field of molecular dynamics on a lower level, with many examples of what was happening at the article's writing. Of particular interest are new experimental techniques that allow the intermediate species present in a reaction to be studied.

Richard W. Schwenz

1986

Chemistry
Dudley R. Herschbach, United States
Yuan T. Lee, China and United States
John C. Polanyi, Canada

Physics
Ernst Ruska, West Germany
Gerd Binnig, West Germany
Heinrich Rohrer, Switzerland

Physiology or Medicine
Stanley Cohen, United States
Rita Levi-Montalcini, United States

Economic Sciences
James M. Buchanan, Jr., United States

Literature
Wole Soyinka, Nigeria

Peace
Elie Wiesel, United States

JOHN C. POLANYI
1986

Born: Berlin, Germany; January 23, 1929

Nationality: Canadian
Area of concentration: Molecular reaction dynamics

Polanyi developed the experimental method of infrared chemiluminescence, which allows chemists to look at the internal state distributions of product molecules in a chemical reaction. He performed a systematic study of the influence of potential energy surface features on the energy distributions in product molecules

The Award

Presentation

Sture Forsén, professor of physical chemistry at the University of Lund, Sweden, and a member of the Nobel Committee for Chemistry, presented John C. Polanyi for the Nobel Prize in Chemistry on December 10, 1986. Forsén's address commended each of the three laureates sharing the prize, Dudley Herschbach, Yuan Lee, and John Polanyi, for their experimental and theoretical investigations into the motions of atoms in chemical reactions, or chemical reaction dynamics. Forsén began by describing the difficulties involved in studying even simple processes such as the burning of a flame. The rate at which a flame burns is actually a function of many variables, including, for example, the position being studied within the flame, the temperature of the flame, the material of which the candle is made, the height above sea level of the candle, and so on. Forsén said it is necessary to simplify, by analyzing individual chemical reactions within the process, to determine each reaction's dependence on the angle at which molecules approach one another, their relative velocities, and the specifics of which products are formed.

What is necessary in experiments that study these supposedly simple processes is a method of controlling the variables to be modified or those held constant. Polanyi and his colaureates undertook and refined this kind of chemical reaction experimentation and became leaders in the developing field of molecular reaction dynamics. Forsén cited Polanyi in particular for his development of the experimental method of infrared chemiluminescence, which allowed him and others to observe the internal energy distributions of the molecules produced, and for his contributions to the refinement and systematization of the theoretical description of reaction dynamics.

Nobel lecture

On Monday, December 8, 1986, John Polanyi delivered his Nobel lecture, entitled "Some Concepts in Reaction Dynamics." As his lecture immediately followed those of his colaureates, Dudley R. Herschbach speaking on "Molecular Reaction

Dynamics of Elementary Chemical Reactions" and Yuan T. Lee on "Molecular Beam Studies of Elementary Chemical Processes," he assumed a familiarity on the part of his audience with the field of reaction dynamics. He started by giving credit to his colaureates and coworkers at Toronto for defining the beginnings of the story of reaction dynamics, a story that he believed was then not far past the introduction.

In the first section of his address, Polanyi described in detail the experimental apparatus which he developed for measuring the infrared spectrum of hydrogen chloride produced in reactions between chlorine atoms and simple species containing hydrogen; he also noted the basics of the method that he used to examine the theoretical aspects of the same reactions. In particular, Polanyi said, he wanted to condense the numerous observations on many different rotational and vibrational quantum states of the products into a single graph explaining the energy disposal within the products of the reaction under study. These graphs could then be compared for many different reaction systems.

Being the most theoretical of the three laureates, Polanyi covered material that is principally theoretical in nature. He described a series of classical trajectory studies, using Isaac Newton's idea of force on different energy descriptors in an investigation of the effects of a wide variety of features of the surface on the product rotational and vibrational state distributions and on the reaction probabilities. In the last portion of the lecture, he covered the principal concepts involved in examining reacting molecules during the course of the reaction rather than preparing the reactants and examining them following the reaction. He described these concepts as doing electronic spectroscopy on the transition state of the reacting system or as using a solid surface to predetermine the orientation of the reacting molecules with respect to one another. While Polanyi's lecture was significant in that it summarized the extensive experimental and theoretical work that he had done prior to the Nobel award, it was unfortunately presented in such a fashion that the extraction of material is difficult at best. Other writers, and even Polanyi himself, have provided a much clearer sense of the immense undertakings of this remarkable man and his science in other sources.

Critical reception

The presentation of the Nobel Prize in 1986 to John Polanyi, Dudley Herschbach, and Yuan Lee for their pioneering work in reaction dynamics was "a gratifying moment to physical chemists," said Richard Zare, Stanford University professor of physical chemistry. He cited the work of the three laureates as being seminal in the study of reaction dynamics.

Polanyi's original work on the chemiluminescence from the reaction of hydrogen with chlorine molecules was published in 1958. In the same year, Arthur L. Schawlow and Charles H. Townes suggested that light could be amplified if it passed through a medium in which the atoms or molecules are in a highly excited state, with more molecules in an upper than lower state—a "population inversion." In 1960, Polanyi realized that the reactions between hydrogen and chlorine provided such a population inversion, which might form the basis for a "chemical laser." In 1965, George Pimentel and J. V. V. Kasper at Berkeley made the first chemical laser. These lasers are so powerful that they have been considered for various military purposes, including the Strategic Defense Initiative proposed by President Reagan's administration. Polanyi himself wrote that "one can certainly question the uses that chemical lasers are being put to, but there's no denying that the work has had practical applications." Polanyi was founding chairman of the Canadian Pugwash group studying arms control and nuclear proliferation and has written articles on arms control and the dangers of nuclear war.

Science magazine wrote that Polanyi's "data on the distribution of energy in product molecules, and how that distribution depends on the state of reactant molecules, have often been the first of their kind." Furthermore, his detailed maps of the potential energy for reactants had given theorists "a simple and elegant way of understanding the process as a whole." Polanyi's cowinner Dudley Herschbach remarked that with the combination of infrared chemiluminescence and molecular beam techniques, the whole picture of a chemical reaction is strengthened because of the complementary nature of the results from the two techniques. This complementary nature arises because infrared chemiluminescence examines the rotational and vibrational state distribution of the product molecules, whereas molecular beams look at the velocity and angular distributions of the product molecules.

Biography

John C. Polanyi was born in Berlin, Germany, on January 23, 1929, to Michael and Magda Elizabeth Polanyi. His father was a renowned professor of physical chemistry and later of philosophy. The family moved to England in 1933, when his father accepted a position as professor of physical chemistry at the University of Manchester. John received his early formal schooling at the Manchester Grammar School and then attended the University of Manchester beginning in 1946, graduating in 1949 with a bachelor's degree in chemistry.

He continued his education at Manchester, attaining a Ph.D. under Ernest Warhurst, one of his father's former students. His Ph.D. thesis involved experimental measurement of the strengths of chemical bonds by thermal dissociation. The impetus for his career in molecular reaction dynamics came with his acceptance of a postdoctoral position with E. W. R. Steacie at the National Research Council of Canada in Ottawa and later with Hugh Taylor at Princeton University. As a result of his work with Steacie and Taylor, Polanyi decided that he wanted to examine the mysteries of the forces between molecules in more depth than that pursued by previous investigators, who had been more interested in producing new molecules than in studying the processes during the collision. In 1956, Polanyi accepted a position as lecturer in chemistry at the University of Toronto. He has remained there, advancing through the various professorial levels, becoming assistant professor in 1957, associate professor in 1960, and professor in 1962. The university awarded him the honorific title of University Professor in 1974. In 1958, he married

Anne Farrar Davidson, a musician and piano teacher, with whom he has written the words and music for several professionally performed skits.

Scientific Career

The scientific career of John Polanyi is somewhat unusual in that he followed in his father's footsteps and built upon his work on the determination of reaction mechanisms. The major focus of the younger Polanyi's work has been examination of the details of chemical reactions—the precise ways in which the motion of reactant molecules is transferred into product molecular motion. His interest in performing these types of experiments and theoretical calculations was piqued during his years as a graduate student and postdoctoral researcher at the National Research Council and Princeton University. His interest was caught by an experiment performed in Taylor's laboratory in Princeton in which an orange glow was observed from the reaction of atomic hydrogen with ozone. This suggested to Polanyi the possibility of infrared radiation from the hydrogen halide products of hydrogen atoms reacting with halogen molecules.

With the aid of his first graduate students, Polanyi began looking in earnest for infrared emission from the hydrogen chloride products of the reaction between hydrogen and chlorine. In 1958, he and J. K. Cashion, one of his students, published their results showing the emission spectra obtained from this process. These experiments were crude in that they did not measure the hydrogen chloride emission before the hydrogen chloride had the opportunity to collide with another molecule in the apparatus. The experimental apparatus was extremely simple, consisting only of a source of hydrogen atoms, a tube down which the reactants flow and are mixed, and an infrared emission detector for viewing light, infrared chemiluminescence, from the hydrogen chloride products of the reaction through windows in the side of the reaction tube. (The pumps and gas-handling systems were much larger and more complicated.) The hydrogen atoms for the reactants were formed in a microwave discharge, the chlorine molecules were purchased in a gas cylinder, and the infrared detector was borrowed from another professor.

The infrared photons from the vibrationally excited hydrogen chloride, at about 5,000 Kelvins (approximately 9,000 degrees Fahrenheit), were detected at various distances down the flow tube from the point where the reactants were mixed. These distances corresponded directly to the length of time following initiation of the reaction for the emitting molecules. It was possible by observing the emission spectra in these early experiments to gain knowledge of the relative numbers of product molecules in each vibrational state. The nascent, zero time, populations observed by using Polanyi's technique of "measured relaxation" were among the first that could be quantified. The technique was useful because it permitted experimental measurements on single pairs of reactants, which could then be compared with theoretical predictions of energy disposal in reactions.

This first study was also important because it provided the first indications that chemical reactions could be used to produce amplified light in the infrared spectrum as long as more molecules were created by the chemical reaction in vibrationally excited states than in the lowest vibrational state. Subsequent experiments by Polanyi and others revealed that the light produced by these reactions could be used as chemical lasers with the population inversion created chemically rather than electrically, as is most commonly done. Meanwhile, Polanyi turned his attention to experiments that would directly measure the amounts of each product vibrational state at zero time rather than determination by extrapolation. With the "arrested relaxation" technique he developed in 1967, a modification of the "measured relaxation" technique used earlier, this goal became a reality. The measurement of the rate of product formation in each vibrational and rotational state became possible. In the arrested relaxation method, only the small fraction of photons that are radiated quickly following product formation are observed, while all other molecules (and the accompanying vibrational excitation that produces photons) are pumped rapidly out of the reaction vessel.

In the early 1960's, several research groups began trying to understand the experimental results of Polanyi's measured and arrested relaxation experiments and the molecular beam results of Dudley Herschbach and others, using computational techniques to qualitatively and quantitatively predict experimental results. The basis for all these first theoretical efforts was the classical mechanics originally developed by Sir Isaac Newton in the 1600's to describe the motion of the planetary masses, thrown rocks, and so forth. The techniques used by these groups treated the reacting molecules as masses that were moving in space as the result of forces acting between them. These forces were calculated in a variety of manners. The interactions among the atoms were first modeled on whatever was suggested by the intuition of the modeler. Later they worked from the first principles of Coulomb's laws of attraction and repulsion of electrically charged particles. This classical trajectory method used a large digital computer to select randomly initial conditions of the reactant molecules for study, to follow the motion of the atoms involved, and then to determine where the energy resided in the final products. It is referred to as the classical trajectory method because it uses classical mechanics, rather than quantum mechanics, to describe the motion (the trajectory) of the particles with respect to one another. Polanyi used classical trajectories from the start, with his efforts directed toward a systematic study of energy disposal rather than concentrating on specific atomic systems. In order to accomplish this, he adapted an existing description of the interaction forces between the atoms called the London-Eyring-Polanyi (Michael, his father)-Sato potential energy surface. It incorporated a number of parameters which, if changed, could change the position of energy barriers or wells, and it could compute enormous numbers of trajectories to determine energy disposal with each feature change.

One example of the new knowledge gained from these studies concerned the amount of energy in a product molecule, and where the energy was found. It was learned that if an energy barrier to reaction occurred early in the course of a reaction, then the product carried away the energy as rotation and vibration, whereas if the barrier occurred late, the product molecule carried away most of its energy as translation of the product molecules with respect to one another. The major flaw in classical trajectory calculations, recognized by Polanyi and everyone else for as long as they have been done, is that atoms do not move as point masses in a classical manner. They are in fact quantum mechanical particles, and should be treated as such. Computer technology, however, was not capable of quantum mechanical calculations on a reactive system until 1976, and there are still only a few systems that can be studied using quantum mechanics. By the time the first quantum mechanical calculation could be done, classical trajectories had allowed a good qualitative understanding of reaction dynamics to be achieved.

The 1970's brought a continuation of the research efforts of the late 1960's. A wider range of experimental systems were studied, and the systematic investigation of the variables using the classical trajectory method continued on a finer scale. At the close of the decade, believing that the possibilities of further reactions involving the halogens were few, Polanyi began work on a new step in the examination of reactions. He concentrated on the examination of reactants during the course of the reaction rather than before and after it, as had been done previously. His method was to watch for the emission of a photon during the reaction, an event that occurs one time in a million collisions, instead of emission after the reaction. By examining the number and wavelengths of these photons, Polanyi's researchers could give some very exact statements about the shapes of the potential energy surfaces during the course of the reaction rather than only at the endpoints. The reaction used for this innovative experiment was that of fluorine atoms with a sodium molecule containing two atoms. It yields an electronically excited molecule with two sodium atoms and a fluorine atom, which is stable for a relatively long period of time and which falls apart to sodium fluoride and an electronically excited sodium atom. The visible chemiluminescence for which Polanyi looked is that from the electronically excited collision complex. At this point, Polanyi came full circle with his father's research, studying in great detail one of the reactions for which his father had provided the mechanistic explanation.

Polanyi's discovery of the hydrogen-chlorine population inversion and its subsequent development as a high-power laser with possible military uses has enhanced his interest in the political arena, particularly in the areas of arms control, nuclear disarmament, and the dangers of nuclear war. He was the founding chairman of the Canadian Pugwash Group and remained its chairman until 1978. He has published more than sixty articles, delivered numerous talks, and organized symposia on the topic of nuclear survivability and is perhaps as well regarded as an authority on this topic as he is for his work on reaction dynamics.

Bibliography

Primary

CHEMISTRY: "The Effect of Changing Reagent Energy on Reaction Probability, and Product Energy-Distribution," *Faraday Discussions of the Chemical Society*, 1973 (with A. M. G. Ding, L. J. Kirsch, D. S. Perry, and J. L. Schreiber); "Magnitude and Orientation of Rotation in Exchange Reactions A + BC → AB + C," *Chemical Physics*, 1975 (with N. H. Hijazi); "The Reaction F + H_2 → HF + H. A Case Study in Reaction Dynamics," *Faraday Discussions of the Chemical Society*, 1976 (with J. L. Schreiber); "Location of Energy Barriers. VII. Sudden and Gradual Late-Energy-Barriers," *Chemical Physics*, 1978 (with N. Sathyamurthy); "Distribution of Reaction Products (Theory). Part 12. Microscopic Branching in H + XY → HX + Y, HY + X (X, Y = halogens)," *Faraday Discussions of the Chemical Society*, 1979 (with J. L. Schreiber and W. J. Skrlac); "Chemiluminescence in the Course of a Reactive Encounter, F + Na_2 → $FNaNa^+$ → NaF + Na*," *Journal of Chemical Physics*, 1980 (with P. Arrowsmith, F. E. Bartozek, S. H. P. Bly, T. Carrington, and P. E. Charters); "Spectroscopy of the Transition State. II. Atomic Fluorine Diatomic Sodium → $FNaNa^{+*}$ → Sodium Fluoride + Excited Atomic Sodium," *Journal of Chemical Physics*, 1983 (with Arrowsmith, Bly, and Charters); "Spectroscopy of the Transition State (Theory) II. Absorption by Triatomic Hydrogen (H_3^+) in Atomic Hydrogen + Molecular Hydrogen → Triatomic Hydrogen (H_3^+) → Molecular Hydrogen + Atomic Hydrogen," *Journal of Chemical Physics*, 1984 (with H. R. Mayne and R. A. Poirier).

EDITED TEXT: *The Dangers of Nuclear War: A Pugwash Symposium*, 1979 (with Franklyn Griffiths).

Secondary

Bernstein, Richard B. *Chemical Dynamics via Molecular Beam and Laser Techniques*. New York: Oxford University Press, 1982. The combination of molecular beam studies with laser technology is examined in this book. Use of these complementary techniques can produce abundant information on reactions by obtaining information on both the angular distribution and the internal state distribution of molecules.

Leone, Stephen R. "Infrared Fluorescence: A Versatile Probe of State-Selected Chemical Dynamics." *Accounts of Chemical Research* 16 (1983): 88. This review summarizes types of work using infrared fluorescence as a detector for molecular reaction dynamics and photochemistry.

——————. "State-Resolved Molecular Reaction Dynamics." *Annual Review of Physical Chemistry* 35 (1984): 109. A chronological review of the field of molecular reaction dynamics from 1979 to 1984, showing the breadth of the field.

Levine, Raphael D., and Richard B. Bernstein. *Molecular Reaction Dynamics and Chemical Reactivity*. New York: Oxford University Press, 1987. This book surveys the field of collisional dynamics up until the time of Polanyi's Nobel award. It explains the relevant experimental and theoretical chemistry, and is written at a fairly advanced (advanced undergraduate) level.

Zewail, Ahmed H., and Richard B. Bernstein. "Real Time Laser Femtochemistry." *Chemical and Engineering News*, November 7, 1988. By giving many examples of work being done at the time it was written, this article conveys the excitement in the field of molecular dynamics. Mentions new techniques that were making it possible to study the intermediate species of a reaction.

Richard W. Schwenz

1987

Chemistry
Donald J. Cram, United States
Jean-Marie Lehn, France
Charles J. Pedersen, United States

Physics
Karl Alexander Müller, Switzerland
J. Georg Bednorz, West Germany

Physiology or Medicine
Susumu Tonegawa, Japan

Economic Sciences
Robert M. Solow, United States

Literature
Joseph Brodsky, United States

Peace
Oscar Arias Sanchez, Costa Rica

DONALD J. CRAM
1987

Born: Chester, Vermont; April 22, 1919

Nationality: American
Areas of concentration: Molecular recognition and host-guest chemistry

Cram helped to develop a detailed understanding of how specific molecules such as an enzyme and its substrate, or an antibody and antigen, recognize each other. He pioneered new ways to synthesize organic molecules large enough to mimic the main functions of an enzyme. His work helped lay the foundation for the extremely broad area known as host-guest chemistry

The Award

Presentation

Professor Salo Gronowitz of the Royal Swedish Academy of Sciences presented Donald J. Cram for the Nobel Prize in Chemistry on December 10, 1987. He opened his address by observing that all life processes involve recognition at the molecular level: Enzymes recognize substrates, antibodies recognize antigens, and so on. As the chemist and Nobel laureate Emil Fischer said in 1902, the molecules must fit together like a key in a lock. Chemists had theorized for years as to how large a portion of each of these large biomolecules is really necessary for proper recognition, and they have sought methods to prepare large molecules to test the theories. Charles Pedersen, one of the three cowinners of the 1987 prize, made a breakthrough in the 1960's when he learned how to prepare cyclic carbon-oxygen ring compounds with between eighteen and forty atoms and studied their peculiar properties. Since they resembled a royal crown in shape, he named them crown ethers. Among other properties, these crown ethers unexpectedly could bind alkali metal ions. Most important, the internal diameter of the crown determined which metal ions would be bound.

Major advances in organic synthetic techniques had been made in the past decades, Gronowitz said, as recognized by Nobel Prizes awarded to chemists Robert Burns Woodward (1965), Herbert C. Brown and Georg Wittig (1979), and Bruce Merrifield (1984). These advances made it possible for Donald Cram and cowinner Jean-Marie Lehn to extend Pedersen's work and to conceive and prepare complex molecules that contain holes or crevices that can selectively bind inorganic or organic molecules, or ions of either positive or negative charge. Furthermore, they can differentiate between mirror-image forms of the same molecule and also mimic the ability of enzymes to accelerate chemical reactions. Cram has called the work "host-guest chemistry," while Lehn gave it the name "supramolecular chemistry." Gronowitz pointed out that this vast field of molecular recognition is fundamental and affects many branches of chemistry, including biochemistry, analytical chemistry, organic synthesis, and coordination chemistry.

Nobel lecture

Donald Cram delivered his lecture, entitled "The Design of Molecular Hosts, Guests, and Their Complexes," on December 8, 1987. He began by describing his early ambitions, in the 1950's, to synthesize simple organic compounds that would imitate the working features of natural molecules such as enzymes, nucleic acids, or parts of the immune system. He immediately recognized Pedersen's first papers (1967) on alkali metal ion binding with crown ethers as being of great general import, and had within ten years defined the general host-guest chemistry approach. A complex is generally defined by Cram to be composed of two or more molecules or ions held together in a unique structural relation by electrostatic forces other than full covalent bonds. This complex, or host-guest relationship, involves a complementary three-dimensional arrangement of atoms and electrons to form binding sites. In the host, one finds an organic molecule or ion whose binding sites converge or enclose to make the complex; in the guest one finds a molecule or ion whose binding sites diverge or reach out when forming the complex. This description shows the host to be a synthetic counterpart of a receptor site in biological chemistry, and the guest is the counterpart of the substrate, inhibitor, or cofactor.

Cram spoke of his many hours spent with models devising suitable complexes for synthesis, for the possibilities seemed endless. They formed an uncharted sea of new compounds as yet unknown. Coworkers then prepared the proposed host molecules and tested them with suitable guests. Cram also compared these with complexes of natural origin (biotic complexes), and, as an important test of the approach, performed X-ray structural determinations on the abiotic (not originating in living things) complexes and hosts to check the fit, or interaction, between host and guest. Displaying a gift for analogy and elegant simplification, Cram noted that complexes could be visualized in three ways: perched like a bird on a limb, nested like an egg in a nest, or encapsulated like a nut in its shell. He then showed that in order to obtain a strong binding interaction, the host must be preorganized; that is, it should be shaped like a nest before insertion of the egg. In solution, a simple host molecule may exist in a thousand or more different spatial arrangements, of which only one or two actually form the nest that can hold the guest. By design, he was able to synthesize host molecules that were more nest-like in solution and therefore had greater binding power.

The other important feature is structural recognition, and structural complementarity is its central determinant. In the biotic world, chiral (mirror-image) recognition is fundamental to complex formation. Amino acids and other important biotic molecules can exist in two mirror-image forms, but in nature only one of them is used. Cram described a machine that he built which could separate mixtures of the mirror-image forms of amino acids, based on chiral recognition by a synthetic host. He then described his work to create a molecule that would mimic an enzyme's ability to form complexes which accelerate a reaction and to be competitively inhibited, that is, to lose its complexing ability in the presence of some other chemical. His model compound mimicked the action of the enzyme chymotrypsin in an acylation reaction and was inhibited by sodium perchlorate, a simple salt.

His last two topics were cavitands and carcerands. "Cavitand" is the name he gave to compounds that have a cavity large enough to embrace a small molecule, and a "carcerand" is a host molecule of sufficient size to trap a small molecule within its structure by forming a cage of covalent bonds without relying on a strong host-guest interaction. He described some of the unusual properties of these compounds and offered ideas for future studies. In his closing remarks, he graciously acknowledged his financial supporters and the more than two hundred coworkers who had participated in these studies.

Critical reception

The press gave a very favorable reception to the news of the award. Since the award in physics that year recognized work on superconductivity (a widely and often reported subject) and was announced simultaneously, it was given a slightly greater emphasis in the general press. Newspapers usually gave combined accounts of the three chemistry cowinners' reactions to their selection on October 14. Lehn was in Strasbourg, Pedersen was in Salem, New Jersey, and Cram was in Los Angeles. Pedersen was recognized as the first to discover that crown ethers could form complexes with metal ions. At the time of the award he was eighty-three; his classic work in the field had been published in 1967. Cram and Lehn used his results in different ways to make their respective contributions. Although the prize was given in recognition of work in the field of organic chemistry, many newspapers emphasized the application of the work to biochemistry and medicine.

The New York Times described some of the many potential medical and industrial uses of their work, which include the creation of artificial enzymes and new medical diagnostic aids. The remarkable nature of the 1987 Nobel Prize was noted, in that it recognized the future possibilities raised by this work rather than only its existing contributions and impact. The international impact of Cram's work was acknowledged in a separate article, which said that his doctoral students (more than one hundred in all) were spreading his ideas all over the world and that the majority of chemists from several countries working in molecular recognition have spent time in his laboratory. *The Washington Post* tried to convey some of the excitement felt by chemists about the field of host-guest interactions by emphasizing their similarities to those of proteins in living cells, which are important in the operation of genes, enzymes, and antibodies. It also expressed the generally optimistic and futuristic mood of the press and quoted Cram as saying that there were still "years of research needed to find out all we don't know. We're really just opening the door." The *Los Angeles Times* interjected a humorous note by observing that the Nobel Committee at first had contacted the wrong person in Los Angeles, a man with a very similar name who was a carpet cleaner by profession. Cram and Lehn were noted to be friendly and to exchange information in order to prevent duplication of research.

An article in *The San Francisco Chronicle* also emphasized potential uses of these compounds. It said that chemical separations of unprecedented precision were now possible; they could allow the removal of poisons from contaminated soil or water and the detection of traces of chemicals in the environment. The journal *Science* featured an in-depth interview with Cram. Lehn was credited with applying Pedersen's ideas to three-dimensional structures by creating cryptands ("little crypts") in 1969 and coining the term "supramolecular chemistry" to describe the phenomenon that Cram calls "host-guest chemistry." Cram's cavitands and carcerands were presented as molecules that could serve as miniature laboratories in which chemistry could be observed taking place or as vehicles for the slow release of drugs or pesticides. The *Science* article also noted that very few synthetic compounds have the concave surfaces found in nature, such as the doughnut-shaped cyclodextrins created by bacteria. Cram does not work with these, although they have host-guest properties that have been explored by researchers, most notably Ronald Breslow at Columbia University. The European press voiced the same optimism expressed in the United States and focused its attention on the implications of the work for biomedical research.

Biography

Donald James Cram was born in Chester, Vermont, the fourth child and only son of a Scottish father and Germanic mother. His father died when he was four, and he grew up in Brattleboro, Vermont. In his own words, his childhood was "idyllic and adventuresome, in the things that mattered." His family dispersed when he was sixteen, and he held many odd jobs that taught him self-discipline. He obtained a scholarship to Rollins College, from which he received a B.S. degree in 1941. He decided on a chemistry career in academic research. He obtained a master of science degree in 1942 from the University of Nebraska and, during the years of World War II, worked on penicillin and streptomycin research at Merck & Co., under Dr. Max Tishler, who then helped him enter Harvard University in 1945 to complete his doctoral studies. At Harvard, he worked as a National Research Council Fellow with Dr. Louis Fieser and was also influenced by Professors Robert Burns Woodward and Paul Bartlett. He completed his doctoral research in eighteen months, receiving his Ph.D. in 1947. Then, after a brief three months at the Massachusetts Institute of Technology, working with Dr. John Roberts, he arrived at the University of California, Los Angeles, in August of 1947. He has taught and conducted research at UCLA since then and, since 1985, has held the position of Saul Weinstein Professor of Chemistry. He has been a Guggenheim Fellow (1955) at the University of London and the Swiss Federal Institute of Technology. He was a visiting professor at the National University of Mexico in 1956 and a guest professor at the University of Heidelberg in 1958. He was elected to the National Academy of Sciences in 1961 and won the American Chemical Society (ACS) Award for Creative Work in Synthetic Organic Chemistry in 1965. In 1984, he was given the Roger Adams Award in Organic Chemistry by the ACS in recognition of his contributions to organic complexation chemistry. In 1985, he received the prestigious Willard Gibbs Medal from the Chicago Section of the ACS for his pioneering work in organic chemistry.

Scientific Career

Cram's career, from his early college days, has embodied a search for new phenomena and an intense interest in research. Almost all of his scientific career has been spent at UCLA. He started there at a time when biochemistry, organic chemistry, and physical chemistry were combining their approaches and methods, and he has drawn upon these fields in his own work. He has made considerable contributions to the organic synthesis of large molecules with selective properties— the important features for molecular recognition—and investigated their biochemical implications. The idea of creating molecules that mimic the behavior of enzymes and other biochemical systems has inspired his work for more than forty years.

In 1952, Cram and his coworkers published their rule of "steric control of asymmetric induction," which enables one to predict the dominant mirror-image product of synthetic organic reactions that begin with a ketone. This same approach led him to the invention and study of a new class of organic compounds, the paracyclophanes. These were found to have interesting properties: Several parts of the molecule could interfere with one another's free movement in space, which in turn affected their chemical reactivity. In addition, their *pi* electron orbitals were extremely avid electron acceptors. In 1970, he began the study of complexes between two organic molecules that were formed with the use of *pi* electrons. The electron donor used electrons in a *pi* orbital to bond with the electron acceptor, or *pi* acid. He realized that it would be necessary to build and study complexes that possessed highly oriented, fairly rigid structures in order to mimic the behavior of enzyme systems—this at a time when relatively little detail was known about the structure and mode of action of enzymes.

Cram saw the implications of Pedersen's work, and by 1973 he was able to synthesize crown ethers that could recognize and selectively form complexes with one of the mirror-image forms of several amino acids. These crown ethers were "chiral"; that is, they had a specific three-dimensional structure that distinguished them from other compounds of the same atomic composition. (The difference is analogous to the differences that distinguish the right hand from the left, its mirror image.) This imparted certain electronic patterns to the "nest," or host, so that only one form of the amino acid "egg," or guest, would form a complex. The other form, or mirror image, would not sit deeply enough in the nest to form a strong complex. Using this approach, Cram was able to take a solution containing equal parts of the two mirror-image forms of the amino acid and separate them by causing one to form a complex with the chiral crown ether and then selectively removing the complex by dissolving it in a solvent that would not dissolve the other uncomplexed amino acid form. He thus not only demonstrated that molecules could be designed to recognize certain other molecules or ions but also made a practical application of this ability by accomplishing an otherwise very difficult feat, the separation of two types of mirror-image molecules which possess almost identical chemical and physical properties. This work established the direction of Cram's research and was published as a general article in *Science*, entitled "Host-Guest Chemistry," in 1974.

A formidable task now presented itself: the design of other host molecules. From an almost endless array of potential host molecules that could be created on paper, Cram had to choose likely candidates to construct and then test experimentally. Hundreds of accurate molecular models of host-guest complexes, with correct interatomic bond distances and three-dimensional structures, were carefully devised. Some years earlier, William Corey, Linus Pauling, and William Koltun had devised a set of atomic models (CPK models) with correct sizes and bond lengths so that chemists could build accurate three-dimensional models of molecules which could be held in the hands for study. Cram made many of these CPK models, which served him "as a compass on an otherwise uncharted sea," in his own words, and were ranked as potential candidates for further study. An important aspect of this work involved relating these abiotic complexes to similar compounds found in nature. Cram started with what was known about the structures of small enzymes (hosts) and their substrates (guests) found in nature. By constructing models of them, he was able to suggest abiotic (nonliving) compounds that might behave similarly and also would be simple enough to be synthesized. The most promising hosts were then prepared by coworkers (a formidable task, in many cases). If they would actually form a complex, they were then analyzed by X-ray crystallography to compare the true experimental structures with those predicted from the models. Within the span of ten years, more than fifty host-guest complexes and twenty-five other hosts were prepared and studied in this way by Cram, working with Kenneth Trueblood, Carolyn Knobler, Emily Maverick, and Israel Goldberg. Given the amount of work necessary to prepare and study only one molecule or complex, this is a prodigious output of X-ray studies. It stands as a tribute to Cram's skill as a synthetic chemist and his insight into the important features of host-guest chemistry.

Several important principles emerged from these studies, one of which came from what was known about complexes in general. Electrons repel each other. If two molecules approach too closely, then their surrounding electron clouds will repel each other and no bonding interaction will occur. Yet they must approach closely in order for the complex to form. A way must be found for the host to minimize repulsions with the guest in its binding site, or nest area, so that the attractive forces are greater than the repulsive forces. Cram called this the complimentarity principle: The host's binding site must cooperatively contact and attract binding sites of guests without generating strong nonbonding repulsions. In effect, the host must "grasp" the guest. Molecules do this in a manner somewhat analogous to a hand that closes when picking up an object. The shape of the host molecule can change to improve the "fit" or bonding interaction as the guest moves toward its correct position in the complex. This is called cooperative contact, and it implies a more dynamic situation than the lock and key analogy drawn by Emil Fischer in 1902 for enzyme action, which implies a more static or rigid nature for the molecules. Indeed, Cram refers to several host molecules as if they were "hinged" to permit a better fit with the guest.

Cram's earlier complexes were of the kind that he described as being like a bird perching on a limb. The smaller guest molecule (containing approximately one to sixteen atoms) sits on one side of the larger, somewhat flattened host molecule, which might be composed of twenty to thirty atoms. As new models were built and new synthetic methods devised, however, more complicated molecules with other shapes could be made. The next type of complex he devised used a nest with a host molecule composed of thirty to forty or more atoms and (usually) a very simple guest, such as a sodium ion. Many of the host molecule's atoms serve as a super-structure to hold the binding site atoms in the correct three-dimensional orientation in the complex. In order to house a larger guest molecule with many atoms, a very large superstructure obviously is needed; in nature, many enzymes contain extensive superstructures in order to form the active site (or nest), which itself may involve only a small percentage of the total atoms present. Cram's genius lay in his ability to reduce the complexity of the molecules to a size small enough to be synthesized, while retaining the essential features governing the operation of an enzyme. The third type of host molecule, which acts like the shell enclosing a nut, was named capsular, since the complex is encapsulated by the host molecule.

Another important principle that Cram found is called preorganization. When a crown ether type of host molecule is placed in solution without the guest being present, it can assume a wide variety of shapes. Many of these shapes are very similar in terms of energy, structural distances, and electronic repulsions. The host can easily shift from one shape to another, and does so rapidly in solution; the locale where the guest will sit is often occupied by one or several loosely associated solvent molecules. Many of these shapes are not suitable for forming a strong host-guest complex, and this reduces the tendency for one to form. In other words, in the uncomplexed state, the hosts possessed no cavities, clefts, or convergently arranged binding sites to attract the guest. This meant that the cavity had to be formed during the association of the guest with the host, and if several binding sites were involved (commonly four, six, or eight are), they would have to swing into correct position sequentially.

Cram realized that by careful analysis of the models, he could design a molecule with its binding sites already locked and positioned favorably for complex formation to occur. By 1981, in a wonderfully conceived and executed synthetic sequence, he made a host that had six binding sites (in this case, oxygen atoms) octahedrally arranged inside the spherical host molecule at just the right separation to contain a sodium or lithium ion as the guest. By choosing oxygen atoms and placing them at the corners of an octahedron, he was taking advantage of the known preferences of sodium and lithium to surround themselves with this environment. In a simple aqueous solution, six different water molecules would provide it, but in the complex, the host would. This was the first host molecule that was completely organized during synthesis rather than during formation of the complex. He gave this type of host the family name "spherand." Spherands were predicted to form strong complexes because of their preorganized structure, and they were found experimentally to do so. Cram's spherands were an important step toward the creation of an abiotic system to mimic enzyme behavior. Many enzymes are preorganized themselves so that they can interact strongly with the correct substrate. This strong interaction is one reason biological systems (enzymes) can perform chemistry at body temperature and normal atmospheric pressure, while the chemist must often use extreme pressures and/or temperatures to accomplish the same work without the aid of preorganization.

In an elegant series of experiments, Cram first synthesized an analogue of the spherand host molecule, called a podand, which differed in one important respect: Its superstructure was cut in two in the middle, so that the preorganization was ruined. He then devised a method to measure the energy of the interaction of the spherand or the podand with several different ionic guests, including lithium, sodium, potassium, and ammonium ions. He discovered that the spherand bound the lithium ion more strongly than the podand by more than 68 kilojoules/mole. This tremendous binding energy difference, which he attributed to preorganization, is much larger than any observed for other factors that could affect the binding. He has continued to study binding energy differences for various families of hosts and has shown that the degree of preorganization determines the binding power.

The third principle that Cram elucidated concerns molecular recognition. A very simple type of recognition can be based on size: If the egg is too large, it will not fit in the nest. Cram devised a series of hosts of different sizes and compared their abilities to form complexes with smaller and larger alkali metal ions in 1985. It proved to be a dramatic demonstration of complimentarity. One of the hosts showed a preference for the sodium ion over the potassium ion of 13,000:1. By simply adding six atoms to enlarge the nest, the larger potassium ion became favored by 10,000:1. This work is important for biology and medicine, for it shows one way that a living cell could construct a channel for the selective movement of sodium or potassium through the cell membrane. The way that a cell pumps these ions in and out is still not completely understood, and many medical problems, such as dehydration and diarrhea, involve this chemical pump.

Not only does nature provide an environment for biochemical reactions that is complementary and preorganized (in Cram's terms), but also it is capable of very sophisticated selection of molecules. Chiral recognition distinguishes between chemically identical mirror-image forms of the same molecule. A good example is amino acids. They are found naturally in only one of two possible chiral forms, often called the left-handed form. The other (right-handed) form can be made chemically but cannot be used metabolically by living systems to form materials such as protein. As early as 1978, Cram had synthesized a chiral host that could recognize a chiral guest, again based on studies using CPK models. It formed a perched type of complex with certain amino acid salts and had the novel feature that the salt could form a complex from either side. The ratio of the preference for one chiral salt over its mirror image was 31:1, which was quite a success. Cram built a machine in 1979 to separate chiral amino acid salts. At this time, man-made amino acids were generally composed of equal mixtures of the right- and left-handed forms, and separation was a laborious process. He attached the chiral host molecules to a polymeric resin backbone and was able to effect complete separation of the mirror-image forms by ion exchange, which is essentially the same process used in home water softeners to remove unwanted metal ions by substituting them with sodium. The ion exchange approach for chiral separation has since been used extensively by analytical and preparative chemists.

Since 1984, Cram has worked on ways to mimic the behavior of enzymes, and he considers it one of the most challenging problems of organic chemistry. Two important properties of enzymes are that they greatly enhance the conversion rate of substrate into product and they are subject to competitive inhibition. Competitive inhibition simply means that in the presence of other specific compounds which compete with the enzyme for the substrate in some way, the enzyme loses its ability to speed the reaction. This is a crucial feature of metabolic regulation. Cram first worked on a host that mimics the action of the enzyme chymotrypsin, because its operation was well studied, and the important molecular features and events during its reactions were known. This enzyme, made in the pancreas, is used in the small intestine to fragment proteins. These fragments are then digested to free amino acids in later reactions. The active site in the chymotrypsin molecule is like a miniature factory. It contains a place to hold the protein for disassembly (pre-organized binding site) and has the tools for the job nearby (chemical species such as hydrogen ions). Cram's challenge was to mimic all these features with a molecule simple enough to be synthesized. His mimic was not intended to fragment protein; instead, it recognized and bound a specific guest, which then reacted with the host molecule using the same type of chemistry that chymotrypsin does. Two critical features were observed. The mimic was able to speed the reaction rate dramatically because of its preorganization, and competitive inhibition occurred when a salt was added. With this encouragement, Cram devised a thirty-step synthesis of another mimic, with the hydrogen ion and other reagents built into place, thus moving one step closer to the goal of mimicking enzyme chemistry. His pioneering work in this area has produced methods to synthesize, analyze, evaluate, and organize research for studying enzyme properties with chemical model systems.

Cram also noted that in biological systems such as enzymes, deoxyribonucleic acid (DNA), and ribonucleic acid (RNA), there exist cavities large enough to contain molecules such as solvent, or substrates. Such cavities are extremely rare among the seven million organic compounds that chemists have synthesized. These cavities are very important biologically, for they provide the shell, or concave framework, on whose internal surfaces are placed the atoms that form the binding sites and catalytic agents. He named his class of abiotic compounds which have such cavities carcerands. As always, careful planning using the CPK models allowed him to design and then synthesize cavitands that resembled bowls or vases of various depths, which stood on four "feet" (actually, methyl groups) in their crystalline forms. Different cavitands can hold small spherical, rod-shaped, or bent molecules, as predicted by the principle of complimentarity. In 1985, he completed this cycle of creating molecules with cavities by synthesizing a synthetic molecular cell, that is, a molecule that completely surrounds a cavity on all sides, which he called a carcerand. Excitement grew as chemists speculated as to what, if anything at all, would be found trapped inside the carcerand after it was recovered from the mixture of solvent and reagents used to form it. Because the carcerand was very insoluble in practically every solvent, purification was difficult. Eventually, the answer was found to be the reaction mixture itself. Many of the different chemicals present in the reaction mixture (as the cell was formed by interlocking rings of atoms) were trapped inside, including positive and negative ions, solvent molecules, and reagents. Even when the carcerand was thoroughly dried, these separate species could not be driven off. Curiously, however, when the dried carcerand was boiled in heavy water (in which the normal hydrogen isotope is replaced with deuterium to give D_2O), the entrapped water was replaced with the D_2O. Cram went back to the CPK models and found that the carcerand has two small portals lined with methyl groups which will only allow passage of the small water molecules in and out of the cage. The presence of these portals is most interesting, for living cells must also have some kind of portals in them to allow oxygen, nutrients, and metabolites to pass through the cell membrane; perhaps they are similar to those he discovered. Cram has continued his work with cavitands and carcerands to explore their unusual physical and chemical properties and to find new chemical and biomedical uses for them.

Cram's career shows the remarkable union that he has created between the seemingly disparate fields of synthetic organic chemistry, biochemistry, physical chemistry, and molecular modeling. He has not only found ways to synthesize and study new molecules but has also described some of the basic and profound properties that molecules in biological systems must possess. Some of his greatest contributions concern his revelations of the essential features of molecular recognition and the proof of their validity with model compounds. His work serves not only as a bridge between organic chemistry and biochemistry but also as a guide for future work on a broad range of problems in these fields. Through his efforts, chemists have begun to see important generalizations for the development of new pharmaceuticals, novel uses of molecular recognition for analysis and separations, new insights into the functioning of enzymes, DNA, and other biomolecules, and new ways to synthesize biomimetic molecules. Using his approaches, chemists may someday be able to follow the detailed course of the molecular events that occur during the remarkable transformations the living cell performs with such seeming ease during metabolism.

Bibliography

Primary

CHEMISTRY: *Reaction Mechanisms*, 1962 (with George Hammond and Albert Lwowski); *Fundamentals of Carbanion Chemistry*, 1965; *Organic Chemistry*, 1967 (with George Hammond); *Elements of Organic Chemistry*, 1970 (with James Hendrickson and George Hammond); *Essence of Organic Chemistry*, 1978 (with Jane Cram); *Concept, Structure, and Binding in Complexation*, 1985 (with Kenneth Trueblood).

Secondary

Fendler, Janos, *Membrane Mimetic Chemistry: Characterizations and Applications of Micelles, Microemulsions, Monolayers, Bilayers, Vesicles, Host-Guest Systems, and Polyions*. New York: John Wiley & Sons, 1982. Provides a good general view of the importance of host-guest chemistry in biological systems. The book relates this field to biochemistry and medicine, showing how the compounds can be used for practical purposes.

Streitweiser, Andrew, Jr., and Clayton Heathcock. *Introduction to Organic Chemistry*. New York: Macmillan, 1985. Crown ethers are described in this introductory textbook and are related to their simpler analogues. Molecular geometry is clearly explained; the different shapes involved in host-guest chemistry can be visualized easily. Some basic knowledge of chemical bonding is assumed.

Voegtle, Fritz, ed. *Cyclophanes*. New York: Springer-Verlag, 1983. This book presents a series of research essays on cyclophane chemistry. This was the first class of compounds Cram developed, intended for studying the effects of molecular structure and interfering groups on the molecules' ability to form *pi* complexes. Other workers have extended and broadened the original ideas he studied, and some of their work is brought together in this book.

Voegtle, Fritz, and Friedrich Boschke, eds. *Host Guest Chemistry*. New York: Springer-Verlag, 1982. This book surveys the literature on host-guest compounds. It discusses in detail the many synthetic steps involved in preparing these molecules. Reviews preparation, structure, and uses of many of these compounds; computer models are discussed, as are X-ray and nuclear magnetic methods of structure determination.

Voegtle, Fritz, and Edwin Weber, eds. *Host Guest Complex Chemistry: Synthesis, Structures, Applications*. New York: Springer-Verlag, 1985. A compilation of methods for preparing host-guest complexes. Their structures are shown in detail, and many applications are given. The basic theories developed by Cram and Lehn are discussed, and numerous compounds are presented that verify and elaborate the theories. Ways in which they mimic enzymes and can act as reagents for selecting metal ions are described.

Volhardt, Peter. *Organic Chemistry*. New York: W. H. Freeman, 1987. This textbook, a general organic chemistry text, provides an introduction to the field of host-guest chemistry. Detailed descriptions are given of some of the synthetic reactions used to make host compounds. Shows the relationship of crown ethers and other cryptands to similar organic compounds.

William Van Willis

1987

Chemistry
Donald J. Cram, United States
Jean-Marie Lehn, France
Charles J. Pedersen, United States

Physics
Karl Alexander Müller, Switzerland
J. Georg Bednorz, West Germany

Physiology or Medicine
Susumu Tonegawa, Japan

Economic Sciences
Robert M. Solow, United States

Literature
Joseph Brodsky, United States

Peace
Oscar Arias Sanchez, Costa Rica

JEAN-MARIE LEHN
1987

Born: Rosheim, France; September 30, 1939

Nationality: French
Areas of concentration: Molecular recognition and host-guest chemistry

Lehn was instrumental in the development of supramolecular chemistry, the chemistry of organic complexing agents that involve noncovalent intermolecular bonds. His work has improved understanding of how molecules "recognize" one another, opening the door for the synthesis of artificial enzymes, cells, and molecular devices

The Award

Presentation

The Nobel Prize in Chemistry was presented to Jean-Marie Lehn, Donald J. Cram, and Charles J. Pedersen by Salo Gronowitz on December 10, 1987. Gronowitz, a member of the Royal Swedish Academy of Sciences and professor of organic chemistry at the University of Lund, cited Lehn and the others for their development and use of "supramolecular chemistry," in which "host" molecules with cavities of precisely defined sizes and shapes recognize and bind to smaller "guest" molecules of a complementary size and shape, much the same way as a key fits into a lock. The host-guest interaction is very specific; only guests of the appropriate structure can be accommodated by a particular host.

Gronowitz explained that this "molecular recognition" is not interesting merely as a chemical curiosity; such interactions are vital to all life processes. The complex functions of sophisticated biomolecules depend largely on their ability to recognize and bind to only certain other molecules. Enzymes, for example, which serve to catalyze specific biochemical reactions, must be able to recognize and act upon only the appropriate "substrate" molecules. A given enzyme might be able to break down the proteins in food but must not also break down the proteins constituting the structural components of the body's own cells.

The rapid progress made in recent decades in the area of synthetic organic chemistry, Gronowitz noted, has allowed for the development of supramolecular chemistry. Through appropriate design and construction, molecules have been synthesized that act as artificial enzymes or that can selectively separate toxic from nontoxic metal ions. The day can be envisioned when synthetic enzymes will perform their functions even more efficiently than the naturally occurring enzymes, or when they will catalyze new or as-yet-unknown chemical reactions.

Nobel lecture

"Supramolecular Chemistry: Scope and Perspectives" was the title of the Nobel lecture given by Jean-Marie Lehn on December 8, 1987. Lehn apologized for not being able to do justice to a discussion of all the developments that are being made by all the workers in this burgeoning field. Although he chose to confine himself primarily to discoveries made within his own research group, one of the most impressive features of the address was the sheer volume of the work that Lehn and his coworkers had produced during the years 1967-1987 and the incredible progress they had made in developing and applying the concepts involved in supramolecular chemistry.

Lehn began his talk, appropriately, by making clear the distinction between "molecular" and "supramolecular" chemistry. Whereas molecules are composed of individual atoms held together by very strong covalent bonds (shared pairs of electrons), supramolecular interactions rely on relatively weak intermolecular attractive forces. These forces are electrostatic in nature: Regions of one molecule bearing a partial positive charge are attracted to complementary regions of another molecule that bear a partial negative charge. Although these forces individually are usually quite weak, the cumulative attractive force may be substantial if there are many such interactions between a given pair of molecules. In Lehn's words, "supermolecules are to molecules and the intermolecular bond what molecules are to atoms and the covalent bond." It may seem surprising, but it is precisely the weakness (and hence the "reversibility") of intermolecular bonds that allows molecules of biological interest to exhibit their highly specialized functions. The actions of enzymes, antibodies, and deoxyribonucleic acid (DNA) are possible only because of the nonpermanent nature of intermolecular interactions.

Lehn described the basic functions of supramolecular species as "recognition, transformation, and translocation." The process begins when a pair of molecules (a "receptor" and a "substrate," with the receptor being the larger of the two) form intermolecular attachments to each other. Once bound, the receptor-substrate pair is referred to as a "complex species," or supramolecule. In order for this complexation to qualify as recognition, however, binding must be selective and it must have a "purpose." Commonly this purpose will entail either transformation (inducing a chemical change in the substrate) or translocation (moving the substrate from one location to another, usually across a barrier or a gradient that it could not or would not cross on its own).

Such supramolecular interactions are common in biological systems. For example, certain naturally occurring antibiotic substances (termed "ionophores") have the ability to mediate cation transport across cell membranes. (Ions are species, either atoms or molecules, that bear an electrical charge; anions are negatively charged, and cations are positively charged.) Lehn recalled his first contributions to the field of supramolecular chemistry—the development and synthesis of artificial cation-complexing agents, which he called "cryptands." These molecules are shaped like hollow spheres, formed from interconnected chains of atoms, most of which are carbon, but some of which are nitrogen and oxygen. By varying the size of the cryptand, and hence the size of the interior cavity where complexation takes place, selectivity between metal cations of various sizes was achieved.

Lehn explained how further variations on this theme allowed him to produce molecular receptors, molecules that are capable of forming supramolecular complexes with anions and with nonspherically shaped ionic substrates, such as the tetrahedral "ammonium" cation, NH_4^+. One receptor molecule outfitted with covalently bound sulfhydryl groups (hydrogen attached to sulfur attached to the rest of the molecule) is appropriate for effecting a chemical reaction known as ester cleavage, which involves the breaking of a particular sort of carbon-to-oxygen covalent bond. When substrate molecules bearing an ester group at one end and an ammonium group at the other were exposed to the specially equipped receptors, very high rates of ester cleavage were observed. Complexation had occurred between the ammonium group and the receptor in such a way that the ester end of the substrate was situated relative to the sulfhydryl groups in a position favoring ester cleavage. Thus, an artificial enzyme had been produced, and the fundamental goal of transformation subsequent to recognition was achieved. (Further efforts have yielded artificial enzymes capable of facilitating the formation of covalent bonds in molecules as well.)

While most of the accomplishments in the area of synthetic enzyme design are "biomimetic," that is, they attempt to imitate processes known to occur in nature, Lehn noted that mere imitation of biological enzymatic catalysis need not be a limit to scientists' aspirations.

The final portion of Lehn's lecture was devoted to areas in which he had recently begun work, and to a discussion of the prospects for future developments in the field of supramolecular chemistry. Among the most exciting of these is the coupling of recognition, transport, and transformation within a single polymolecular assembly, thus creating a microreactor, or "artificial cell." The transport and synthesis functions could be light-activated, having applications in the areas of artificial photosynthesis or solar energy conversion. Additionally, the development of supramolecular electronic devices can be envisaged. If signal processing could be achieved "artificially" at the molecular level, the field of electronics would experience a revolution similar to that caused by the replacement of vacuum tubes with semiconductors. Lehn concluded his lecture by thanking his collaborators.

Critical reception

Of the three Nobel Prize winners for 1987, Pedersen is credited with having established the basis for his cowinners' achievements through his discovery of the "crown ethers." The first of these to be synthesized was "18-crown-6," the overall structure of which is doughnut-shaped, with the oxygen atoms forming a hexagon along the inner circumference of the doughnut (the hole) and the carbon atoms occupying positions around the exterior circumference. Lehn's first contribution to the field of supramolecular chemistry was the extension of Pedersen's idea from two dimensions to three. Cram's approach was similar to Lehn's, but his molecules are even more elaborately shaped than the cryptands. According to the Nobel Committee, the three prizewinners had been selected "for the development and use of molecules with structure-specific interactions of high selectivity." The specificity of these interactions has numerous practical applications.

The response of the scientific community to the awarding of the Nobel Prize to Lehn, Cram, and Pedersen was uniformly positive and vigorous. As *Time* magazine reported, the scientists were able to "bask in the traditional praise of colleagues around the globe" after the announcement. According to *The New York Times*, these colleagues describe Lehn as a "leader whose ideas are so compelling that he draws a faithful crowd of followers." François Diederich of the University of California at Los Angeles, said of Lehn that "you can talk to him on any chemical topic whatsoever, and he will reply with answers and reasoning at the highest scientific level in the next moment." Diederich also noted that in 1987 the Nobel Committee had recognized rapidly expanding fields having "great futures before them." Evidence from the chemical literature bears out this contention. There were fewer than twenty scientific papers published in the area of "inclusion compounds" in 1969, when Lehn's work on cryptands first appeared. By 1987, the number had risen to almost two hundred.

Ronald Breslow of Columbia University, himself a major proponent of biomimetic chemistry and enzyme models, described Lehn as "the leading chemist of France" even though Lehn was "still a very young man." The French were duly proud of their "enfant terrible," particularly because it was the first time in more than fifty years that someone from France had won the Nobel Prize in Chemistry. In an interview with Fabien Gruhier of *Le Nouvel Observateur*, however, Lehn said, "It is the work that matters, not the country."

Biography

On September 30, 1939, Jean-Marie Lehn was born in Rosheim, France, the first of Pierre and Marie Lehn's four sons. Pierre was a baker, and Jean-Marie had occasion to help in the shop along with his mother and oldest brother. Lehn entered high school in 1950, studying classics with an emphasis on philosophy but developing an interest in science as well. In the summer of 1957 he received his *baccalauréat* in both philosophy and experimental sciences. In the fall of 1957, Lehn entered the University of Strasbourg. He had originally planned to study philosophy, but he was so taken with his science courses that he began to reconsider his intended field of study. He was, in his own words, "particularly receptive to the experimental power of organic chemistry, which was able to convert at will, it seemed, complicated substances into one another following well defined rules and routes." Lehn received his B.S. degree in 1960 and entered Guy Ourisson's laboratory as a Ph.D. candidate that fall. Upon receiving his doctorate in 1963, Lehn traveled to Harvard University, where he spent a year as a postdoctoral research associate in the laboratory of Robert Burns Woodward, working on the total synthesis of vitamin B_{12}.

In 1965, Lehn returned to the University of Strasbourg, where he was appointed assistant professor of chemistry in 1966. Although the initial focus of his work was in the area of physical organic chemistry, Lehn's interest in the chemistry of the nervous system brought a change in direction to his research efforts. Cation transport across nerve cell membranes, so critical to their function, led Lehn to synthesize the cryptands, which have remarkable cation-complexing abilities. Out of this development grew the field of supramolecular chemistry in general, the study of which began to occupy the bulk of Lehn's time.

Lehn was promoted to associate and then to full professor in 1970 at the University of Strasbourg. While keeping his research group in Strasbourg, he was elected to a chair at the Collège de France in Paris, where he also began directing a research group in 1980. He has held positions as a visiting professor at several academic institutions, including Harvard, the University of Cambridge, and the Eidgenössiche Technische Hochschule in Zurich. In these research settings, Lehn has produced well in excess of three hundred scientific papers in collaboration with more than one hundred coworkers from more than twenty different countries.

Lehn's honors and awards are too numerous to list in detail, but they include the Bronze (1963), Silver (1972), and Gold (1981) Medals of the Centre National de la Recherche Scientifique (the French national research institute). He is a member of the French National Order of Merit (1976) and the Legion of Honor (1983) and has received honorary doctorates from several major research universities.

Outside science, his main interest is music, having learned to play the piano and the organ while in high school. He was married to Sylvie Lederer in 1965, and they have two sons, David (born in 1966) and Mathias (1969).

Scientific Career

Lehn's research work can be separated into two periods. Prior to 1968, his interests were in the area of physical organic chemistry; that is, he studied the relationship between the structure of a molecule and its properties. After the first cryptand was prepared, he became increasingly involved in the field of molecular recognition, which he extended into what he later termed "supramolecular chemistry." A common thread unites these two seemingly disparate lines of research. During each period, Lehn was interested in knowing how a molecule's structure and shape determine its physical properties and behavior. Exploring the relationship between form and function on a molecular level has always been a focal point for his work.

As a graduate student, Lehn examined the physicochemical properties of a class of compounds known as the triterpenes. He was placed in charge of his research group's first nuclear magnetic resonance (NMR) spectrometer, an instrument that provides detailed structural information about the compound being analyzed. Although NMR spectroscopy was in its infancy at the time, it was soon to become an indispensable technique for virtually every practicing organic chemist. Lehn's early exposure to what he calls "this very powerful physical method" certainly gave him a head start on the rest of the chemical community with regard to the use and application of this new technology.

After receiving his Ph.D. in 1963, Lehn spent a year at Harvard working on the total synthesis of vitamin B_{12} with Robert Burns Woodward, winner of the 1965 Nobel Prize in Chemistry. This project (finally completed in 1973) required the efforts of numerous researchers working for many years, but it illustrates the power of synthetic organic chemistry. Even though vitamin B_{12} is an exceedingly complex molecule, it can be built up from simpler substances in stepwise, logical fashion.

While at Harvard, Lehn had the opportunity to take a course in quantum mechanics and to perform computer calculations with Roald Hoffmann (who would win the Nobel in 1981) on problems of significant theoretical interest. Upon returning to Strasbourg, he combined the knowledge he had acquired in organic synthesis, quantum theory, and physical methods (primarily NMR) in the study of physical organic chemistry. For example, NMR was used to determine which of two possible "conformations" (relative spatial orientation of the atoms) that a particular molecule could have is actually the preferred one, or how quickly the interconversion between these two forms occurs. Lehn was also actively engaged in theoretical studies of "stereoelectronic effects," which had to do with predicting the relative stabilities of various conformations of a given molecule. These studies involve *ab initio* (from the beginning) quantum chemical calculations, and many of Lehn's predictions based on these theoretical calculations have been borne out by experimental evidence.

In 1967, a new line of research was opened. Lehn stated:

> . . . my interest for the processes occurring in the nervous system (stemming diffusely from the first year courses in biology as well as from my earlier inclination toward philosophy) led me to wonder how a chemist might contribute to their study. The electrical phenomena in nerve cells depend on sodium and potassium ion distributions across membranes. A possible entry into the field was to try to affect the processes which allow ion transport and gradients to be established. I related this to the then very recent observations that natural antibiotics were able to make membranes permeable to cations. It thus appeared possible to devise chemical substances that would display similar properties.

Another observation that Lehn took into account was the work of Charles Pedersen of the Du Pont Company, whose discovery of the crown ethers and their fascinating chemical behavior was just being made public. Lehn certainly was the very first to make the logical extension from two dimensions to three. Function follows form, he reasoned, and if an essentially two-dimensional crown ether can form a strong complex with specific metal cations, then a three-dimensional analogue should be able to do the job even better. This hypothesis proved to be true.

Work on the synthesis of Lehn's first cryptand began in October, 1967, and was completed the following September. This molecule (referred to simply as [2.2.2]) forms a complex with a potassium ion that is almost ten thousand times stronger than that formed by 18-crown-6 and potassium.

In devising a name for his new class of compounds (there were others besides [2.2.2] in development), Lehn decided on the term "cryptand," because it was equally suggestive in French, English, and German of the behavior of these molecules. Their interior cavities resembled "crypts," in which a substance could be "entombed." Once formed, the complex is referred to as a "cryptate."

By the mid-1970's, hundreds of topologically distinct receptors had been prepared and studied. Cryptands that were appropriate for binding substrates of different sizes, shapes, and electrical charges had been successfully designed and synthesized. Yet, Lehn was not satisfied to leave it at that. Molecular recognition had been achieved, but he wanted to make receptors that could do something to the substrate once it was bound, be it a chemical change or a physical one. Complexation in and of itself does alter the properties of the bound substrate. For example, the ammonium cation (NH_4^+), which is acidic, is almost one million times less acidic when complexed by one particular cryptand than it is in its uncomplexed form.

Lehn, who always had an eye out for biochemical analogies in his work, wanted to prepare receptors that could perform more active operations on their substrates than the passive sorts of change just described. Specifically, he wanted molecules that could serve as carriers (such as hemoglobin, which carries oxygen through the bloodstream) or as enzymes (such as ptyalin, present in saliva, which breaks apart starch molecules). Efforts along both of these lines have met with considerable success. In the area of transport, a particularly simple example involves the carrying of materials into solvents in which those materials are ordinarily insoluble. In another set of systems on which Lehn has worked, the "cotransport" of two ions (similarly or oppositely charged, transported in opposite or identical directions, respectively) has been achieved. In some cases, the energy necessary to drive the process is provided by light. This has clear implications in the area of solar energy conversion, a field in which Lehn became actively involved in 1976.

The production of artificial enzymes is a particularly promising line of research. Receptors have been designed and synthesized that have the capacity to facilitate specific chemical reactions, either covalent bond-making or bond-breaking. Some of these molecules imitate processes carried out by enzymes found in nature, while others perform functions for which there are no obvious natural analogues. Ultimately it is hoped that catalysts can be tailor made for any given chemical reaction. Such compounds could be of great economic importance in industrial chemical production.

The 1980's have seen Lehn take supramolecular chemistry one step further, attempting to combine the functions of transport and catalysis in the production of microscopic chemical reactors, or artificial cells. Although far from creating life, he has made substantial progress in this direction. Much of the work in this area centers on the production of systems that exhibit the properties of "self-assembly" and "self-recognition."

The notion that chemists can imitate some of the fundamental components and behaviors of living cells is met by some people with skepticism, shock, or even outrage. It is not, however, as inconceivable an idea as it might seem. Highly organized molecular systems analogous to some of the cellular substructures (like the fatty membrane constituting the wall of animal cells, a "lipid bilayer") assemble themselves spontaneously under appropriate conditions. An interesting example of molecular self-assembly was achieved by Lehn and his coworkers in 1987, when they produced the first "inorganic double helix." (A double helix is the structural form of DNA, arguably the most important molecule of biological significance.) Two identical chains of carbon, nitrogen, and oxygen atoms, each containing the repeating unit -C-C-N-C-C-N-C-C-O-, will twist around each other to form a double helix in the presence of copper ions. In this system, the nitrogen atoms form intermolecular attachments with the metal ions, and the oxygen atoms serve as additional points about which the chain twists in a helical fashion.

It is important to note that the binding of one copper ion by nitrogen atoms from each strand facilitates the binding of the next copper ion. Such "positive cooperativity" would be an essential characteristic of a molecular "amplifier." In fact, the construction of molecular scale versions of electronic circuit components became one of Lehn's principal research interests. Molecules that serve as "wires" (that carry electronic information from one location to another) have been produced, and more complex circuit elements can be envisioned. The long-term goal of this research is, in Lehn's words, to "design and realize 'molecular devices,' molecular components that would eventually be able to perform signal and information processing at the molecular level." This is not such a far-fetched endeavor; the brain performs exactly this sort of molecular-level information processing all the time.

Aside from its many practical applications, the purely scientific implications of Lehn's work are staggering. Like the work of other notable Nobel Prize winners, such as Linus Pauling, Lehn's work occurs not only at the cutting edge of theory and technology but also at the interface of several disciplines. He has made fundamental contributions to the understanding of organic chemistry, inorganic chemistry, biochemistry, and biophysics. Much of his work blurs the distinction between these disciplines. While the specific accomplishments that Lehn has made to date in the area of supramolecular chemistry are impressive, the field is still very new. Lehn and the other winners of the 1987 Nobel Prize have opened the door for the rapid development of the vast potential of "chemistry beyond the molecule."

Bibliography

Primary

CHEMISTRY: "Design of Organic Complexing Agents: Strategies Towards Properties," *Structure and Bonding*, vol. 16, 1973; "Cryptates: The Chemistry of Macropolycyclic Inclusion Complexes," *Accounts of Chemical Research*, vol. 11, 1978; "Cryptates: Inclusion Complexes of Macropolycyclic Receptor Molecules," *Pure and Applied Chemistry*, vol. 50, 1978; "Macrocyclic Receptor Molecules: Aspects of Chemical Reactivity. Investigations into Molecular Catalysis and Transport Processes," *Pure and Applied Chemistry*, vol. 51, 1979; "Physicochemical Studies of Crown and Cryptate Complexes," in *Coordination Chemistry of Macrocyclic Compounds*, 1979 (with A. I. Popov); "Cryptate Inclusion Complexes: Effects on Solute-Solute and Solute-Solvent Interactions and on Ionic Reactivity," *Pure and Applied Chemistry*, vol. 52, 1980; "Inaugural Lecture," presented before the Collège de France on March 7, 1980 (in his capacity as Chair of Chimie des Interactions Moléculaires); "Dinuclear Cryptates: Dimetallic Macropolycyclic Inclusion Complexes. Concepts—Designs—Prospects," *Pure and Applied Chemistry*, vol. 52, 1980; "Supramolecular Chemistry: Receptors, Catalysts, and Carriers," *Science*, vol. 227, 1985; "Multidentate Macrocyclic and Macropolycyclic Ligands" in G. Wilkinson, ed., *Comprehensive Coordination Chemistry*, vol. 1 1987 (with K. B. Mertes); "Photophysical and Photochemical Aspects of Supramolecular Chemistry," in V. Balzani, ed., *Supramolecular Photochemistry*, 1987; "Supramolecular Chemistry—Scope and Perspectives," *Angewandte Chemie, International Edition in English*, vol. 27, 1988.

Secondary

Colquhoun, Howard, Fraser Stoddart, and David Williams. "Chemistry Beyond the Molecule." *New Scientist* 110 (May 1, 1986): 44-48. A very well-written, clear, concise presentation of the fundamentals of intramolecular bonding (ionic and covalent) and of intermolecular forces and their consequences, leading to a discussion of the crown ethers and their properties and descriptions of some of the authors' pet projects. These include the use of crown ethers in facilitating drug delivery and in altering the normal course of certain chemical reactions.

Dye, James L. "Electrides." *Scientific American* 257 (September, 1987): 66-75. Complexation by supramolecular species alters the chemical and physical properties of the bound substrate. A particularly striking example of this is found in the electrides, which are prepared from crown ethers or cryptands and alkali metals. Many branches of chemistry and physics (conductivity, optical spectroscopy, magnetic susceptibility, and NMR) have been brought into play in analyzing the electrides. Each of these techniques is described in a way that makes it readily understandable to readers with even minimal background in science. A short bibliography.

Iverson, Brent L., and Richard A. Lerner. "Sequence-Specific Peptide Cleavage Catalyzed by an Antibody." *Science* 243 (March 3, 1989): 1184-1188. In addition to the "supramolecular" method, other approaches to artificial enzyme synthesis include protein engineering, chemical mutation, and antibody induction. The one most nearly related to Lehn's work is the last. Antibodies are raised to one substance that, if the original substance is chosen carefully, have shapes and properties appropriate for catalyzing chemical reactions of different substances. Iverson and Lerner describe a recent advance in this area and give many references to similar work.

Koshland, Daniel E. "Protein Shape and Biological Control." *Scientific American* 229 (October, 1973): 52-64. Since much of Lehn's work is centered on the synthesis of artificial enzymes (biomimetic catalysts), it is important to understand something about the way that natural enzymes work. Koshland's article provides the information necessary for the interested reader to develop this sort of understanding, in addition to describing some of the other functions of proteins, as receptors and as antibodies.

National Research Council. *Opportunities in Chemistry*. Washington, D.C.: National Academy Press, 1985. The "Pimentel Report," so called because chemistry professor George C. Pimentel of the University of California at Berkeley chaired the NRC committee that prepared the report, describes the current state of chemistry and speculates about opportunities for the future. Developments in the areas of molecular recognition, artificial enzyme production, and molecule-scale electronic devices are among the many topics covered. Index and appendices. Highly recommended as a general reference.

Nickon, Alex, and Ernest F. Silversmith. *Organic Chemistry: The Name Game*. Elmsford, N.Y.: Pergamon Press, 1987. A fascinating book that deals with the origins of nonsystematic nomenclature of specific organic compounds, many of which are interesting merely by virtue of their shapes. The cryptands are covered, as are Pedersen's crown ethers and Cram's spherands. Contains illustrations, index, and many appendices, including one that lists the Nobel Prize winners (and their research areas) in Chemistry, Physiology or Medicine, and Physics. Requires some knowledge of basic organic chemistry.

Peterson, Ivars. "Cages, Cavities, and Clefts." *Science News* 132 (August 8, 1987): 90-93. Intended for a general audience, this article deals with similarities and differences in the work of three of the key players in the field of molecular recognition: Ronald Breslow, Donald J. Cram, and Julius Rebek, Jr. Illustrations of the structures of cavitands (Cram), cyclodextrins (Breslow), and molecular clefts (Rebek) are provided, along with easily understood analogies between the behaviors of these molecules and the functions of naturally occurring "supermolecules" such as antibodies, enzymes, DNA, and the ionophores.

"Self-Organization in Chemistry." *Journal of Chemical Education* 66 (March, 1989): 187-212. The first half of this issue is devoted to chemical systems exhibiting molecular self-organization. A basic understanding of such behavior is vital if artificial cells are ever to become a reality. The articles are geared for chemistry teachers and professionals, but much of it is well within the grasp of a nonspecialist.

Thomas H. Eberlein

1987

Chemistry
Donald J. Cram, United States
Jean-Marie Lehn, France
Charles J. Pedersen, United States

Physics
Karl Alexander Müller, Switzerland
J. Georg Bednorz, West Germany

Physiology or Medicine
Susumu Tonegawa, Japan

Economic Sciences
Robert M. Solow, United States

Literature
Joseph Brodsky, United States

Peace
Oscar Arias Sanchez, Costa Rica

CHARLES J. PEDERSEN
1987

Born: Fusan, Republic of Korea; October 3, 1904

Nationality: American
Area of concentration: Macrocyclic polyethers (crown ethers)

Pedersen synthesized and characterized the first compounds to form complexes with alkali metal ions, called crown ethers. His work provided the basic concept and molecular framework for others to develop more complex molecules and initiate the field of molecular recognition, which is extremely important to biochemistry and chemical synthesis

The Award

Presentation

Professor Salo Gronowitz of the Royal Swedish Academy of Sciences delivered the presentation address for Charles J. Pedersen on December 10, 1987. His speech began with the observation that all life processes involve recognition at the molecular level: Enzymes recognize substrates, antibodies recognize antigens, and so forth. These molecules have to fit together like a key in a lock, in the words of Emil Fischer, the 1902 Nobel laureate in chemistry. For years, chemists had theorized as to how large a portion of each of these large biomolecules is really necessary for proper recognition, and they sought methods to prepare large molecules to test the theories. Charles Pedersen (one of three cowinners of the 1987 prize), made a breakthrough in the 1960's when he learned how to prepare compounds with between eighteen and forty carbon and oxygen atoms formed in a zigzag ring and studied their peculiar properties. These compounds functionally belonged to the chemical class called ethers. Because they were shaped like a king's crown, he named them crown ethers. One of their unusual and totally unexpected properties was that they could bind alkali metal ions. Significantly, the internal diameter of the crown determined which metal ions would be bound inside it.

Major advances in organic synthetic techniques were made after the time of Pedersen's initial work, as recognized by Nobel Prizes awarded to the chemists Robert Burns Woodward (1965), Herbert C. Brown and Georg Wittig (1979), and Bruce Merrifield (1984). These men made it possible for Donald Cram and Jean-Marie Lehn, cowinners with Pedersen, to extend his work and to conceive and prepare complex molecules that contain holes or crevices that can selectively bind inorganic or organic molecules, as well as ions of either positive or negative charge. Gronowitz pointed out the fundamental nature and broad impact of this work, particularly on many branches of chemistry, including biochemistry, analytical chemistry, organic synthesis, and coordination chemistry. He then called for Cram, Lehn, and Pedersen to step forward and receive their prizes.

Nobel lecture

Pedersen delivered his Nobel lecture, entitled "The Discovery of Crown Ethers," on December 8, 1987. He opened with some autobiographical remarks that were intended to provide insight into his personal life and his beginnings as a chemist, including a description of the exciting research atmosphere at the Du Pont Company when he arrived there in 1927. By the mid-1940's, he had firmly established himself as an independent researcher of the highest level at Du Pont. In 1960, colleague Herman Schroeder suggested that he study the factors that governed the catalytic activity of vanadium in oxidation and polymerization. It was his work in this relatively unexplored area that was to lead to the discovery of crown ethers.

The oxidation of petroleum and rubber products is greatly accelerated or catalyzed by the presence of traces of metals, such as copper, which are always present as a result of the manufacturing process. Pedersen spent many years working on metal deactivators, which are compounds that suppress metal catalysis by forming inactive metal complexes (compounds formed by reacting a metal with another compound or ion, called a ligand). He decided to study the effects of multidentate phenolic ligands (aromatic alcohols having several points of attachment to the metal) on the catalytic properties of the vanadyl ion, VO^{+2}. In his attempts to purify the ligand he synthesized, he came across a small collection of white crystals that had an unexpected silky, fibrous appearance and was insoluble in water or alcoholic solvents. It obviously was not the intended product, but luckily he decided to study it, and it became known as the first crown ether. Again fortunately, he decided to examine its ultraviolet spectrum in solution. A typical experiment for phenolic ligands would be to dissolve the crystals in methanol, take the spectrum, and then add sodium hydroxide. Change in the spectrum would indicate that the alcohol groups were present as $-OH$; the absence of change would indicate that the hydrogens of OH had been replaced to form ethers.

The compound was only slightly soluble in methanol, and when sodium hydroxide was added, not only were the expected spectral changes absent, but an entirely different spectrum had been obtained as well, and the compound became extremely soluble in the methanol. What could cause the compound, which had no free $-OH$ groups (as shown by the spectra), to become so soluble in the presence of sodium hydroxide? Pedersen found that it was not the hydroxide ion but instead the sodium ion that was important. Further studies showed the compound to be an eighteen-member ring of twelve carbons and six oxygens, which he visualized as a crown sitting on the spherical sodium ion. This was the first crown ether, which he named dibenzo-18-crown-6.

He was able to prepare this large ring of atoms (called a macrocycle) in a one-step reaction, which is most unusual. Previous preparations of these compounds in the 1930's and 1950's required many steps and did not recognize these compounds' ability to form complexes with alkali metals. With the help of his laboratory assistant, Pedersen prepared more than sixty of these compounds and studied their properties. Using Pedersen's results as a basis, Jean-Marie Lehn added a third strand across the top of the crown to form cyptands, and Donald J. Cram added different features to form cages that he called spherands and cavitands. All these molecules are three-dimensional networks of atoms that surround a central cavity in which an ion or molecule can be physically trapped without forming a strong chemical bond with the cage. Pedersen closed his lecture with a discussion of the properties of some of the crown ethers and with acknowledgments of his coworkers, the Du Pont Company, and his fellow laureates.

Critical reception

The press gave a favorable and polite reception to the news of the award. Because the award in physics that year recognized work on superconductivity (a highly publicized subject) and was announced simultaneously, it received greater emphasis in the general press. Newspapers usually combined the accounts of the three chemistry cowinners' reactions to their selection on October 14. Lehn was in Strasbourg, Pedersen was at his home in Salem, New Jersey, and Cram was in Los Angeles. Pedersen, holder of a master's degree from the Massachusetts Institute of Technology, was recognized as the first to discover that crown ethers could complex with metal ions. At the time of the award, reports noted, he was eighty-three and retired from industry; he had obtained sixty-five patents during his career, and his classic work in the field was published in 1967. Cram and Lehn used Pedersen's result in different ways to make their respective contributions. Although the prize was given in recognition of work in the field of organic chemistry, newspapers emphasized the application of the work to biochemistry and medicine. *The New York Times*, for example, described the potential for creating artificial enzymes and new medical diagnostic aids. The remarkable nature of this Nobel Prize, it was noted, was that it recognized the future possibilities raised by the work rather than only existing applications and previous impact.

The Washington Post tried to convey some of the excitement felt by chemists about the field of host-guest interactions by emphasizing their similarities to those of proteins in living cells, which are important in the operation of genes, enzymes, and antibodies. The reporter also expressed the generally optimistic and futuristic mood of the press. Pedersen, soft-spoken and having lived in quiet retirement for twenty years, was reported as saying that his award had come as a great surprise: "I'm not used to this sort of thing. . . . It is a great honor," he said, and added, "You don't have to be thirty-five to be a hit." The *Los Angeles Times* noted that Pedersen had made the key discovery of the metal-binding properties of crown ethers shortly before his retirement, and Cram and Lehn had built their work on this discovery. An article in *The San Francisco Chronicle* also emphasized potential uses of these compounds. It said that chemical separations of unprecedented precision, now possible, could allow the removal of poisons from contaminated soil or water and the detection of traces of chemicals in the environment. The journal *Science* printed an in-depth interview with Cram. Lehn was credited with applying Pedersen's ideas to three-dimensional structures by creating cryptands ("little crypts") in 1969 and coining the term "supramolecular chemistry" to describe the phenomenon that Cram calls "host-guest chemistry." Cram's cavitands and carcerands were presented as molecules that could serve as miniature laboratories in which chemistry could be observed taking place, or as vehicles for the slow release of drugs or pesticides. The press in Europe voiced the same optimistic views expressed in the United States, generally focusing attention on the implications of the work for biomedical research.

Biography

Charles J. Pedersen was born in Fusan, in the Republic of Korea, to Brede Pedersen, a mechanical engineer, and Takino Yasui, the daughter of a Japanese family engaged in the soybean and silkworm trades. His father worked for a large American gold and lumber concession, administered by Americans, who made an effort to make their life-style there as American as possible. He grew up learning English and was sent to Nagasaki, Japan, to a convent school at the age of eight, as there were no such schools in Korea at that time. When he was ten, his mother took him to Yokohama, where he studied at St. Joseph College, a Marianist secondary school. It was there that he took his first chemistry course.

Pedersen chose to study in America, with his father's encouragement, and attended the University of Dayton, as it was a Marianist school and there were family and friends in Ohio. He then attended the Massachusetts Institute of Technology, obtaining a master's degree in 1927. As he was anxious to begin working, he decided not to take a Ph.D., but with the help of his research adviser, Professor James F. Norris, he obtained employment at the Du Pont Company in Wilmington, Delaware. He remained there for his entire forty-two-year career.

Pedersen established a career studying antioxidants, and by 1947 he had risen to the highest levels of research in the company. At that time, he married Susan Ault, and they moved to Salem, New Jersey. He returned to the study of coordination chemistry in 1960 and published his seminal papers on crown ethers in 1967, two years before his retirement, which he would devote to his interests in ornithology, gardening, fishing, and poetry.

Scientific Career

Throughout his schooling and professional career, Pedersen showed a preference for independence, self-sufficiency, ingenuity, and a hands-on approach to his work. His career generally reflects his interest in and expertise at problem solving. Rather than working strictly within one area of chemistry, such as organic chemistry, he used several approaches to solve the problems of current interest and his knowledge of organic, physical, inorganic, and analytical techniques in his work. Although he excelled at the University of Dayton, where he earned a bachelor's degree in chemical engineering, it was in graduate school at the Massachusetts Institute of Technology (MIT) that he felt the freedom to take charge of his own life and affairs. Thus, after one year there, he was graduated with a master's degree in organic chemistry and took an industrial position in 1927 in order to be self-supporting. His research adviser at MIT, James F. Norris, encouraged him to stay on and take a Ph.D. but, seeing his determination, helped him to obtain a job at Du Pont Chemical Company in Wilmington, Delaware. Most industrial laboratories of the day were oriented toward solving specific problems (what is now called "applied research") rather than exploring novel chemistries and ideas for their own merits ("basic research," considered more the province of academic laboratories at that time). Du Pont was different: It had created a department of basic research that was to employ scientists such as Wallace Carothers and Paul Flory (who developed the polymers that led to nylon), Julian Hill (who made the first oriented polyester fiber), and Roy Plunkett (the discoverer of Teflon). This laboratory produced other highly successful compounds, such as tetraethyl lead, new elastomers, fluorocarbons for refrigerants and aerosols, antifreezes, dyestuffs, petroleum products, and many industrially useful chemicals. In this exciting atmosphere, where success was expected, Pedersen took his place.

He was initially given a set of, in his words, "typical problems" to solve, and he did so quite successfully. He started by developing a method for recovering tetraethyl lead during its manufacture, a method for preparing alkali metal salts of selenium and tellurium, a noncorrosive antifreeze solution for automobile radiators, and a way to stabilize hygroscopic (water-absorbing) salts to facilitate their handling in the textile industry. These led to the awarding of his first five patents during the years 1935-1938, which gave a strong impetus to his career. He next turned to the problem of finding a way to scavenge copper particles from internal combustion engines by having them dissolve in the motor oil, which could be easily removed from the engine and discarded. It was important not only to dissolve them but also to render them passive, so that they did not accelerate the breakdown of the motor oil. This led to the first good deactivator for petroleum products, and another patent. This deactivator prevented the traces of copper released during normal engine wear from accelerating the decomposition (autooxidation) of the motor oil by combining with the copper to form a new compound with different properties.

Pedersen became more interested in ways to combine metals with organic molecules so as to change their catalytic properties, an interest that would eventually lead him to discover crown ethers some twenty years later. One result of the early work was a compound that greatly improved the efficacy of antioxidant materials used in rubber and petroleum products. In 1947, Pedersen was appointed a Research Associate, which was the highest research title attainable at Du Pont. His career was fully established, and he was known for his work in oxidative degradation and stabilization. He could now turn his attention to whatever problems he chose to tackle. Thus, in the next decade, his interests became more varied. He developed several new polymers, studied problems which involved light-induced chemical reactions (photochemistry), worked on organic dyes for textiles, and discovered an antiknock compound for gasoline.

Wishing to work more in the field of elastic polymers (elastomers), Pedersen next took the suggestion of Herman Schroeder, a colleague at Du Pont, and in 1960 started to study the factors that determined the catalytic activity of vanadium during oxidation and polymerization reactions, where it serves as a catalyst. These two types of chemical reaction are very important in the production of elastomers. Although Pedersen did not know it at the time, he was beginning the work that would lead to the discovery of crown ethers. Based on his extensive experience and knowledge of the kinds of organic compounds that affected the catalytic properties of metals, he chose to make an organic molecule starting from a simple, cheap organic alcohol and a chlorinated ether. The organic molecule so created would attach itself to the vanadium metal ion at several points, via oxygen atoms, to form an organometallic compound called a chelate and alter the metal's properties during chemical reactions. Through a series of serendipitous events, Pedersen discovered, on July 5, 1962, that he had synthesized, in one simple chemical reaction step, a compound composed of eighteen atoms in a ring, with some side attachments. He visualized these ring atoms, twelve carbons and six oxygens, as forming a zigzag circular chain that would fit around a sodium ion like a crown, and he named the compound as a crown ether, dibenzo-18-crown-6. Although known to chemists as early as the 1930's, the ability of the ring atoms to form complexes (that is, to chelate) with sodium was not discovered until Pedersen's work, and the synthetic methods had been much longer and more difficult.

This initial success had several important features. Foremost, the crown ether was the first molecule known that could trap the sodium ion in a chelate. Many other organic molecules were known, but none had this property, which had great implications for both organic synthesis and biochemistry. Another important feature was that the synthetic method used showed the way to form an eighteen-member ring of atoms in one step. This was most unexpected: How does one end of the chain find the other, in order to close the ring? The presence of the sodium ion was found to be crucial, for it acts as a form around which the chain can develop and helps to link the ends together when eighteen atoms are built into the chain. Fewer atoms could not span the circumference of the sodium ion. Once there were eighteen atoms, the chain closed on itself and ended the lengthening process.

Later experiment showed this to be the same process operative during the formation of the atomic skeleton of chlorophyll and hemoglobin, two molecules of major biochemical importance which, respectively, contain magnesium and iron atoms at their centers. The metal atom at the center serves as a central guide or armature on which the reactants "stick" to build up the molecule, just as the sculptor builds his clay model upon a metal frame. Pedersen then spent several years working with Ted Malinowski, his laboratory assistant, on the creation of other crown ethers. They discovered that rings having different hole sizes (from 12 to 43 nanometers) best accommodated different metal ions, mostly from groups I and II in the periodic table. They also discovered many other useful properties of these compounds, and Pedersen published his first paper on the subject in 1967. He continued on this project until his retirement, two years later. Other publications and patents bearing his name followed for the next eight years.

It was the ability to form an eighteen-member ring in such a simple and elegant fashion that attracted the attention of synthetic organic chemists. Here, at last, was an easy way to form a molecule with a hole in it large enough to accommodate another ion or molecule. With only slight modifications to the starting reactants, crowns of different sizes could be made. The discovery might prove to be the key to the formidable problem of creating the larger molecules such as are found in living systems, particularly enzymes. Cram and Lehn saw these possibilities in Pedersen's work, and each, in his own way, set about finding ways to convert the crown into a three-dimensional cage. Their work extended Pedersen's into areas much closer to biochemistry and provided ways to create molecules that could mimic natural enzymes (biomimetic chemistry).

To paraphrase Pedersen's acknowledgment of his colaureates, they mined rich veins in the goldfield he had discovered. Many, many other applications of crown ethers have been investigated in a very broad spectrum of disciplines, including chemical synthesis, environmental cleanup, purification of metals, biophysics, atomic energy, pharmaceuticals, and electrochemistry. All these areas capitalize on the ability of crown ethers to capture, separate, or transport cations, or to solubilize inorganic salts in organic solvents. We may be approaching the fulfillment of Pedersen's wish, expressed in his Nobel address, that "something of great benefit to mankind will be developed about which it may be said that were it not for the crown compounds it could not be."

Bibliography

Primary

CHEMISTRY: "Antioxidants," in *Encyclopædia Britannica*, 1953; "Symposium on Chelate Chemistry," *Advances in Chelate Chemistry*, 1954; "Cyclic Polyethers and Their Complexes with Metal Salts," *Journal of the American Chemical Society*, 1967; "Cryptates," *Endeavour*, 1971 (with M. R. Truter); *Synthetic Multidentate Macrocyclic Compounds*, 1978.

Secondary

Fendler, Janos. *Membrane Mimetic Chemistry: Characterizations and Applications of Micelles, Microemulsions, Monolayers, Bilayers, Vesicles, Host-Guest Systems, and Polyions*. New York: John Wiley & Sons, 1982. A general view of the uses and importance of host-guest chemistry in biological systems is given and related to other types of chemical compounds with similar roles. This book helps to show how the compounds can be used for practical purposes and relates host-guest chemistry to the broader fields of biochemistry and medicine and to industrial applications.

Hiraoka, Michio. *Crown Compounds: Their Characteristics and Applications*. New York: Elsevier, 1982. An attempt to review and systematize the research done on crown ethers, starting with Pedersen's work in 1967. Covers preparation, characteristics, applications, and toxicity of these substances.

Izatt, Reed M., and James J. Christensen, eds. *Synthetic Multidentate Macrocyclic Compounds*. New York: Academic Press, 1978. Each of the six chapters summarizes one area of knowledge about crown ethers. The first chapter is by Charles Pedersen and expands the basic information he summarized in his Nobel address about the discovery, properties, and toxicity of crown ethers.

Patai, Saul, ed. *The Chemistry of Ethers, Crown Ethers, Hydroxyl Groups, and Their Sulphur Analogues*. New York: John Wiley & Sons, 1980. Five of the twenty-four chapters deal with different aspects of the chemistry of crown ethers, and each is written by an expert in the field. The emphasis is on organic chemistry, primarily from the viewpoint of the synthetic chemist.

Streitweiser, Andrew, Jr., and Clayton Heathcock. *Introduction to Organic Chemistry*. New York: Macmillan, 1985. A first textbook in organic chemistry for the student who is interested in learning more about the field. Crown ethers are described and related to their simpler analogues. This book is similar in purpose and content to Peter Volhardt's textbook (see below). The authors assume some knowledge of the basic ideas of chemical bonding. They explain molecular geometry from first principles so that the ethers, macrocycles, and crown compounds described by Pedersen can be easily visualized.

Voegtle, Fritz, and Friedrich Boschke, eds. *Host Guest Chemistry*. New York: Springer-Verlag, 1982. A review of the research literature on the preparation, structure, and uses of a number of these compounds. Because many synthetic steps are needed to prepare such molecules, each one must be very efficient. These are discussed in detail. Structures are determined by X-ray, nuclear magnetic, and infrared methods. Computer models of proposed structures are also discussed.

Volhardt, Peter. *Organic Chemistry*. New York: W. H. Freeman, 1987. A general organic chemistry textbook that introduces the reader to the field and shows the relationships of crown ethers and cryptands to similar organic compounds. Many of the synthetic chemical reactions used to make host compounds are described in detail but are discussed in terms of their general utility to the synthetic chemist. Explanations are given for the uses of various reactions, and strategies for multistep syntheses are exemplified.

William Van Willis

1988

Chemistry
Johann Deisenhofer, West Germany
Robert Huber, West Germany
Hartmut Michel, West Germany

Physics
Leon M. Lederman, United States
Melvin Schwartz, United States
Jack Steinberger, Germany and United States

Physiology or Medicine
Sir James W. Black, Great Britain
Gertrude B. Elion, United States
George H. Hitchings, United States

Economic Sciences
Maurice Allais, France

Literature
Naguib Mahfouz, Egypt

Peace
U.N. Peacekeeping Forces

JOHANN DEISENHOFER
1988

Born: Zusamaltheim, Germany; September 30, 1943

Nationality: German
Areas of concentration: X-ray crystallography and structural analysis

Using X-ray crystallography, Deisenhofer determined the complete structure of the photosynthetic reaction center of the bacterium Rhodopseudomonas viridis. *This membrane-bound protein is crucial to the bacterium's ability to perform photosynthesis*

The Award

Presentation

In the traditional awards ceremony, held on December 10, 1988, Bo G. Malmström, a biochemist from Gothenburg University, presented Johann Deisenhofer to the King of Sweden for receipt of his Nobel medal and diploma. Deisenhofer shared the moment with two of his former colleagues from the Max Planck Institute, Hartmut Michel and Robert Huber. Each researcher was honored for his pivotal contributions to the understanding of the complex series of chemical events known as photosynthesis. Their interest in this chemical process, which is fundamental to all life on the planet Earth, had led the trio to investigate a photosynthesizing purple bacterium, *Rhodopseudomonas viridis*; more specifically, their attention had focused on a large protein, the photosynthetic reaction center, which some have called the very heart of photosynthesis.

A complete map of the photosynthetic reaction center, Malmström stated, is important not only because it explains the intimate details of the way sunlight is converted into chemical energy but also because the photosynthetic reaction center is a membrane-bound protein. Heretofore, no protein embedded in a cell membrane had been successfully isolated and crystallized so that X-ray studies could determine its three-dimensional atomic structure. A perfect crystalline sample is necessary for complete structure determination via X-ray crystallographic methods. As a team, Deisenhofer, Huber, and Michel discovered one of nature's most important and elusive secrets.

Malmström acknowledged other original works in chemistry previously recognized by the Royal Swedish Academy of Sciences. These works ultimately contributed to the brilliant success of the 1988 Nobel laureates. Specifically mentioned was the work of Henry Taube, the 1983 Nobel laureate in chemistry. Taube's pioneering work exploring electron transfer in simple metallic materials assisted scientists in the comprehension of all electron migrations, including those within living systems. Electron transfer is an essential aspect of photosynthetic chemistry.

Also acknowledged was Peter Mitchell, a British biochemist who was awarded the 1978 Nobel Prize in Chemistry. Mitchell postulated that the membrane of a cell was actively involved in the transport of electrons and protons, or positively charged hydrogen ions, during the production of chemicals such as adenosine triphosphate (ATP). Mitchell recognized that the cell membrane had little "pumps" that move both electrons and hydrogen ions across the membrane. This migration is a fundamental aspect of the biosynthesis of high-energy chemical bonds, such as those found in ATP.

Finally, Aaron Klug, a 1982 Nobel laureate in chemistry, was acknowledged for providing yet another important link. Klug had attempted to show the structure of two membrane-bound proteins using electron microscopy techniques. While his work was an important step forward, the quality and details of his structural analyses were crude in comparison to the refined and exacting image produced by Deisenhofer's X-ray crystallographic techniques.

As Malmström spoke on behalf of the Royal Swedish Academy of Sciences, he stated that the Academy presented the award to Deisenhofer, Michel, and Huber for unraveling the full details of how a membrane-bound protein is built.

Malmström closed by noting that the work of the three laureates was a major step forward not only for scientists' understanding of photosynthesis, which continues to be regarded as the most important chemical reaction in the earth's biosphere, but also for the understanding of other complex biological processes. The laureates' work now made it possible to begin to determine the structures of other important membrane proteins. In addition, it may even be possible, Malmström noted, that research in this area might one day lead to synthetic photosynthesis.

Nobel lecture

At 9:00 A.M. on Thursday, December 8, 1988, Johann Deisenhofer and his colleague, Hartmut Michel, delivered their joint Nobel lecture at the Royal Swedish Academy of Sciences. It was entitled "The Photosynthetic Reaction Center from the Purple Bacterium *Rhodopseudomonas viridis*." The two chemists worked to provide a harmonious and contiguous presentation of their research, and each chemist expressed his own perspective on the work. Once Michel had completed his explanation of how he had successfully isolated and produced crystalline samples of the photosynthetic reaction center, Deisenhofer presented a description of his structural studies on the so-called "heart of photosynthesis."

Deisenhofer described the complexities and problems encountered during the early stages in his research. Starting with an overview, Deisenhofer explained how the huge protein molecule of the reaction center appeared as a whole. He then surveyed various substructures, paying particular attention to the spatial arrangement of atoms as it correlated with the unique functions of the photosynthetic reaction center.

Much to the chagrin of any crystallographer, the X-ray studies of chemistry are not as simple as those of medicine. Unlike the black and white photographic images of bones and teeth, X-ray studies of solid, crystalline molecules result in images that look as though someone has randomly drawn dots all over the photographic film. The trick to being an excellent crystallographer is not only in knowing how to get the best "dots" on photographic film but also in knowing how to interpret the patterns of dots: Encoded in the film is all the information needed to reveal where every atom is located, even within the most challenging molecule.

According to Deisenhofer, the crystals of the photosynthetic reaction center of *Rhodopseudomonas viridis* have a large unit cell and form tetragonal crystals. A unit cell is the simplest portion of a crystal that builds upon itself to make a large solid. Considering the extreme bulk of the membrane-bound protein, it is not surprising that the unit cell is large. The entire protein is made of more than ten thousand atoms, each one of which contributes to the mass of the reaction center. For this reason, the molecular mass of the reaction center has a high value of 145,000 daltons, or atomic mass units.

Deisenhofer stated that it took about two years to accumulate the original data on the reaction center. As indicated earlier, it is the analysis of the data that becomes the more rigorous task, even to a proficient and experienced crystallographer. He also mentioned some of the methods used in his data analysis and recognized persons who significantly contributed to this aspect of the project; among them were Hartmut Michel, Irmgard Sinning, and Gerhard Schertler.

Deisenhofer next discussed what is known as the phase problem. During this stage, the critical and essential X-ray data must be coupled with other data and resources in order to elucidate the protein structure fully. Two assistants, Kunio Miki and Otto Epp, were acknowledged for their fastidious efforts in the careful processing of the films. Since the films have all the structural information required for analysis recorded upon them, processing the film with the greatest care is critical.

In an effort to build a complete model of the reaction center, contributions from smaller projects were necessary. In particular, prosthetic groups were identified, as were polypeptide chains, those portions of the reaction center made of amino acids. To guarantee that the composition of the peptide chains was correctly determined, a genetic sequencing of the reaction center subunits was performed. This technique confirmed that, indeed, the correct structure of the polypeptide portions of the reaction center had been properly identified. (For clarification purposes, a peptide may be considered to be a small protein.)

As Deisenhofer proceeded with his presentation, his attention shifted from techniques to results. The molecular models of the photosynthetic reaction center were colorful, complex, computer-generated images, and Deisenhofer showed several of these visual images to his audience. He spoke at length about the structure of the *Rhodopseudomonas viridis* photosynthetic reaction center, being careful to point out the strange and unusual attributes of this protein complex. Deisenhofer stated that what he and his colleagues had done would open exciting new avenues in the understanding of photosynthesis.

Critical reception

The announcement of the 1988 Nobel Prize in Chemistry was joyfully received, perhaps in part because it was a refreshing decision by the Nobel Committee to recognize excellence in such a young research team. Deisenhofer, Michel, and Huber had compressed into eight years what other scientists have waited a lifetime to achieve.

What had been a waning interest in studies of photosynthesis was, in 1988, at a peak as a direct result of this research. For protein chemists, interest was aroused in applying the techniques demonstrated by the West German group to study other important membrane-bound proteins. Many of the proteins under investigation play a vital role in sustaining the necessary balance of chemistry within and without a cell. Some are directly involved in fighting and recognizing disease, while others perform the chemical work of pumping energy or nutrients into and out of the cell.

Crystallographers reveled in the fact that another one of their colleagues had succeeded in gaining Nobel recognition; Deisenhofer would enjoy the respect accorded fellow Nobel crystallographers such as Dorothy Crowfoot Hodgkin (1964), who determined the structure of vitamin B_{12}, and Hermann Staudinger (1953), who determined the structure of the genetic coding material DNA, or deoxyribonucleic acid.

In an interview with *The New York Times*, Michael Garavito of the University of Chicago proclaimed that the Nobel work of this German team had captured the heart of photosynthesis. Another professor interviewed in the same article, Keith Moffat of Cornell University, explained that "a whole important range of materials has been brought into view." Wayne Hendrickson of Columbia University stated that the work of the West German threesome had "revitalized investigation in photosynthesis." Photosynthesis could now be understood as a sequence of events that originates in the reaction center.

The editor of *Nature* lamented their refusal, several years earlier, to publish Michel's original paper describing the method by which he obtained the large, lovely crystals of the photosynthetic reaction center. The editors had refused to publish the work until Michel could produce structural information to accompany the crystallization methods. Since that time, however, *Nature* has printed other pertinent articles about photosynthetic reaction center research. Maxine Clarke, in a *Nature* article, described the work of Michel, Deisenhofer, and Huber as "an impressive technical feat" and went on to say that the center was one of the most important biological structures found in nature. The opening to her article also contained an accurate description of a membrane-bound protein, which she said can be visualized as a beast that has its "body immersed in a lipid bilayer [while] its head and legs are in water."

An article in *Science* quoted Douglas Youvan of the Massachusetts Institute of Technology as saying, "What was so beautiful about the structure was that immediately you could see how the time series of events would fit into the spatial framework." Youvan, along with Barry Marrs, had previously published, in 1987, an excellent article in *Scientific American* entitled "Molecular Mechanisms of Photosynthesis." These two scientists had investigated similar reaction centers of another bacterium, and the two scientists were combining molecular genetics and spectroscopic methods in their studies. In their jointly written article, Youvan and Marrs referred to the work of Michel and Deisenhofer as "a tremendous achievement; the reaction center is to date the only integral membrane protein whose structure is known to atomic resolution." Their article acknowledges the significance of the *Rhodopseudomonas viridis* work. Diagrams printed in the Youvan and Marrs article help in explaining the overall events that occur within bacterial photosynthetic reaction centers.

The city of Dallas, Texas, and the University of Texas Southwestern Medical Center at Dallas were exuberant at the news of their third Nobel recipient within three years—Deisenhofer had moved to Dallas and joined the University of Texas earlier in 1988. The president of the Howard Hughes Medical Institute, a branch of the University of Texas Southwestern complex, Dr. Purnell Choppin, said that "the understanding of the detailed structure of important biological molecules that these scientists are providing is opening new avenues for prevention and treatment of disease."

Biography

The firstborn child of a German farmer and his wife, Johann Deisenhofer began his life in 1943 in the Bavarian countryside. His parents, Thekla and Johann, were members of a traditional German farming community. It was there, among the fields and farm animals, that young Hans performed his earliest experiments. One of them involved manufacturing his own black powder, putting it in a metal pipe, and detonating the device. Deisenhofer admits recalling that he "felt proud of [his] accomplishment [although] somewhat frightened" upon observing the results of his explosion. He remembers thinking that he should exercise more caution next time. Deisenhofer always had a desire to know how things worked and, in his rural setting, also had the luxury of a large outdoor laboratory. Deisenhofer once reminisced about a moment of discovery in his early primary school years. His fascination with the workings of a camera had led him to a childhood scientific postulate: There must be a little machine inside doing all the work. When he at last got his hands on a camera to investigate further, he was amazed to find that there was no machinery inside at all. He saw only emptiness, save the lenses—which he then began to ponder.

In school, he found that science was often taught in a boring manner; in spite of that, he fed his scientific curiosity through avid reading about physics and astronomy and about the life and works of Albert Einstein. As he matured, his parents gradually began to realize that their only son had no interest in being a farmer. Therefore, at a time when schooling was not something that everyone had a chance to experience, Hans was granted permission to attend high school. There had been some delays in making the decision to send him to school, however, so he stayed at the same school level for three years while awaiting family approval to continue his studies. His extra three years of early schooling served only to heighten his desire to learn as much as possible while in middle and high school.

At the close of his high school years, Deisenhofer performed extremely well on his final exit exams, which won for him a college stipend for four years of study in a West German college. The stipend, awarded by the Bavarian Ministry for Education and Culture, enabled him to pursue a college education. His selection of Technische Universität München (Technical University in Munich) came easily, since he knew he would study physics. News of a new organizational hierarchy within the physics department at this particular university appealed to Deisenhofer. It had also lured the great German physicist, Rudolf Mössbauer, into moving his research team to Munich. In addition to the attraction of such a famous physicist being at the Munich campus, the university was not far from the Deisenhofer farm, which had a special appeal to the young man.

As a physics student, Deisenhofer selected the laboratory of Klaus Dransfeld, another physicist who had been attracted to the university during the reorganization, as a place to begin his research work. Dransfeld, who had previously worked for Bell Laboratories, had been exposed to the new area of research that would become known as biophysics. As Deisenhofer's research adviser and mentor, Dransfeld planted as much intrigue for this field as he could into the mind of his young associate.

There is no bachelor's degree in the West German college system; a diploma in physics, which is equivalent to a master's degree, was awarded to Johann Deisenhofer in 1971 from Technische Universität München. The stipend, along with the financial supplements, support, and love from his family, had nurtured him to a fruitful conclusion of his college years. At the same time, the newly degreed physicist realized that more advanced training was necessary in order to satiate his growing desire to work in the newly evolving discipline of biophysics.

Deisenhofer actively searched for a modern laboratory within which he could conduct advanced biophysical research. At the Max Planck Institute for Biochemistry in Martinsreid, he found exactly what, and who, he was looking for, in a laboratory headed by Robert Huber. It was under Huber's supervision that Deisenhofer learned the art and science of X-ray crystallography. He received his Ph.D. in 1974 from the Max Planck Institute, and his link with Huber proved to be vital to Deisenhofer's success as a scientist.

Deisenhofer moved to Dallas, Texas, early in 1988 to become a member of the Howard Hughes Medical Institute. In June, 1989, he married Kirsten Fischer-Lindahl, a woman of Swedish ancestry. She is a researcher in immunology at the institute, and they met when he first visited Dallas for interviews.

Scientific Career

Since the beginning of his scientific career, Deisenhofer has remained loyal to his original desire to seek new truths and knowledge through the application of physics to biological investigations. Klaus Dransfeld was an important influence in the early years of Deisenhofer's training. In his original projects with Dransfeld, Deisenhofer had investigated the properties of electronic transitions in ruby crystals. The studies required low temperatures in order to detect phonons, or quantized vibrations of atoms in the ruby crystal lattice. His research continued for one and a half years at Technische Universitaet. His master's thesis was entitled "Detection of Tetrahertz-Phonons in Rubies at 4 Kelvin."

According to Deisenhofer, his move to explore biophysics was attributable to the influence of Dransfeld, from whom he had sought advice on career goals. Dransfeld had cultivated Deisenhofer's own interest in biophysics; Deisenhofer read avidly about the newly forming branch of science and organized some lectures on the topic. His research adviser was convincing; biophysics was a rising and interesting field that Deisenhofer decided he would pursue.

When he entered the doctoral program at the Max Planck Institute, Deisenhofer's association with Robert Huber was securely established. His three years as a doctoral student culminated in his dissertation, "Structural Refinement of the Basic Pancreatic Trypsin Inhibitor." Upon earning his physics doctorate in 1974, Deisenhofer completed his training with Huber, one of the original pioneers in establishing applications of crystallographic techniques to protein structural analysis.

Immediately after completing his doctoral work, Deisenhofer became a research associate within the Huber laboratory. (In some nations, this period of research is called a postdoctoral position.) During this period, Deisenhofer directed his own research interests and trained or assisted other researchers in the Huber group. His extended stay with Huber as a research associate is largely attributable to the strangely slow and painfully restricted access to the title of independent science investigator in West Germany. Unlike in the United States, where the number of research directors or group leaders may be twenty or more within one small department, such as molecular biology, in West Germany there may be only three such directors in a department of comparable size. In the West German hierarchy, a patriarchal system holds academic intellectuals in a rigid grasp. Unless an individual investigator is willing to seek other opportunities in a freer environment, the climb to the prestigious position of group leader is greatly inhibited. As he attempted to groom his career within the confines of West German academia, Deisenhofer continued to publish his research findings and cultivate professional collaborations.

Several of Deisenhofer's publications addressed the structural traits of human immunoglobulins, or fragments thereof. An immunoglobulin is like an antibody: It is able to recognize foreign bodies, or antigens, and prompt the attack on those antigens. An antigen-antibody complex is formed upon recognition of the invading antigen. Oddly enough, both antigens and immunoglobulins are often protein macromolecules. Their structures reveal the secrets of how the antigen and antibody chemically bind to one another. In other studies, the structures of biologically active enzymes, which are protein molecules that serve a unique role as biological catalysts, were examined. Enzymes allow numerous metabolic reactions to occur; some require a helper molecule called a coenzyme. As an enzyme functions, it will attach to a substrate, or material it works upon, and cause a chemical change. The so-called "lock and key" enzyme model was an early attempt to describe the specific match in structure that is required of both enzyme and substrate.

The concept that molecular structure dictates biological function is repeatedly upheld in Deisenhofer's work. His journal articles generally include large, scrawled diagrams that resemble space vessels from a science fiction film or pieces of modern art. To Deisenhofer, each turn in the molecular structure, every repeated pattern, each plane of symmetry and region of asymmetry reveals more clues about where the atoms are located. Eventually he pieces the puzzle together, resulting in a full image that explains why an atom has to be in a certain position in order for the molecule to perform its natural biological role.

In 1982, Johann Deisenhofer began collaborating with Hartmut Michel, who claims that Deisenhofer "was just the partner I needed." According to Deisenhofer, "It was immediately clear to me that this [the photosynthetic reaction center] would be the most interesting molecule that one can find." Robert Huber continued to provide the essential instrumentation and intellectual feedback on the project.

In 1984, the *Journal of Molecular Biology* published an article entitled "X-Ray Structure Analysis of a Membrane Protein Complex." This work was the now-famous paper on the photosynthetic reaction center of *Rhodopseudomonas viridis*. One decade after receiving his Ph.D., his reputation as an excellent scientist was becoming well established. In the article, Deisenhofer reported that he was able to identify structural features, which were numerous and complicated, within the reaction center. The entire photosynthetic reaction center is a huge chemical entity; in fact, there are four protein subunits plus four heme groups present in the complex. Other components can be classified as: four chlorophyll units; two pheophytin units, which are similar to chlorophyll; two quinone units, one at the end of each branch; and a strangely situated iron ion nestled between the two quinones but not trapped as if in a claw (that is, nonheme).

The four protein subunits were found to be different from one another and were labeled as such: H was the largest unit; M denoted the protein unit having a molecular mass of medium range; L represented the lightest protein substructure; and C denoted the c-type cytochrome. Two other features are the "special pair" and the distinct preference for electrons to move along only one branch of the complex, even though the two branches appear to be very similar. As reported in *Science*, Deisenhofer considered finding "what looked like a pair of closely associated chlorophyll molecules in the electron density patterns" to be one of his most exciting moments as a researcher. The notion had been proposed by an American team in the early 1970's, but at the time it was not a well-received idea and could not be rigorously proven.

In spite of the reasonably symmetric arrangement of atoms and substructures around the special pair, a distinct preference is exhibited as to which side of the complex is useful. When an electron (which is generated at the special pair immediately after the infrared radiation of the sun is absorbed there) begins its journey through the complex, it would seem as though the electron could travel on either side. There does not appear to be any overwhelming difference between the two paths; this, however, is not the case. Only one route is selected, and it is consistently selected. The information is still a puzzle to Deisenhofer, who has ample questions to address about how each subunit functions in nature.

Johann Deisenhofer continued his career at the Max Planck Institute after his 1984 publication, completing another stage in his professional advancement called *Habilitation*. This is a necessary move if a researcher desires a career in the academia of West Germany. A person in *Habilitation* must already possess a Ph.D., must have completed postdoctoral work, and must be planning a career at a university. Deisenhofer passed both the exams and the scrutiny of his scientific research, and in 1987 completed *Habilitation* at the Technical University in Munich. The only problem he faced now was a personal one: He did not really like classroom teaching. If his career continued in its current direction, soon he would not only be doing research but also be teaching undergraduate and graduate classes. This seemed a bleak destiny to a man who loved his laboratory work and much preferred it to teaching. Deisenhofer, however, avoided classroom lecturing by seeking employment elsewhere. Several universities in the United States expressed an interest; Deisenhofer elected to become a member of the Howard Hughes Medical Institute of the University of Texas Southwestern Medical Center in Dallas, Texas.

Upon receiving the 1988 Nobel Prize, Deisenhofer was suddenly not only a respected name in the scientific community but also a focal point for media attention. It was only three years since the *Rhodopseudomonas viridis* paper had been published. In a press conference, he explained, "I was in the shower. I had just gotten reasonably wet and the telephone began to ring. I finally answered it and it turned out to be the secretary of the Royal Academy." At the news that his team had been awarded the prestigious award, Deisenhofer said, he felt "absolute shock" and "disbelief." In a short synopsis of his work that appeared some months later, he noted that winning the Nobel Prize was more than he ever expected. He stated, "I was never sure of the magnitude of my discovery."

The Nobel Prize carries with it a certain burden, or expectation, along with the prestige and honor. As Deisenhofer became more comfortable with his success as a research chemist and with his Nobel fame, his research instinct once again took control of his scientific creativity. His new collaborations with other researchers in Dallas continued to be cultivated. Among those with whom he established research liaisons were Michael Brown and Joseph Goldstein, both Nobel laureates, whose work in cholesterol metabolism received international acclaim in medical communities. Researcher Betsy Goldsmith and Deisenhofer embarked on a project to determine the protein structure of a low density lipoprotein (or LDL) receptor soon after Deisenhofer set up his laboratory in Dallas.

Deisenhofer has explained that he enjoys doing research because "it is an opportunity to do something no one has done before." He described how the challenges

of research come during the "long stretches of time when there are no results . . . it requires patience and confidence . . . and you cannot predict when the
results will come." Although the results of daily laboratory work may not be
predictable, the excellence of Deisenhofer's research is. As he himself has phrased
it, a "mixture of patience and impatience" has guided his career.

Bibliography

Primary

CHEMISTRY: "Structure of the Complex Formed by Bovine Trypsin and Bovine
  Pancreatic Trypsin Inhibitor," *Journal of Molecular Biology*, vol. 89, 1974; "Crystallographic Structure Studies of an IgG Molecule and an Fc Fragment," *Nature*,
  vol. 264, 1976; "Crystallographic Refinement of a Human Fc Fragment and Its Complex with Fragment B of Protein A from *Staphylococcus aureus* at 2.9- to 2.8-
  Ångstrom Resolution," *Biochemistry*, vol. 20, 1981; "X-Ray Structure Analysis of
  a Membrane Protein Complex," *Journal of Molecular Biology*, vol. 180, 1984;
  "Crystal Structure Analysis and Molecular Model of a Complex of Citrate Synthase with Oxaloacetate and S-Acetonyl-coenzyme A," *Journal of Molecular
  Biology*, vol. 174, 1984; "Structure of the Protein Subunits in the Photosynthetic
  Reaction Centre of *Rhodopseudomonas viridis* at 3-Ångstrom Resolution," *Na-
  ture*, vol. 318, 1985; "The Structural Basis of Photosynthetic Light Reactions in
  Bacteria," *Trends in Biochemical Science*, June, 1985; "Experience with Various
  Techniques for the Refinement of Protein Structures," *Methods in Enzymology*,
  vol. 115, 1985 (with S. J. Remington and W. Steigemann); "Relevance of the
  Photosynthetic Reaction Center from Purple Bacteria to the Structure of Pho-
  tosystem II," *Biochemistry*, vol. 27, 1988.

Secondary

Bloom, Myer, and Ole Mouritsen. "The Evolution of Membranes." *Canadian Journal of Chemistry* 66 (1988): 706-712. Proposing that prokaryotic cell membranes
  (in bacteria and blue-green algae) manifest as eukaryotic membranes (in multi-
  cellular organisms) in the presence of an oxygen-rich biosphere, this article
  explores possible pathways of membrane evolution. A well-written, concise account of the physical and chemical properties of bacterial membranes is given.
  While portions require intense reading, the overview provided is easily understood and worth the reader's investigation.
Feyer, George, J. P. Allen, et al. "Structure and Function of Bacterial Photosynthetic Reaction Centres." *Nature* 339 (1989): 111-116. Written as a review on the topic
  of photosynthetic reaction centers, this article compares two reaction centers
  from two related, but different, bacteria, *Rhodopseudomonas viridis* and *Rhodopseudomonas sphaeroides*. Photographs showing stereo views of these reaction
  centers are excellent. The paper provides an excellent assessment of how the
  Deisenhofer, Michel, and Huber work will affect future research efforts.
Gregory, Richard P. F. *Biochemistry of Photosynthesis*. 2d ed. New York: John

Wiley & Sons, 1977. This book provides a summary of the photosynthetic process. The early chapters are not rigorous, but as the book progresses, many will find it difficult to comprehend without some biological or chemical background. For the more scientifically astute reader, it presents a thorough overview of complex photosynthetic processes.

Hall, D. O., and K. K. Rao. *Photosynthesis*. 4th ed. London: Edward Arnold, 1987. This book is information intensive, but it is an excellent survey of developments in understanding photosynthesis. It will be advantageous to the reader to have some prior chemistry or biochemistry knowledge. Otherwise, it is a challenging text.

Lascelles, June, ed. *Microbial Photosynthesis*. Stroudsburg, Pa.: Dowden, Hutchinson & Ross, 1973. This book is composed of several independent papers that address different aspects of microbial photosynthesis. The introductory papers are easily understood by an untrained, but curious, reader. The first seven articles are worth investigation for an overview of bacterial photosynthesis.

Lewin, Roger. "Membrane Protein Holds Photosynthetic Secrets." *Science* 242 (1988): 672-673. This article gives insight into the personal associations of Deisenhofer, Michel, and Huber. It provides the beginner with an easily understood introduction into the research and its significance. Some portions may become too technical for a novice, but it is brief and interesting to read.

Reigchel, Diane. "Johann Deisenhofer: Can a Nobel Prize Winner Find Happiness in Dallas? Naturlich, He Says." *Dallas Morning News*, June 11, 1989, sec. E: 1-2. This is a delightful article showcasing Deisenhofer's personal and professional life. Reveals some of his unique professional and personal quirks.

Youvan, Douglas C., and Barry L. Marrs. "Molecular Mechanisms of Photosynthesis." *Scientific American*, June, 1987: 42-48. This is a good overview of how spectroscopy, X-ray crystallography, and molecular genetics reveal the secrets of photosynthetic processes. While the information may overwhelm some, the images are clear representations of some of the specialized events that occur in photosynthesis. The bacterial reaction center discussed in this article is actually less complex than the one studied by Deisenhofer, Michel, and Huber.

Mary C. Fields

1988

Chemistry
Johann Deisenhofer, West Germany
Robert Huber, West Germany
Hartmut Michel, West Germany

Physics
Leon M. Lederman, United States
Melvin Schwartz, United States
Jack Steinberger, Germany and United States

Physiology or Medicine
Sir James W. Black, Great Britain
Gertrude B. Elion, United States
George H. Hitchings, United States

Economic Sciences
Maurice Allais, France

Literature
Naguib Mahfouz, Egypt

Peace
U.N. Peacekeeping Forces

ROBERT HUBER
1988

Born: Munich, Germany; February 20, 1937

Nationality: German
Areas of concentration: X-ray crystallography and structural analysis

Huber pioneered in applying X-ray crystallographic techniques to protein struc-
ture analysis. Together with cowinners Hartmut Michel and Johann Deisenhofer, he
determined the structure of the photosynthetic reaction center of the bacterium Rhodopseudomonas viridis

The Award

Presentation
"In the beginning there was light." So began Professor Bo G. Malmström's
presentation of the winners of the 1988 Nobel Prize in Chemistry to the Swedish
royalty and to the members and guests of the Royal Swedish Academy of Sciences
on December 10, 1988. Malmström's opening sentence alluded to the vital role that
light plays in maintaining the balance of life on earth. He focused the audience's
attention on the photosynthetic research performed by Robert Huber, Johann Deisenhofer, and Hartmut Michel. The scientific team had investigated protein structures found within a photosynthetic bacterium, structures essential for the conversion of incident solar energy into stored chemical energy. In other words, these
structures actually perform the chemistry of photosynthesis.

Malmström emphasized the significant role that photosynthesis plays in processing solar energy and creating the nutrients necessary for all life forms on earth to
exist. He briefly gave a summary of earlier Nobel Prize-winning research that laid
foundations upon which the West German trio built their research. Henry Taube, a
Nobel chemistry laureate in 1983, delineated the fundamental principles involved in
electron transfer in metallic compounds, which have been extrapolated into the
comprehension of electron transfers that are involved in photosynthesis. Malmström
recognized Peter Mitchell for his Nobel Prize-winning (1978) research in mechanisms of adenosine triphosphate, or ATP, production. Malmström also acknowledged the research of Aaron Klug, who had devised applications of electron microscopy in the structural analysis of both simple and complex molecules; Klug won the
1982 Nobel Prize in Chemistry.

The research of Huber, Deisenhofer, and Michel incorporated these fundamental
scientific concepts and embellished them so that the "determination of the structure
of a photosynthetic reaction center [that caused] a leap in our understanding of the
perhaps most important chemical reaction on earth" could occur. Malmström concluded by noting that this research also opened new avenues of investigation in the
fields of immunology, pharmacology, and biological systems.

Nobel lecture

Robert Huber was unable to attend the Nobel ceremonies or to deliver his portion of the Nobel lecture. On Thursday morning, December 8, 1988, his colleagues, Hartmut Michel and Johann Deisenhofer, jointly presented their research to an audience of Swedish scientific intellectuals and special guests. Huber, however, subsequently submitted his own paper to the Nobel Foundation, entitled "A Structural Basis of Light Energy and Electron Transfer in Biology."

He described the most basic physical and chemical principles involved in the absorption of light energy and the accompanying electron migrations that ultimately allow the radiant energy to become stored chemical energy. He focused on three protein-cofactor complexes: the reaction center of *Rhodopseudomonas viridis* (a purple bacterium), light-harvesting cyanophycobilisomes, and blue multicopper oxides. (All three of these systems had been explored in depth under Huber's guidance in his own laboratory.) The dominant theme of his paper was that the structure of nature holds the key to a detailed understanding of the complicated series of events collectively known as photosynthesis. In order to grasp the key, one must discover every small detail of the molecular structure: the atoms involved, their spatial distributions, and the interactions between small segments of the large protein-cofactor entities.

The protein and its associated cofactors, such as pigments or metal ions, together form such a difficult molecule that the term "complex" is used to describe it; thus, the photosynthetic reaction center is a molecular complex. Huber described chemical models that attempt to explain the subtle shifts that occur as a photon of light prompts chemical reactions to begin within the complex. The chemical reactions can induce a charge separation and form ions, or the complex can store the energy via excited electronic states. Most models include a donor of electrons, an acceptor of electrons, a bridging ligand that often connects the donor to the acceptor, pendant groups which are not in the direct line of electron or energy transfer, and, finally, a large matrix within which the other components are housed. As Huber readily acknowledged, no one model serves well for every system, but a model can provide a perspective from which these systems can be further explored. Geometry, spatial gaps, and surrounding environments all merge to reveal how, when, and why light-absorbing complexes function as they do.

In his closing paragraphs, Huber described new methodologies in protein chemistry and advances in computer systems associated with crystallographic instrumentation and noted that such advances continue to fuel protein crystallography research. He also alluded to significant breakthroughs in the comprehension of photosynthetic reaction centers, virus structures, protein DNA complexes, and multi-enzyme complexes, and stated that advances in these areas were the result of the powerful investigative technique of X-ray crystallography. He cited likely future endeavors in drug designs and protein designs, many of which play essential immunological roles in living organisms, and explained how future successes in these areas depend upon gathering detailed, accurate structural information about each system.

Critical reception

The announcement of the 1988 Nobel Prize in Chemistry pleasantly surprised many chemists. The three German researchers had first published their results in the *Journal of Molecular Biology* in 1984. They determined the structure of a complex protein "which sits astride the bacterial membrane with one part inside the cell and one part outside," and many biochemists recognized that this publication was a likely candidate for a Nobel award. The question, How long would it take? was answered only four years later.

According to Bo Malmström, the chairperson of the 1988 Nobel Committee for Chemistry, the scientific trio was "the first to succeed in unraveling the full details of how a membrane-bound protein is built . . . atom by atom." Not only did the committee find that the research altered science's understanding of photosynthesis in bacteria as well as in plants, but also they found the research to be fundamental to future investigations of membrane proteins.

Many scientists described the photosynthetic reaction center as the "heart" or the "engine" of photosynthesis, and protein chemists universally admired Hartmut Michel's success in crystallizing a protein complex that others had spent decades unsuccessfully trying to extract from cell membranes. In an article in *The New York Times*, Keith Moffat of Cornell University was quoted as saying that Michel was "spectacularly successful." William Parson of the University of Washington elaborated in *Science*, saying that "people thought it couldn't be done. It was a psychological barrier, like the 4-minute mile." As for crystallographers, both Robert Huber and Johann Deisenhofer were familiar and respected names. Even prior to the 1988 award, Huber had been described (in *Nature*) as operating "one of the most productive protein structure groups in the world." Soon after their 1984 publication, Deisenhofer was being lured to American universities by researchers who recognized his astuteness as a crystallographer; moreover, his youth would mean many years of productive research to come. Huber and Deisenhofer both would join the ranks of Nobel Prize-winning crystallographers, including Hermann Staudinger (1953) and Dorothy Crowfoot Hodgkin (1964).

The complete structural determination of a membrane-bound protein to atomic detail heightened interest in areas of pharmacology, immunology, and molecular genetics of bacteria. An article in *New Scientist* stated that Jim Barber of Imperial College in London had recommended the research on the *Rhodopseudomonas viridis* reaction center to the Nobel Committee since its 1984 publication. Barber was quoted as saying that the research would make a "tremendous contribution to membrane biology, particularly to understanding receptors in the membrane." Membrane-bound proteins play important roles in cells whose function may fail, and analysis of more such proteins could provide insight into elusive diseases such as diabetes and cancer.

The overall reception of the 1988 announcement was marked by a real sense of excitement over the relatively young group of researchers receiving the prize shortly after publishing their work, because the Nobel Committee seldom rewards scientists during their early professional years. There was also great excitement over the new possibilities that this research had prompted in the work of other scientists who could apply the same methods and techniques in their research.

Although the majority of the reaction to this prize was favorable, some negative comments were made about the selection of laureates. The rigorous, competitive, and sometimes unsatisfying world of research can foster resentment and frustration among members of the scientific community. The result of these forces can be seen in an article entitled "A Whiff of Cordite over Chemistry Prize" in *New Scientist* (October 29, 1988). The article identifies three factions: those who believed that George Feher, a scientist at the University of California performing related studies, should have been included; another group who believed that Dieter Österhelt of the Max Planck Institute in Martinsreid should have been included; and a faction that believed that only Michel should have received the prize, for his creative separation method. All three factions could even be found within the halls of the Max Planck Institute. When several people are involved in a project at a variety of levels and intensities, alliances, loyalties, and schisms are quite likely to occur. This involvement of so many researchers increasingly complicates the Nobel selection process; the Nobel Committee must decide whom to include and whom to exclude based upon its own judgment.

In a *Science* article, Michel expressed frustration over the omission of his postdoctoral adviser, Dieter Österhelt. Michel is quoted as saying, "Without his help, I would have given up." Österhelt had certainly worked closely with Michel in developing the purification techniques he used to isolate the reaction center. Michel was not alone in his sentiment; other researchers at Martinsreid expressed the same frustration. There were also complaints about the inclusion of Huber, whom some said had contributed little or nothing to the research. They maintained that Huber's name appeared as coauthor on many research publications with which they believed he was not actually involved.

Many more favorable comments about Huber, however, can be found. In *The New York Times*, he was identified as being "already an internationally known expert in X-ray crystallography," while in *Science*, the Huber laboratory was called "a powerhouse of structural analysis." Certainly Huber provided the instrumentation for the X-ray work, and it is probable that his intellectual feedback, comments, and criticisms assisted profoundly in the final success of the *Rhodopseudomonas viridis* work.

Biography

Robert Huber was born on February 20, 1937, in Munich, Germany. At the age of twenty-five, Huber had completed his doctoral degree at the technical university of Munich. He decided to pursue his scientific research in an academic setting, and he became one of the original pioneers in applying X-ray crystallographic techniques to protein structural analysis. He is frequently described as a dedicated, hardworking spectroscopist. According to Harmut Michel, Huber "spends the most time in the lab of anyone I have ever seen." *The New York Times* reported that Huber works about ten hours a day in his laboratory Monday through Saturday and generally spends another five hours there on Sunday.

At the age of fifty-one, when he received his Nobel Prize, Huber was the father of several adult children as well as an eight-year-old. In spite of his grueling laboratory hours, he has remained a devoted family man. He balances the rigors of professional life and the demands and joys of family life by staying physically active and healthy. His friends have said that he rides his bicycle to the laboratory every day; the seven-mile trek from home to laboratory is covered without fail, no matter what the weather conditions are.

Scientific Career

Robert Huber studied at the technical university of Munich during his graduate years, completing his doctoral degree there in 1963. Once he decided to continue his research interests in an academic setting, he went on to do his *Habilitation* program at the same university where he had earned his doctorate. *Habilitation* is a uniquely German stage in the making of a professor and independent researcher of science within a college or university. In order to begin the *Habilitation* program, one must be dedicated to an academic career, must have completed both a doctoral and postdoctoral program, and must be willing to prepare for and master several advanced examinations.

Huber completed this advanced training period at the technical university of Munich in 1968, only five years after receiving his doctoral degree. Soon thereafter, his academic career began to flourish. By 1972, Huber had become the division head, or chairman, at the Max Planck Institute for Biochemistry in Martinsreid. His research work had been fruitful, and his associations and collaborations were on the increase. Johann Deisenhofer was then a promising young graduate student in his first year of graduate studies. At the age of thirty-five, Huber had established himself as an astute and productive scientist. His X-ray crystallography laboratory continued to grow, and his focus on determining the structures of biologically active proteins continued to sharpen. In 1974, Deisenhofer received his doctorate degree and became the new postdoctoral fellow in Huber's research group.

Huber became a full professor at the technical university in Munich in 1976. Only two years later, Deiter Österhelt and his junior scientist, Hartmut Michel, would move their research laboratory to the Max Planck Institute in Martinsreid. (The Max Planck Institute is a part of the technical university system.) Huber's group had become a rather large team of X-ray crystallographers who were producing a high number of publications that described the structural details of biologically significant proteins. Deisenhofer became a productive researcher, and Huber coauthored several papers, with the assistance of other researchers and technicians, beginning in 1974.

In 1980, Österhelt had established his department in biophysics at the new location in Martinsreid. He and Huber immediately began collaborative investigations. Michel had obtained his very fine, pure sample of the *Rhodopseudomonas viridis* crystals by September of 1981. In February, 1982, he began collecting data from X-ray analysis. He soon found that, although he had some familiarity with X-ray crystallography, he lacked the expert knowledge needed to perform the structural analysis alone. Therefore, Michel logically sought the advice of crystallography experts—Huber and his group. As Michel recalls it, he gave a seminar in either April or May of 1982 to the Huber group, and it was at this time that he officially requested a collaboration with members of the Huber group.

Michel's postdoctoral adviser, Österhelt, had made it clear that he believed that the young scientist should be given the reaction center project to investigate. After some internal discussions, Huber agreed to collaborate with Michel and suggested his postdoctoral fellow Deisenhofer for the project. It is fateful that Österhelt had purchased an X-ray generator in 1980 to assist Michel in his investigations. The generator was wisely installed in the Huber department, which ultimately guaranteed that Michel would have access to the crystallography wisdom of Deisenhofer and Huber. The three scientists published their photosynthetic reaction center article only two years after the collaboration officially began. Three years after that, in 1987, they separated to pursue their career interests and research.

In 1987, Huber was promoted to director of the Max Planck Institute for Biochemistry in Martinsreid; Deisenhofer moved to Dallas, Texas, to establish his own research group, becoming an independent (no longer under postdoctoral supervision) investigator. Hartmut Michel became a department head and director at the Max Planck Institute for Biophysics in Frankfurt/Main. Approximately one year later, in separate worlds, the three would learn of their shared Nobel Prize. Huber continued his research and leadership role at the university at which he had been educated and to which he remained faithful and loyal. An article in *Nature* described the structural analysis of the *Rhodopseudomonas viridis* photosynthetic reaction center as a "witness to the tremendous and continuously growing power of protein crystallography."

Bibliography

Primary
CHEMISTRY: "Chemistry of the Ecdysones: 7, Crystal and Molecular Structure Analysis of the Insect Pupation Hormone Ecdysone with the Automatic Molecular Method," *Chemische Berichte*, vol. 98, 1965 (with W. Hoppe); "Structures of Deoxy- and Carbonmonoxy-erythrocruorin," *Journal of Molecular Biology*, vol. 52, 1970 (with O. Epp and H. Formanek); "Basic Trypsin Inhibitor of Bovine Pancreas: 1, Structure Analysis and Conformation of the Polypeptide Chain," *Naturwissenschaften*, vol. 57, 1970 (with D. Kukla, A. Ruehimann, O. Epp, and H. Formanek); "Crystal and Molecular Structure of a Dimer Composed of the Variable Portions of the Bence-Jones Protein REI," *European Journal of Biochemistry*, vol. 45, 1974 (with O. Epp, P. Colman, W. Bode, R. Huber, et al.); "Structure of the Complex Formed by Bovine Trypsin and Bovine Pancreatic

Trypsin Inhibitor: 2, Crystallographic Refinement at 1.9 Å Resolution," *Journal of Molecular Biology*, vol. 89, 1974 (with D. Kukla, W. Bode, P. Schwager, et al.); "Structure of the Human Antibody Molecule Koll (Immunoglobulin G1): An Electron Density Map at 5 Å Resolution," *Journal of Molecular Biology*, vol. 100, 1976 (with P. M. Colman, J. Deisenhofer, and W. Palm); "Crystallographic Structure Studies of an IgG Molecule and an Fc Fragment," *Nature*, vol. 264, 1976 (with J. Deisenhofer, P. M. Colman, M. Matsushima, and W. Palm); "X-Ray Structure Analysis of a Membrane Protein Complex. Electron Density Map at 3 Å Resolution and a Model of the Chromophores of the Photosynthetic Reaction Center from *Rhodopseudomonas viridis*," *Journal of Molecular Biology*, vol. 180, 1984 (with J. Deisenhofer, H. Michel, O. Epp, and K. Miki); "Structure of the Protein Subunits in the Photosynthetic Reaction Center of *Rhodopseudomonas viridis* at 3 Å Resolution," *Nature*, vol. 318, 1985 (with J. Deisenhofer, H. Michel, O. Epp, and K. Miki).

Secondary

Bragg, Sir William Lawrence. *The Development of X-Ray Analysis.* Edited by D. C. Phillips and H. F. Lipson. New York: Hafner Press, 1975. The author's father, William Henry Bragg, was a founder of X-ray analysis, and he wrote an interesting introduction for this volume. (The two Braggs shared the 1915 Nobel Prize in Physics for their pioneering X-ray work.) This is a clear, easily understood presentation, divided into two sections; one discusses the art of X-ray analysis, the other its applications and significance.

Clarke, M. "1988 Nobel Prizes." *Nature*, October 27, 1988: 752-753. Summarizes the research and findings of the three prizewinners, referring to primary citations.

Dagani, Ron, and Stephen Stinson. "Nobel Prizes: Photosynthesis, Drug Studies Honored." *Chemical and Engineering News*, October 24, 1988: 4-5. Presents a good short summary of the work that won the prize for Huber, Deisenhofer, and Michel and quotes reactions of some United States scientists to the award announcement.

Feyer, George, J. P. Allen, et al. "Structure and Function of Bacterial Photosynthetic Reaction Centres." *Nature* 339 (1989): 111-116. This review article compares the centers from *Rhodopseudomonas viridis* and *Rhodopseudomonas sphaeroides*, two related bacteria. Includes excellent photographs; provides an assessment of how the prizewinners' work will affect future research.

Hall, Nina, and Debora MacKenzie. "A Whiff of Cordite over Chemistry Prize." *New Scientist* 29 (October 29, 1988): 31-32. This article discusses the disagreements over who should (or should not) have been included in the 1988 chemistry award, noting sources that questioned Huber's role in the work.

Lewin, Roger. "Membrane Protein Holds Photosynthetic Secrets." *Science* 242 (1988): 672-673. Provides good insights into the association of Huber, Michel, and Deisenhofer. An easily understood introduction to their research and its significance.

Stryer, Lubert. *Biochemistry.* 3d ed. New York: W. H. Freeman, 1988. Chapter 3, "Exploring Proteins," presents a clear introduction to protein chemistry. Includes a section on the use of X-ray crystallography to determine the three-dimensional structure of proteins.

Wilson, Herbert Rees. *Diffraction of X-Rays by Proteins, Nucleic Acids, and Viruses.* London: Edward Arnold, 1966. The early chapters of this book provide a good introduction to the principles of X-ray diffraction and explain how it is used to understand protein structure. Also presents a good, brief introduction to the principles behind protein chemistry.

Mary C. Fields

1988

Chemistry
Johann Deisenhofer, West Germany
Robert Huber, West Germany
Hartmut Michel, West Germany

Physics
Leon M. Lederman, United States
Melvin Schwartz, United States
Jack Steinberger, Germany and United States

Physiology or Medicine
Sir James W. Black, Great Britain
Gertrude B. Elion, United States
George H. Hitchings, United States

Economic Sciences
Maurice Allais, France

Literature
Naguib Mahfouz, Egypt

Peace
U.N. Peacekeeping Forces

HARTMUT MICHEL
1988

Born: Ludwigsburg, West Germany; July 18, 1948

Nationality: German
Areas of concentration: Protein chemistry and macromolecular structure

Michel isolated the photoreaction center protein from a bacterium and obtained highly ordered three-dimensional crystals of the protein. With his cowinners, he revealed the spatial arrangement of the molecules that carry out the primary steps in photosynthesis

The Award

Presentation

Bo G. Malmström, a biochemist and a member of the Royal Swedish Academy of Sciences, presented the Nobel Prize in Chemistry to Hartmut Michel on December 10, 1988. Malmström began with a familiar declaration: "In the beginning there was light." He then noted the central role that light played in the early evolution of life on Earth, particularly as it enabled the development of photosynthetic organisms. These organisms are capable of making complex molecules from simple ones by using sunlight. Michel's achievement in crystallizing the photoreaction center protein from a photosynthetic bacterium and eventually determining its structure by X-ray crystallography provided science with a great leap forward in the understanding of how light is converted into chemical energy in the form of separated charges by electron transfer.

The principles for electron transfer between simple molecules had been laid down previously, Malmström said, in the pioneering work of Henry Taube, winner of the Nobel Prize in Chemistry in 1983. The photoreaction center structure provided the first glimpse into how electron transfer steps could occur in large molecular aggregates embedded within a biological membrane. The early steps in photosynthesis culminate in the movement of protons across a biological membrane and ultimately in the synthesis of ATP by a mechanism formulated by the Nobel Prize winner for chemistry in 1978, Peter Mitchell. Malmström concluded by noting that many biological functions, including hormone action and nerve impulses, are associated with membrane-bound proteins, and he stressed that the work of Michel and his associates might enable the determination of detailed structures for many other membrane proteins.

Nobel lecture

Michel began his Nobel lecture, entitled "The Photoreaction Center from the Purple Bacterium *Rhodopseudomonas viridis*," by introducing the observation that first stimulated his interest in crystallizing membrane proteins. In August, 1978, while working as a postdoctoral associate in the laboratory of Dieter Österhelt in the Max Planck Institute in Martinsreid, he observed the formation of "glass-like aggregates" upon freezing solutions of bacteriorhodopsin, a membrane protein, that had been completely stripped of all the lipid molecules that formed the membrane. Michel believed that it should be possible to induce these aggregates to form well-ordered three-dimensional crystals, which are a prerequisite for determination of the atomic level structure using high-resolution X-ray crystallographic analysis. This idea was supported by the observation that some membrane proteins exhibit two-dimensional crystalline order even in their native membrane.

A new strategy had to be developed, however, in order to crystallize membrane proteins that are water insoluble. It had been previously known that detergents make membrane proteins soluble by surrounding them within micelles. Micelles, in their simplest form, are spherically shaped aggregates of detergent molecules in which the polar head groups face toward the aqueous phase and the nonpolar hydrocarbon chains are buried in the interior. This asymmetry in polarity is the characteristic feature of ampiphatic molecules, of which detergents are one example. Unfortunately, micelles do not generally crystallize. The key to inducing crystallization, as Michel showed in systematic studies, was to use shorter-length detergent molecules, which form small micelles. This enables the polar ends of the protein to protrude outside the micelle into the aqueous phase, where they can contact other protein/micelle particles and thereby form an extended lattice. Another problem also had to be overcome. The smaller the detergent molecule, the more likely it is to cause the protein to deactivate (denature) by unfolding. He solved this difficulty by making mixed micelles, in which some of the detergent molecules were replaced by even smaller ampiphatic molecules. At low concentrations, these partition into the micelles and are nondenaturing to the protein. After switching from bacteriorhodopsin to the photoreaction center protein from the purple bacterium *Rhodopseudomonas viridis*, large crystals were obtained almost immediately.

Michel then discussed the relationship between the bacterial photoreaction center protein and that found in the majority of higher plants and certain algae, which are capable of oxidizing water to molecular oxygen in a related photoreaction center II complex. From an analysis of the protein sequences, he had predicted which proteins in the more complex higher plants had to make up the reaction center. This proposal was at variance with one of the prevailing views, but later studies confirmed his proposal. The structural and functional homology between bacterial reaction centers and the reaction center II protein complex is now generally accepted.

At the end of his lecture, Michel surveyed the highlights of the atomic structure of the photoreaction center protein. A striking feature was the arrangement of the twelve molecular cofactors involved in light absorption and electron transfer. Four bacteriochlorophyll, two bacteriopheophytin, and two quinones were found to be supported by the protein backbone in an arrangement forming two parallel branches, such that electron transfer occurs from the outer to the inner surface of the membrane. The evolutionary origin of the two parallel branches has evoked much speculation, particularly since only one of the branches is known to be functional in electron transport. The protein also revealed a remarkable asymmetry in the location of polar and charged amino acids and bound water molecules. These were found almost exclusively in regions of the protein known to be external to the nonpolar membrane spanning region.

Critical reception

The awarding of the Nobel Prize to three West Germans, Johann Deisenhofer, forty-five; Robert Huber, fifty-one; and Hartmut Michel, forty, was widely acclaimed. The award came a short four years after the initial structural results were reported. Their work in unraveling the three-dimensional structure of the photosynthetic reaction center protein provided a great leap in the understanding of photosynthesis, since it was the first photoreaction center structure known. It also was the first membrane protein to be crystallized using a systematic approach that allowed the atomic structure to be solved. Articles favorable to the award appeared in *Chemical and Engineering News* as well as in *New Scientist*. According to Stephen G. Boxer, a chemistry professor at Stanford University, scientists seeking to create artificial photosynthetic systems for energy storage were now focusing their efforts on mimicking the bacterial structure revealed by the Max Planck Institute researchers: "The whole world of electron transfer research has heated up because of this work."

Solution of the structure of the photoreaction center was said to have been an enormous challenge, because it was one of the largest asymmetric unit cells ever to be solved. Protein crystallographer Bonnie A. Wallace of Rensselaer Polytechnic Institute, whose own work has dealt with the important protein gramicidin, had these words of praise: "Because the West German research provides a model for the structure of membrane proteins in general, it also may lead to new insights to many diseases and other biological processes that involve membrane function." James Barber, from Imperial College in London, noted that "this structure will make a tremendous contribution to membrane biology, particularly to understanding receptors in membranes." The reaction center structure has greatly improved understanding of the molecular bases of certain types of herbicides, which bind within the reaction center by displacing one of the two quinones. Efforts have already begun to engineer the reaction center complex genetically in related crops so that it is no longer susceptible to herbicide activity.

Some mild controversy surrounded the selection of the three laureates, and it was summarized in an article in *New Scientist* by Nina Hall and Debora MacKenzie. The controversy concerned who should and who should not be recognized as having contributed to the photoreaction center structure. Advances as complex as this one invariably require the collaboration of many scientists with skills in different areas. Michel's conceptual innovation of coaxing photosynthetic reaction centers into forming crystals was clearly recognized by all scientists. Deisenhofer performed the crystallographic analysis of what was then the most complex biological structure known at an atomic level. Huber, in whose laboratory the crystallography was performed, was credited with expediting the solution of the structure through his rich experience in protein crystallography. Some argued that Dieter Österhelt, in whose laboratory Michel worked, should also have been recognized if Huber was, since his expertise in membrane proteins stimulated much of the early advances on the bacteriorhodopsin protein. Another group of scientists thought that George Feher should also have been recognized by the Nobel Committee because of the extensive earlier characterization of the reaction center which his group at the University of California, San Diego, had contributed, long before the crystal structure was in hand.

Biography

Hartmut Michel was born in Ludwigsburg, West Germany, on July 18, 1948, the eldest son of Karl and Frieda Michel. Thanks to the influence of his mother he was allowed to enter high school, even though the family and regional traditions were mainly farming. He became an avid reader, which often interfered with his assigned homework. He enjoyed the sciences, especially physics, in which he had excellent instruction. In 1969, after obligatory military service, he applied to study biochemistry at Tübingen University. At the time, this was the only place in Germany where one could study biochemistry from the first year. The experimental work for his biochemistry diploma was done under the supervision of Dieter Österhelt in the Max Planck Institute in Tübingen, where he characterized the ATPase activity of halobacteria. He began his Ph.D. thesis work with Österhelt in 1975 at the University of Würzburg and received his degree in 1977 for his work in membrane bioenergetics.

From 1977 to 1979, he continued working with Österhelt as a postdoctoral associate and began efforts to crystallize bacteriorhodopsin. It was at this time that his collaboration with Richard Henderson at the University of Cambridge began. Henderson had an important influence on Michel's early training in structural biology. In 1979, Michel moved with Österhelt to the Max Planck Institute for Biochemistry at Martinsreid, near Munich, and, in 1981, established his own research group. In 1987 he became head of the department and director at the Max Planck Institute for Biophysics in Frankfurt and professor at the University of Frankfurt.

Scientific Career

Hartmut Michel was only forty years old when he was awarded the Nobel Prize in 1988, and his scientific career was still at a relatively early stage of development. His graduate research training in bioenergetics had provided him with the desire to understand how membrane proteins function as energy-transducing machines capable of pumping electrons and protons across membranes. Michel's attempts to crystallize the membrane protein began with bacteriorhodopsin. This is the major protein component of the so-called purple membrane, a simple photosynthetic system found in halobacteria. Bacteriorhodopsin resembles the protein rhodopsin, which is the principle visual pigment-protein complex found in the eyes of mammals. Dieter Österhelt and Walter Stoeckinus were the first to discover bacteriorhodopsin, and when Michel joined Österhelt in Martinsreid as a postdoctoral associate, he began working on the protein.

At the time that Michel began his efforts, there was much anticipation of the possibility of obtaining three-dimensional crystals of this protein. In 1975, Richard Henderson and Nigel Unwin of Cambridge had demonstrated that highly ordered crystals in two dimensions could be obtained from which electron microscopy would give a low-resolution structure of the helical fingers making up this protein. The absence of long-range order in a third dimension, however, meant that these crystals would be unsuitable for determination of an atomic-level map of the full protein structure. Michel's first attempt to crystallize bacteriorhodopsin focused on efforts to reduce the negative surface charge of the protein where it is exposed to the aqueous interface. To do this, he crystallized the protein in the presence of long-chain amines and detergents. Amines are positively charged at neutral and low pHs, and a long-chain hydrocarbon can substitute for the missing lipids from the membrane. In about four weeks, this resulted in the formation of "needles," which were examined in collaboration with Henderson at Cambridge. This showed that they were yet another two-dimensional crystalline form of bacteriorhodopsin, one in which the sheets are rolled up like tobacco leaves in a cigar.

Michel decided to try another approach that would utilize the particular properties of membrane proteins. Membrane proteins are water-repellant (hydrophobic) on one surface, which is in contact with the lipid layer in which they are embedded, and they are polar on another surface that is in contact with the aqueous phase. He added detergent molecules to bacteriorhodopsin to make the protein soluble (the detergent molecules form micelles, which act on the protein). He was able to obtain needle-like crystals and unstable cubes that converted into a threadlike material but unable to obtain the three-dimensional crystallization that he sought. Michel thought that he could not get the detergent micelles small enough to isolate properly the bacteriorhodopsin because it was too unstable in small detergents. Frustrated, he looked for a "more promising" membrane protein to crystallize.

The breakthrough in forming three-dimensional crystals came when Michel decided to attempt to isolate the photoreaction center protein from the bacterium *Rhodopseudomonas viridis*. Groundwork leading to the success of Michel's work began in the late 1960's, in work done by Dan Reed and Rod Clayton at Cornell University. They had first shown how to isolate a photosynthetic reaction center from a related bacterium. Much information had also been learned about the protein structure on the basis of biochemical and spectroscopic studies, including studies performed by George Feher and his coworkers at the University of California at San Diego. The *Rhodopseudomonas viridis* protein accomplishes photosynthesis by electron transfer rather than by direct proton pumping, as is the case with bacteriorhodopsin. Consequently, the two proteins are structurally very different. A comparison with the two-dimensional structure of bacteriorhodopsis revealed that this protein also possesses several membrane-splitting helical fingers, but it lacks the domains which extend into the aqueous phase and are critical to the formation of crystals in three dimensions.

Michel began work on *Rhodopseudomonas viridis* with Österhelt at the institute in Martinsreid, and they developed their own method of isolating its photoreaction center. Success came quickly, and they obtained starlike crystals of a very good quality. Michel then began the work, with Robert Huber, Johann Deisenhofer, and W. Bode, of collecting X-ray data on the protein's three-dimensional crystallization.

Michel's research career illustrates the breadth of experience which scientists working at the interface of chemistry, physics, and biology must acquire in order to solve important problems. His early training as a biochemist provided the experience necessary to isolate and crystallize the photoreaction protein. Later, he needed to acquire skills in molecular biology in order to deduce the amino acid sequence of the protein subunits by isolation and sequencing of the gene. Finally, he became a practicing crystallographer in the course of solving the reaction center structure by X-ray diffraction techniques.

Bibliography

Primary

CHEMISTRY: "Three-Dimensional Crystals of a Membrane Protein Complex," *Journal of Molecular Biology*, vol. 158, 1982; "Crystallization of Membrane Proteins," *Trends in Biochemical Sciences*, vol. 8, 1983; "X-Ray Structure Analysis of a Membrane Protein Complex," *Journal of Molecular Biology*, vol. 180, 1984 (with J. Deisenhofer, O. Epp, K. Miki, and R. Huber); "Structure of the Protein Subunits in the Photosynthetic Reaction Center of *Rh. viridis* at 3 Å Resolution," *Nature*, vol. 318, 1985; "The Structural Basis of Photosynthetic Light Reactions in Bacteria," *Trends in Biochemical Sciences*, June, 1985; "The 'Light' and 'Medium' Subunits of the Photoreaction Center from *Rh. viridis*: Isolation of the Genes, Nucleotide and Amino Acid Sequence," *EMBO Journal*, vol. 5, 1986 (with K. A. Weyer, H. Gruenberg, I. Dunger, D. Österhelt, and F. Lottspeich); "Pigment-Protein Interactions in the Photosynthetic Reaction Center from *Rh. viridis*," *EMBO Journal*, vol. 5, 1986 (with O. Epp and J. Deisenhofer); "Relevance of the Photosynthetic Reaction Center from Purple Bacteria to the Structure of Photosystem II," *Biochemistry*, vol. 27, 1988 (with J. Deisenhofer).

Secondary

Clarke, M. "1988 Nobel Prizes." *Nature*, October 27, 1988: 752-753. Presents a summary of the important findings of the prizewinners, using primary citations of their publications.

Dagani, Ron, and Stephen Stinson. "Nobel Prizes: Photosynthesis, Drug Studies Honored." *Chemical and Engineering News*, October 24, 1988: 4-5. This short news article quotes the reactions of some U.S. scientists to the announcement of the Nobel award. The authors also include brief, clear summaries of the work.

Hall, Nina, and Debora MacKenzie. "A Whiff of Cordite over Chemistry Prize." *New Scientist* 29 (October 29, 1988): 31-32. This article discusses the mild controversy over the prizewinners, citing the scientists who were perhaps being overlooked and noting sources questioning Huber's role in the research.

Lewin, Roger. "Membrane Protein Holds Photosynthetic Secrets." *Science* 242 (1988): 672-673. Presents a good overview of the research done by the 1988 prizewinners and examines the association of Michel, Deisenhofer, and Huber.

Youvan, Douglas C., and Barry L. Marrs. "Molecular Mechanisms of Photosynthesis." *Scientific American*, June, 1987: 42-48. Surveys advances in understanding how the photoreaction center protein of bacteria works. The article brings together studies done using several techniques, including X-ray crystallography, spectroscopy, kinetics, and site-directed mutagenesis.

Charles Dismukes

1989

Chemistry
Sidney Altman, Canada and United States
Thomas R. Cech, United States

Physics
Hans G. Dehmelt, United States
Wolfgang Paul, West Germany
Norman F. Ramsey, United States

Physiology or Medicine
Harold E. Varmus, United States
J. Michael Bishop, United States

Economic Sciences
Trygve Haavelmo, Norway

Literature
Camilo José Cela, Spain

Peace
Dalai Lama, Tibet

SIDNEY ALTMAN

THOMAS R. CECH

SIDNEY ALTMAN and THOMAS R. CECH
1989

Sidney Altman

Born: Montreal, Canada; May 7, 1939

Nationality: Canadian, American
Areas of concentration: Molecular biology and processing of DNA precursors

Thomas R. Cech

Born: Chicago, Illinois; December 8, 1947

Nationality: American
Areas of concentration: Molecular biology and processing of DNA precursors

Altman and Cech, working independently, discovered that RNA can function as a catalyst, as only proteins had been known to do. Altman discovered the catalyst RNase P, which consists of both protein and RNA, and demonstrated that the RNA is the catalytic part of the molecule. Cech showed that ribosomal RNA catalyzes its own splicing reaction, and he named the catalyst a "ribozyme"

The Award

Presentation

On December 10, 1989, Professor Bertil Andersson, member of the Royal Swedish Academy of Sciences and of the Nobel Committee for Chemistry, presented an overview of the work of Sidney Altman and Thomas R. Cech, recipients of the Nobel Prize in Chemistry "for their discovery of catalytic properties of RNA." First, Professor Andersson identified proteins and nucleic acids as highly significant carriers of genetic information within cells. He traced the current understanding of the storage of genetic information in deoxyribonucleic acid (DNA), the copying of the information into ribonucleic acid (RNA), and finally the use of the RNA as a template for the correct formation of a protein. Then he turned to a discussion of the role of protein catalysts, termed enzymes, in speeding up reactions in cells, a role that in effect makes life's properties possible. Until the early 1980's, only such enzymes were thought to have catalytic ability in cells. Then Sidney Altman found that the enzyme RNase P needed only its RNA component to be an effective catalyst, and Thomas Cech discovered self-catalytic splicing of precursor (or immature) RNA molecules. These findings showed that RNA could function as an enzyme: Proteins do not have a monopoly on this role. Professor Andersson characterized the enzyme-equals-protein concept as a "fundamental dogma of biochemistry," one now overthrown by the new laureates. Finally, he brought out the possible role of RNA in the origin of life. In trying to decide what sort of molecules evolved first, researchers debated the roles of DNA and proteins: DNA requires protein catalysts to be copied and produce new DNA molecules today, whereas protein requires DNA information to specify its structure. Prebiotic evolution thus had the sort of paradox that the question Which came first, the chicken or the egg? presents: Either DNA or protein could be the entry into the circle. Professor Andersson noted that since now RNA is known to be both a catalyst and an information-storage molecule, many scientists support a view that the first macromolecules at the dawn of life were RNA molecules.

Nobel lectures

Sidney Altman's Nobel lecture was entitled "Enzymatic Cleavage of RNA by RNA." First, he gave his perspective on the flow of genetic information within cells, highlighting the role of transfer RNA (tRNA) in the translation of information from RNA into protein. In studying how tRNA is formed from its longer precursor RNA, Altman discovered the enzyme RNase P. This enzyme made a single cut within the longer precursor, cutting it at the site required to produce one particular end of the mature tRNA, an unusually precise reaction for an RNase. Early in his studies of this enzyme, its strong negative charge made him suspect that it might be associated with some type of nucleic acid.

Professor Altman's graduate student, Benjamin Stark, succeeded in purifying and identifying a high-molecular-weight RNA called M1 RNA as a component of RNase P in 1978. He also found that the M1 RNA was required for enzymatic activity. Altman described his own mental reaction: The involvement of an RNA subunit was enough heresy; neither he nor Stark suggested or even suspected that the RNA component of RNase P could in itself be a sufficient catalyst for the reaction. Another associate of Altman, Ryszard Kole, then found that the large M1 RNA and the small associated C5 protein of RNase P could be separated into inactive components and then recombined to recover their catalytic ability. By analogy with the ribosome, a very large RNA-protein complex, they thought seriously about the M1 RNA contributing to the active site of the enzyme. The analogy with the ribosome helped them to prevail over some who had criticized their conclusions in 1981.

At this point, the techniques of recombinant DNA enabled the Altman group to prepare large quantities of the M1 RNA and the C5 protein and to characterize their structures in detail. In an experiment designed to reconstitute RNase P from two different bacterial species, using *Escherichia coli* M1 RNA and *Baccilus subtilis* C5 protein, Cecilia Guerrier-Takada made the breakthrough discovery. When she tested the M1 RNA alone, under the conditions recommended for the *Baccilus subtilis* RNase P, the M1 RNA alone catalyzed the reaction. Although the protein increased the rate of the reaction, the M1 RNA alone, at a high enough concentration of magnesium ion, was a true catalyst. It was unchanged in the reaction, followed classic "enzyme" rates described by Michaelis-Menten kinetic analysis, was stable, and was needed only in small quantities. Altman attributed his group's success to the careful groundwork in purification and characterization of both precursor tRNA and M1 RNA. Subsequent experiments have sought to model the folded structure of M1 RNA, to identify those regions necessary for catalytic activity, and to determine the mechanism of the chemical reaction.

A fascinating feature of the RNase P is that it makes one specific cut in each of approximately sixty different precursor RNAs that have no particular similarities in sequence of components at the sites cut. The folding of the precursors to produce a particular shape susceptible to RNase P cutting is thought to be the likely mechanism of recognition. Model compounds have been used to define the required shape. An "external guide sequence" that can guide RNase P to its target can be base-paired with the RNA to be attacked. The RNase P will cut at the joint between the base-paired region and the single-stranded region on the target RNA. This procedure suggests that, if the proper guide sequence can be expressed inside a cell, any RNA of choice (for example, an RNA virus) could be attacked and cut apart.

Professor Altman concluded his lecture with a discussion of the concept of an RNA world before the dawn of life. He discussed the role that a molecule such as M1 RNA could play in a system without the constraints of intracellular harmony. He speculated that the protein subunit could have been added to catalytic RNAs to fine-tune their specificities and proposed several reasons why the RNA enzymes now known cannot break bonds other than phosphodiester bonds that form RNA structure. He also acknowledged his indebtedness to his relatives, teachers, colleagues, coworkers, and funding agencies.

Professor Thomas R. Cech's Nobel lecture was entitled "Self-Splicing and Enzymatic Activity of an Intervening Sequence RNA from *Tetrahymena*." Cech began by describing the role of enzymes in catalyzing the thousands of reactions in cells. He pointed out that since 1926, when James B. Sumner crystallized the enzyme urease, biological catalysis had been attributed solely to proteins. In 1981 and 1982, however, Cech's research group found a particular RNA that could cleave and rejoin its own structural backbone, a process termed "self-splicing." This finding was the first known example of catalytic action of an RNA.

When Cech started his own laboratory in 1978, he planned to focus his research group's efforts on a particular gene; he chose the gene for the large ribosomal RNA of the ciliated protozoan *Tetrahymena*. The group's early characterization of this gene showed that it had an intervening sequence (IVS), or intron, that interrupted the coding sequences. After the RNA was copied from the gene, this IVS had to be removed.

Professor Cech and his associates first devised a system to transcribe the precursor of ribosomal RNA from its gene in isolated macronuclei. Art Zaug showed that a small RNA molecule, which accumulated after the precursor had been transcribed, was encoded by the IVS. The Cech group realized that their preparation was carrying out the splicing reaction needed to remove the IVS in the test tube. They decided to pursue this line of investigation. They thought that their nuclei should contain an unusually high concentration of the supposed splicing enzyme, since there were ten thousand copies of the ribosomal RNA genes producing precursor to be spliced. They planned to purify unspliced precursor ribosomal RNA, then treat it with nuclear proteins that could be extracted, and then purify the splicing protein.

Zaug set up the tests, both with and without the "nuclear enzyme extract." His very first set of reactions worked well, producing easily detected small RNA of the IVS. Cech thought that Zaug had made a mistake with the control reaction without nuclear enzyme, however, since it also produced the small RNA. When this result proved repeatable, Cech worried that some sort of release of IVS RNA that had already been spliced in the cell could be occurring. Meanwhile, Cech had discovered that magnesium ion and guanosine triphosphate (GTP) were essential for the release of the IVS from precursor RNA in the test tube. Cech tested directly for attachment of labeled GTP to the IVS during the splicing reaction, although he felt that this experiment was based upon such an unlikely premise (catalytic formation of a covalent bond by RNA) that he did not even let his coworkers know what he was investigating. That unlikely premise was absolutely correct, and the experiment worked.

The group then proposed how splicing might work by a trans-esterification reaction substituting guanosine (G) for the entire rest of the molecule in the first step. They still thought that some very tightly bound protein was probably the catalyst, though they at least entertained the possibility that the RNA itself could fold into an active site in their 1981 paper.

After many negative results when attempting to identify the "protein," they tried a direct test of the catalytic RNA idea. The RNA was copied in the test tube from a recombinant DNA molecule using only one pure enzyme, RNA polymerase. This RNA was then highly purified to rid it of this single enzyme. When GTP, magnesium, and salt were added, the IVS RNA was released, breaking at the exactly correct site. At the ensuing champagne party in the laboratory, they coined the term "ribozyme" to describe an RNA with the properties of an enzyme.

In a section of his talk entitled "Enzymologists Outraged," Professor Cech contrasted the quick acceptance of the self-splicing mechanism itself with the strong resistance to such terms as "enzyme-like" and "catalysis" as descriptors. The rate accelerations were quite similar between these RNAs and enzymes; the site specificities were also similar. Enzymologists, however, focused on the fact that the IVS RNA is not unchanged by the reaction, as classical catalysts must be, and claimed that self-splicing therefore could not be considered catalysis. Zaug and Cech decided to remove the attackable site from their precursor to see whether it could then splice other RNA molecules while remaining unchanged, and their attempt succeeded.

Professor Cech also concluded his lecture with a passage on the RNA world, tracing early related ideas of Carl Woese, Francis Crick, and Leslie Orgel. In 1985 and 1986, several groups proposed the scenario of RNA as the first biomolecule, based on catalytic roles of RNA. Cech and his coworkers had described a reaction catalyzed by their RNA enzyme that could assemble RNA chains, for example. Although the versatility of RNA enzymes had not yet been thoroughly tested, Cech stated that he doubted that they would ever equal or surpass the catalytic abilities of protein enzymes. In closing, Cech acknowledged his relatives and coworkers and the agencies that funded his work.

Critical reception

The announcement on October 12, 1989, that Sidney Altman of Yale University and Thomas R. Cech of the University of Colorado, Boulder, would share the Nobel Prize in Chemistry was well received. *The New York Times* featured Altman and Cech in an article on October 13, 1989, on the chemistry and physics prizes. The article heralded the revolutionary nature of their findings, with the implications for theory of biocatalysts, ideas of the nature of life, and the creation of new defenses against viruses. The article also mentioned Altman's dual Canadian/American citizenship and Cech's American citizenship, noting that Americans have won or shared the Nobel Prize in Chemistry twenty-three of the eighty-one times it has been awarded since 1901.

Chemical and Engineering News for October 16, 1989, covered these Nobel laureates, citing the alteration of Francis Crick's "central dogma of molecular biology" made necessary by their work as well as revisions of concepts of how life began. The chronology of Altman's discovery of RNase P with an essential catalytic RNA component, then of Cech's finding that RNA alone could self-splice, was traced. *Maclean's* for October 23, 1989, highlighted Altman's Canadian roots and dual citizenship, also praising the potential benefits of the discovery.

Chemical Week for October 25, 1989, featured the RNA world implications and further suggested that primitive cells could have used RNA rather than proteins as regulatory molecules. In addition, the possible future role of designed molecular shears for RNA viruses was mentioned. The article noted that Cech did not expect the award, although his friends had warned him that he might well be a candidate. Altman was quoted as stating that winning the Nobel Prize was "a wonderful experience" but that scientists should "do the best work you possibly can" rather than aspiring to win awards.

Biographies

Sidney Altman was born on May 7, 1939, in Montreal, Canada. He was the second son of poor immigrants; his father ran a small grocery store in the Notre-Dame-de-Grâce district, and his mother worked in a textile mill. When Altman was young, his family made it clear that education was the path to opportunity; study was expected. Albert Einstein was presented as a worthy role model. The role of scientists in developing the atom bomb, which appeared when he was six years old, was a major early nudge toward science. At approximately age thirteen, Altman received a book about the periodic table of the elements. This book impressed him with the elegance of scientific theory and its ability to organize and direct scientific experiments by its predictive power.

By the time he reached high school, his father's grocery store was providing a comfortable living for the family. Sidney completed West Hill High School in 1956 and then left Montreal to begin his undergraduate studies at Massachusetts Institute of Technology (MIT) near Boston. He describes his years at MIT as "four years of over-stimulation among brilliant, arrogant and zany peers and outstanding teachers." He was graduated with a degree in physics in 1960. Altman spent the years from 1960 to 1962 as a graduate student and teaching assistant in physics at Columbia University. He then enrolled in graduate work in biophysics at the University of Colorado Medical Center, where he was granted a Ph.D. in 1967. A Damon Runyon Fund Cancer Research Fellowship in molecular biology enabled Altman to pursue molecular biology research at Harvard University from 1967 to 1969. In 1968-1969 he also served as a tutor at Radcliffe College. His postdoctoral training continued with an Anna Fuller Fund Fellowship to the Medical Research Council (MRC) Laboratory of Molecular Biology at the University of Cambridge from 1969 to 1970, followed by an MRC fellowship there from 1969 to 1971.

Altman became an assistant professor in the biology department at Yale University in 1971. In 1972, he married Ann Korner. Their first child, Daniel, was born in 1974. A daughter, Leah, was born in 1977. Altman was promoted to associate professor in 1975 and to full professor in 1980. He became a U.S. citizen in 1984 but retained his Canadian citizenship as well. Altman was chairman of the Yale University biology department from 1983 to 1985. In 1985, he became Dean of Yale College (that is, the dean of the Yale undergraduate program), a position he held concurrently with that of professor of biology until 1989, when he returned to the teaching and research faculty. In 1990, he was a Sherman Fairchild Distinguished Scholar at California Institute of Technology.

Thomas Robert Cech was born on December 8, 1947, in Chicago, Illinois. His father, Robert, was a physician; his mother, Annette, was a homemaker. Both sides of his family were of Czech extraction. Cech attended elementary, junior high, and high schools in Iowa City, Iowa.

Cech attended Grinnell College, where he received a liberal arts education and majored in chemistry. There he met his wife, Carol Lynn Martinson, who also majored in chemistry. He was graduated from Grinnell with a B.A. in chemistry in 1970, and he married Carol that same year. They both went to the University of California, Berkeley, to pursue graduate study. Cech received a National Science Foundation Graduate Fellowship. In 1975, both Thomas and Carol received Ph.D.'s in chemistry and moved to Boston. Thomas Cech became a National Cancer Institute fellow in molecular biology at the biology department of Massachusetts Institute of Technology (MIT) from 1975 to 1977. In 1978, both Cechs received faculty appointments at the University of Colorado, Boulder. In 1983, Thomas Cech was promoted to professor of chemistry and biochemistry and, concurrently, professor of cell and developmental biology. He received a Guggenheim Fellowship in 1985-1986, became a Research Professor of the American Cancer Society in 1987, and was appointed an Investigator of the Howard Hughes Medical Institute in 1988.

Professor Cech has received many national and international awards and lectureships; he received the Albert and Mary Lasker Award in 1988, which is sometimes considered to be a prognosticator for future Nobel recognition. Others include the Pfizer Award in Enzyme Chemistry and the Heinecken Prize from the Royal Netherlands Academy of Arts and Sciences. He received an honorary doctor of science degree from Grinnell College in 1987. In 1986, he presented one of the prestigious Harvey Lectures. He was elected to the U.S. National Academy of Sciences in 1987 and to the American Academy of Arts and Sciences in 1988.

Scientific Careers

Sidney Altman was introduced to research in the field of nuclear physics when he conducted an undergraduate honors project supervised by Lee Grodzins. He first encountered molecular biology through a course taught by Cyrus Levinthal. He took the course during his final semester at MIT because there was so much excitement about this area that Altman became curious about it. He was not an immediate convert to the field. Instead, he spent eighteen unhappy months as a graduate student in physics at Columbia University, waiting for an opportunity to work in a laboratory that failed to materialize. He then left Columbia and pursued a summer program in physics while working in Colorado. George Gamow, the physicist, recommended that he consider Leonard Lerman as a mentor. Lerman was a biophysicist studying intercalation of acridines into DNA at the University of Colorado Medical Center, Denver. Altman decided to take this chance to move into biophysics, and he enjoyed productive interactions with Lerman as well as with department chairman Theodore T. Puck. He completed his dissertation, entitled "Bacteriophage-T4 DNA Replication in the Absence and Presence of 9-Aminoacridine," in 1967.

Then, Altman joined Matthew Meselson's laboratory at Harvard University to study an enzyme that was important in both replication and recombination of the DNA of T4, the virus he had studied during his dissertation work. After two years at Harvard, he moved to the Medical Research Council Laboratory of Molecular Biology at the University of Cambridge, England, where he joined a group led by Sydney Brenner and Francis Crick, an experience Altman characterized as "scientific heaven." There, he started the work that eventually revealed the catalytic role of RNA.

Several colleagues at Cambridge helped Sidney Altman hone his ideas, notably Sydney Brenner and John D. Smith. Altman's signal scientific achievement of this period was the discovery of the first radiochemically pure tRNA precursor molecule. He credits this discovery with his being offered the position of assistant professor at Yale University in 1971. As his academic career progressed at Yale, Altman continued to focus upon and unravel the mysteries of how a tRNA molecule matures, and, in 1978, he discovered that RNase P, an important enzyme in tRNA maturation, cannot fulfill its catalytic role without an essential RNA component. Later, in 1983, he and his colleagues demonstrated that the RNA is actually the catalytic subunit of the RNase P; this was the finding on which his selection as Nobel laureate was based.

Thomas Cech's father loved physics as much as medicine, and family discussions sparked an early interest in geology. By junior high school, Thomas was discussing his rocks with University of Iowa geology professors.

At Grinnell College, he meant to go into physical chemistry, and he structured off-campus research experiences at the Lawrence Berkeley Laboratory and the Argonne National Laboratory to follow that interest. Yet he returned after a term at Argonne to undertake the final semester of his senior year with the feeling that the interplay between experimental design and data interpretation was too slow in physical chemistry. He tried a guided reading course in biochemistry with Gene Wubbels and has subsequently stayed in that area of investigation.

At the University of California, Berkeley, Thomas Cech's thesis adviser was John Hearst. Cech studied chromosome structure and function using physico-chemical methods with a fairly global perspective. On his postdoctoral project at MIT, working with Mary Lou Pardue, he became more knowledgeable about biology and used psoralen cross-linking to approach global questions about chromosome structure and function.

Upon moving to the University of Colorado, Boulder, and establishing his own laboratory, he felt the need to look at the chromatin structure and function of a single gene rather than the entire genome. Cech chose the large ribosomal RNA gene of *Tetrahymena* for study because ten thousand copies of the gene are present and active in its macronucleus in extra-chromosomal circles. He hoped this plethora of genes in their native packaging could help him to characterize proteins important in gene expression. Instead, it led him to a very different and startling finding: that RNA itself could serve as a catalyst. This finding was the basis for his Nobel Prize.

Bibliography

Primary

Sidney Altman

CHEMISTRY: "Effects of 9-Amino Acridine on Bacteriophage T4 Deoxyribonucleic Acid Synthesis," *Journal of Molecular Biology*, vol. 50, 1970 (with L. S. Lerman); "Isolation of Tyrosine tRNA Precursor Molecules," *Nature (London), New Biology*, vol. 229, 1971; "Tyrosine tRNA Precursor Molecule Polynucleotide Sequence," *Nature (London), New Biology*, vol. 233, 1971 (with J. D. Smith); "Purification and Properties of a Specific *Escherichia coli* Ribonuclease Which Cleaves a Tyrosine Transfer Ribonucleic Acid Precursor," *Journal of Biological Chemistry*, vol. 247, 1972 (with Hugh D. Robertson and Smith); "Ribonuclease P: An Enzyme with an Essential RNA Component," *Proceedings of the National Academy of Sciences, USA*, vol. 75, 1978 (with Benjamin C. Stark, Ryszard Kole, and Emma J. Bowman); *Transfer RNA*, 1978; "Reconstitution of RNase P Activity from Inactive RNA and Protein," *Proceedings of the National Academy of Sciences, USA*, vol. 76, 1979 (with Kole); "*Escherichia coli* RNase P Has a

Required RNA Component in Vivo," *Cell*, vol. 19, 1980 (with Kole, Madeline Baer, and Stark); "The RNA Moiety of Ribonuclease P Is the Catalytic Subunit of the Enzyme," *Cell*, vol. 35, 1983 (with Guerrier-Takada, Kathleen Gardiner, Terry Marsh, and Norman Pace); "Aspects of Biochemical Catalysis," *Cell*, vol. 36, 1984; "Enzymatic Cleavage of RNA by RNA," *Trends in Biochemical Sciences*, vol. 11, 1986 (with Baer and Guerrier-Takada); "Identification and Characterization of an RNA Molecule That Copurifies with RNase P Activity from Hela Cells," *Genes and Development*, vol. 3, 1989 (with M. Bartkiewicz and H. Gold); "Specific Interaction in RNA Enzyme-Substrate Complexes," *Science*, vol. 246, 1989 (with Guerrier-Takada and Nadya Lumelsky).

Thomas R. Cech

CHEMISTRY: "Characterization of the Most Rapidly Renaturing Sequences in Mouse Main-Band DNA," *Journal of Molecular Biology*, vol. 81, 1973 (with Alita Rosenfeld and John E. Hearst); "Partial Denaturation of Mouse DNA in Preparative Cesium Chloride Density Gradients at Alkaline pH," *Biochemistry*, vol. 15, 1976 (with Gary Wiesehahn and Hearst); "Electron Microscopy of DNA Crosslinked with Trimethylpsoralen: Test of the Secondary Structure of Eukaryotic Inverted Repeat Sequences," *Proceedings of the National Academy of Sciences, USA*, vol. 73, 1976 (with Mary Lou Pardue); "In Vitro Splicing of the Ribosomal RNA Precursor in Nuclei of *Tetrahymena*," *Cell*, vol. 19, 1980 (with Arthur J. Zaug); "The Intervening Sequence of the Ribosomal RNA Precursor Is Converted to a Circular RNA in Isolated Nuclei of *Tetrahymena*," *Cell*, vol. 23, 1981 (with Paula H. Grabowski and Zaug); "In Vitro Splicing of the Ribosomal RNA Precursor of *Tetrahymena*: Involvement of a Guanosine Nucleotide in the Excision of the Intervening Sequence," *Cell*, vol. 27, 1981 (with Zaug and Grabowski); "RNA Splicing: Three Themes with Variations," *Cell*, vol. 34, 1983; "RNA as an Enzyme," *Scientific American*, vol. 255, 1986; "The Intervening Sequence RNA of *Tetrahymena* Is an Enzyme," *Science*, vol. 231, 1986 (with Zaug); "A Model for the RNA-Catalyzed Replication of RNA," *Proceedings of the National Academy of Sciences, USA*, vol. 83, 1986; "Biological Catalysis by RNA," *Annual Review of Biochemistry*, vol. 55, 1986 (with Brenda L. Bass); "Biological Catalysis by RNA," *Harvey Lectures*, vol. 82, 1986-1987; "The Chemistry of Self-Splicing RNA and RNA Enzymes," *Science*, vol. 236, 1987; "RNA as an RNA Polymerase: Net Elongation of an RNA Primer Catalyzed by the *Tetrahymena* Ribozyme," *Science*, vol. 239, 1988 (with Michael D. Been); "Defining the Inside and Outside of a Catalytic RNA Molecule," *Science*, vol. 245, 1989.

BIOLOGY: "Chromatin Structure in Living Cells," *Cold Spring Harbor Symposium in Quantitative Biology*, vol. 42, 1978 (with D. Potter and Mary Lou Pardue); "DNA-Protein Interactions in the *Drosophila virilis* Mitochondrial Chromosome," *Nucleic Acids Research*, vol. 12, 1984 (with Pardue and J. M. Fostel); "Self-Splicing RNA: Implications for Evolution," *International Reviews of Cytology*, vol. 93, 1985; "Telomeric DNA-Protein Interactions of *Oxytricha* Macromolecular DNA,"

Genes in Development, vol. 1, 1987 (with Carolyn M. Price); "Phylogenetic Relationships and Altered Genome Structures Among *Tetrahymena* Mitochondrial DNAs," *Nucleic Acids Research*, vol. 16, 1988.
MEDICINE: "Ribozymes and Their Medical Implications," *Journal of the American Medical Association*, vol. 260, 1988.

Secondary

Campbell, Neil A. *Biology*. 2d ed. Redwood City, Calif.: Benjamin/Cummings, 1990. This is an introductory college biology textbook that discusses the idea of an "RNA world" in a section of "The Origin of Genetic Information." The hypothesis, attributed to Cech, is discussed in a three-page, illustrated essay as part of a chapter entitled "Early Earth and the Origin of Life." This material is accessible to the nonscientist.

Corelli, Rae. "Chemistry of Life: A Native of Montreal Shares a Major Award." *Maclean's* 102 (October 23, 1989): 58. This article in a Canadian journal particularly notes Altman's contributions. His early life in Montreal is briefly touched on. The way in which Altman's and Cech's experiments revolutionized biology and the idea that they might be used to defend against viruses is described in layperson's terms.

Darnell, James, Harvey Lodish, and David Baltimore. *Molecular Cell Biology*. New York: Scientific American Books, 1986. This advanced college text has a long, detailed chapter on the evolution of cells that describes the splicing reactions catalyzed by RNA in detail, with many clear illustrations. The work of both Cech and Altman, in its context in molecular biology, is covered clearly, but at an advanced level. The diagrams include some showing the possible secondary structures of the catalytic RNA regions. There is also a section on how RNA chains could grow longer by transferring the spliced-out RNA onto another RNA. The possibility that the first genes were RNA is brought out briefly at the end of this chapter. Numerous references to the original literature follow this chapter, including papers by both Cech and Altman.

Pendlebury, David. "The New Nobelists: A Look at Their Citation Histories." *The Scientist* 3 (November 13, 1989): 18, 21. In addition to a brief summary of the chronology of catalytic RNA discoveries by Altman and Cech, this article shows that the seminal paper by each author was actually only the third most cited work by the end of 1988. Altman's breakthrough paper was published in 1978, and citations peaked in 1980; Cech's was published in 1981, and citations peaked in 1986. The article briefly alludes to the establishment of a new paradigm of biological catalysis as a result of this work, as well as to its evolutionary and medical implications.

Waldrop, M. Mitchell. "Catalytic RNA Wins Chemistry Nobel." *Science* 246 (1989): 325. This article gives the chronology of the catalytic RNA discovery, with much coverage of the scientific logic of the progression of understanding in this area. The evolutionary implications of the discovery are briefly discussed as well. The article conveys the flavor of a major discovery that arose unexpectedly from detailed, careful analysis of two highly specialized test systems.

_____. "Did Life Really Start Out in an RNA World?" *Science* 246 (1989): 1248-1249. The pros and cons of the idea that RNA was the first informational molecule in the primordial soup form the core of this article. The views of Nobel laureate Christian de Duve, arguing against the RNA hypothesis, are prominently featured, as are the arguments for the RNA world based upon the work of Cech and Altman.

Watson, James D., Nancy H. Hopkins, Jeffrey W. Roberts, Joan Argetsinger Steitz, and Alan M. Weiner. *Molecular Biology of the Gene*. 4th ed. Menlo Park, Calif.: Benjamin/Cummings, 1987. Chapter 28 of this advanced college textbook, "The Origin of Life," deals in detail with the possibility that RNA was the first bio-molecule in prebiotic evolution. The claims for both RNA and DNA to be called "the first living molecule" are evaluated. Evidence that RNA enzymes work like protein enzymes is presented. The ability of the core of the self-splicing RNA enzyme to assemble RNA, acting as an RNA polymerase, is described in detail. Also refers to much primary literature in its extensive bibliography, including many works by Cech and collaborators. Chapter 14, "The Involvement of RNA in Protein Synthesis," explains the splicing of pre-tRNAs and highlights the work of Altman on RNase P. The catalytic RNA of RNase P is modeled in one of the figures in this chapter. The bibliography of chapter 14 refers to Altman's work.

Laura Mays Hoopes

THE NOBEL PRIZE WINNERS

Chemistry

INDEX

Note: Entries appearing in small capitals are intended to help the reader locate all Nobel laureates from a particular country or branch of physics. Boldface page ranges direct the reader to primary articles.

Abelson, Philip, 569-570.
Absorption spectra, 72.
Adenosine diphosphate (ADP), 998; synthesis of, 675.
Adenosine triphosphate (ATP), 993-994, 997-999; synthase, 999; synthesis of, 675.
Adiabatic calorimeter. See Calorimeter, adiabatic.
ADP. See Adenosine diphosphate.
Adsorption, 355-356; chromatography, 521-528, 589; indicators, 856-857.
Advanced Inorganic Chemistry (Wilkinson, with Cotton), 931.
Advisory Council on Scientific Policy (ACSP), 676.
AGRICULTURAL CHEMISTRY: Virtanen, Artturi Ilmari, 471-479.
AIV method, 473.
Alcohol fermentation. See Fermentation.
Alder, Kurt (1950), 543-545, 547, **551-559.**
Aldol reaction, directed, 1022.
ALICYCLIC CHEMISTRY: Wallach, Otto, 143-152.
Alkali metal complexes, 1192.
Alkaloid chemistry, 962-963.
Alkaloids, 421, 511-516.
Alpha displacement rule, 245.
Alpha helix, 627.
Alpha particles, 121-128.
Alpha-ray bombardment of elements, 381-382, 385-386.
Altman, Sidney (1989), 1233-1246.
Aluminum trialkyl compounds, 751-752.
Amino acid analysis, automated, 904, 906.
Ammonia, industrial production of, 337-343; synthesis of, 220, 223-225.
Analine dye, 213.
ANALYTICAL BIOCHEMISTRY: Moore, Stanford, 897-909.
Androsterone, 433, 435, 441, 446.
Anemia. See Pernicious anemia.
Anfinsen, Christian B. (1972), 687, **885-895,** 900-901.
Ansichten über die organische Chemie (van't Hoff), 55.

Anthocyanins, 213-214, 511-516.
Anti-Semitism in Nazi Germany, 212, 225-226, 342-343, 467.
"Antivitamins," 427.
APPLIED CHEMISTRY: Sabatier, Paul, 175-186.
Applied Radiochemistry (Hahn), 468.
ARGENTINA: Leloir, Luis F., 863-872.
Argon, 81-83, 85-87.
Arrested relaxation technique, 1159.
Arrhenius, Svante August (1903), 22-24, 26, 29, 55, 56, **69-78,** 455; *The Life of the Universe*, 76.
Arrhenius' law and chain reaction theory, 655-656, 660.
"Artificial cell." See Microreactors.
Ascorbic acid. See Vitamin C, structure and synthesis of.
Asilomar conference on genetic engineering research, 1032.
Aston, Francis William (1922), 249-257; *Isotopes*, 256; *Mass-Spectra and Isotopes*, 256.
Astronomical spectroscopy, 880.
ATMOSPHERIC PHYSICS: Arrhenius, Svante August, 69-78.
Atom bomb, 570-572, 792-793, 838-839; testing, 627-628.
Atomic Bomb Project, 372.
ATOMIC CHEMISTRY: Aston, Francis William, 249-257.
Atomic Energy Commission, 579, 582, 707, 708, 710.
Atomic fallout, risks of, 707.
Atomic fission. See Nuclear fission.
Atomic weights, 252, 255-256.
ATOMIC WEIGHTS: Richards, Theodore William, 197-206.
Atoms, Molecules, and Quanta (Urey, with Ruark), 370.
ATP. See Adenosine triphosphate.
Atropine, synthesis of, 213.
AUSTRALIA: Cornforth, John Warcup, 947-956.
AUSTRIA: Pregl, Fritz, 259-267.
Avogadro's law, 51.

I